A BASIC COURSE IN SOCIOLOGICAL STATISTICS

GENERAL EDITOR
WILLIAM J. GOODE
COLUMBIA UNIVERSITY

A TEXTBOOK AND WORKBOOK COMBINE

A Basic Course in

Sociological Statistics

Y MORRIS ZELDITCH, Jr. • COLUMBIA UNIVERSITY

A HOLT·DRYDEN BOOK

HENRY HOLT AND COMPANY • NEW YORK

29856-0119

© 1959 by Henry Holt and Company, Inc.
Printed in the United States of America
Library of Congress Catalog Card Number 59-9172

Preface

THIS is probably among the most elementary of all elementary texts on statistics. The book is designed with the specific and pleasant intention of attracting the student who is frightened of mathematics. There are no mathematical derivations whatsoever in the text. We presume only some knowledge of arithmetic.

Yet the book is built around what appears to be a paradoxical conjunction of purposes. On the one hand we want to be elementary; but on the other hand, we want to be advanced. We intend to dispense with mathematical derivations; yet we want to say something about the mathematical theory underlying statistical techniques. Almost every serious student of the application of statistics recognizes the essential part that knowledge of this theory plays in the choice of appropriate techniques. Mood, we think, expresses it well:

> The use of statistical tools is not merely a matter of picking out the wrench that fits the bolt; it is more a matter of selecting the correct one of several wrenches which appear to fit the bolt about equally well, but none of which fit it exactly . . . there is nothing magic about the [algebraic] formula; it is merely a tool, and, moreover, a tool derived from some simple mathematical model which cannot possibly represent the actual situation with any great precision. In using the tool one must make a whole series of judgments relative to the nature and magnitude of the various errors engendered by the discrepancy between the model and the actual experiment. [Mood, 1950, pp. 5–6.]

The central problem of the application of statistics is in the relation of model to practical circumstance. By "model" we mean the definitions and assumptions which the mathematician makes in order to create the statistical methods we use. It is from these definitions and assumptions that he is able to derive the principles of practical procedure, the formulas, the tables, etc., that make up the statistician's working tools. The model is prerequisite to precise conclusions. Nevertheless, it sometimes involves assumptions about the actual situation that are so far from being fulfilled that to apply methods based on the model is both pretentious and useless. This happens to be the case, for instance, in the application of some of the more rigorous and powerful techniques to sociological problems.

Statisticians themselves are well aware of this problem, and they are aware, furthermore, that they should communicate an understanding of it to others. Their usual form of communication, however, is mathematics; and the attractions of mathematics—elegance, power, precision—are not easily given up by those who have managed to perceive them. Thus the assumptions underlying a given mathematical model are frequently treated as part of its advanced mathematics. As descriptions of statistical techniques gradually filter down to those who have to apply them, somehow these assumptions begin to drop out of the discussion until at the most elementary level they disappear from sight. The really interested student is expected to master the mathematics of the subject in order to arrive at a more fundamental understanding of it.

In this book we take a different view. We may be wrong, of course. But the book was undertaken with the idea that even the most elementary and mathematically unprepared student can, and should, learn from the very beginning the conditions under which the more popular methods can and cannot be applied. Our entire interest, of course, is devoted to techniques appropriate to sociological data; this dominates to a large extent the choice of emphasis. In particular, this specific interest has led us to give a great deal of attention to attributes and orders. This is, clearly, a book for sociologists. But more important, it is a book in which we are concerned, throughout, that the student should learn how to recognize just when to apply a given technique and when not to, and to understand what kinds of assumptions are implied in the application.

I am indebted to Professor Sir Ronald A. Fisher, Cambridge, to Dr. Frank Yates, Harpenden, and to Messrs. Oliver & Boyd Ltd., Edinburgh, for permission to reprint in the appendix the chi-square and *t*-tables from their book, *Statistical Tables for Biological, Agricultural and Medical Research*.

I am more than usually indebted to those who have read and offered suggestions for the book, among them: W. J. Goode, Jiri Nehnevajsa, Hanan Selvin, Leda Burnshaw, and John Meyer.

A Note on the Workbook Exercises

Following each chapter there is a set of workbook exercises designed to fix the important elements of the chapter in the student's mind. Each of the basic concepts discussed is the subject of several questions, which should make them so familiar to the student that he will not be misled by their free use in the later chapters.

At the same time, the exercises are designed to be of general sociological interest. Our intention is to place statistical method in its proper context as *part* of research as a whole; and also, of course, to preserve the student's interest in statistics by giving the sometimes tedious calculations required in later exercises *meaning* in terms of the total context of a study. Each of the exercises, therefore, is organized around the summary of a part, or of the whole, of a report from the current sociological literature; and in this summary we have made an effort to include findings and conclusions of general interest, whenever they are not directly suggested already by the answers to the questions in the exercise.

M. Z. JR.

Columbia University
April 1958

Acknowledgments

GRATEFUL acknowledgment is made to the following authors and publishers for their permission to reproduce material from their publications. Page references are to this book.

Anderson, R. L., and Bancroft, T. A., 1952. *Statistical Theory in Research*. New York: McGraw-Hill. Table, p. 18.

Asch, S. E., 1952. "Effects of Group Pressures upon the Modification and Distortion of Judgments." In Swanson, G. E., Newcomb, T. M., and Hartley, E. L., eds., 1952. *Readings in Social Psychology*. New York: Henry Holt. Table, p. 328.

Berelson, B. R., Lazarsfeld, P. F., and McPhee, W. N., 1954. *Voting*. Chicago: The University of Chicago Press. Copyright 1954 by The University of Chicago. Tables, pp. 132, 146, 149, 202, 207.

Blau, P. M., 1955. *Dynamics of Bureaucracy*. Chicago: The University of Chicago Press. Copyright 1955 by The University of Chicago. Tables, pp. 113, 322.

Centers, R., 1949. Marital Selection and Occupational Strata." *Am. Jour. Soc.*, 54:530–535. Table, p. 182.

Clark, K. B., and Clark, M. P., 1941. "Racial Identification and Preference in Negro Children." In Swanson, G. E., Newcomb, T. M., and Hartley, E. L., eds., 1952. *Readings in social Psychology*. New York: Henry Holt. Tables, pp. 294, 297, 302, 303.

Clark, R. E., 1949. "Psychoses, Income, and Occupational Prestige." *Am. Jour. Soc.*, 54:443–440. Tables, p. 336.

Clarke, A. C., 1952. "An Examination of the Operation of Residential Propinquity as a Factor in Mate Selection." *Am. Soc. Rev.*, 17:17–22. Table, p. 86.

Edwards, A. L., 1955. *Statistical Methods for the Behavioral Sciences*. New York: Rinehart. Table, p. 79.

Festinger, L., Schachter, S., and Back, K., 1950. "The Operation of Group Standards." From *Social Pressures in Informal Groups*. New York: Harper. Tables, pp. 4, 341.

French, R. L., 1951. "Sociometric Status and individual Adjustment among Naval Recruits." Jour. Abnorm. and Soc. Psychol., 46:64–72. Table, p. 82.

Goode, W. J., 1956. *After Divorce*. Glencoe: Free Press. Table, p. 147.

Hagood, M. J., and Price, D. O. *Statistics for Sociologists. Revised Edition*. New York: Henry Holt. Copyright, 1941, by Margaret Jarman Hagood; copyright, 1952, by Henry Holt & Co. Table, p. 275.

Hatt, P., and Reiss, A., eds., 1951. *Urban Sociology*. Glencoe: Free Press. Tables, p. 57.

Hawley, A. H., 1956. *The Changing Shape of Metropolitan America*. Glencoe: Free Press. Table, p. 58.

Henry, A. F., and Short, J. F., 1954. *Suicide and Homicide*. Glencoe: Free Press. Table, p. 6.

Horowitz, E. L., 1936. "Development of Racial Prejudice." In O'Brien, R. W., Schrag, C. C., and Martin, W. T., eds., 1951. *Readings in General Sociology*. Boston: Houghton Mifflin. Tables, p. 56.

Hyman, H. H., and Sheatsley, P. B., 1947. "Some Reasons Why Information Campaigns Fail." In Swanson, G. E., Newcomb, T. M., and Hartley, E. L., eds., 1952. *Readings in Social Psychology*. New York: Henry Holt. Table, p. 151.

Kaplan, B., 1954. "A Study of Rorschach Responses in Four Cultures." *Papers of the Peabody Museum*, Vol. 42, No. 2, Cambridge, Mass. Table, p. 33.

Katz, E., and Lazarsfeld, P. F., 1955. *Personal Influence*. Glencoe: Free Press. Table, p. 211.

Kaufman, H., 1944. "Prestige Classes in a New York Rural Community." In Bendix, R., and Lipset, S. M., eds., 1953. *Class, Status, and Power*. Glencoe: Free Press. Reprinted from Cornell Agricultural Experimental Station Memoir 260, Ithaca, N.Y. Table, p. 88.

Lemert, E., 1951. *Social Pathology*. New York: McGraw-Hill. Tables, p. 38.

Lipset, S. M., 1955. "Social Mobility and Urbanizaiton." *Rural Soc.*, 20:220–228. Table, pp. 147, 148.

Loomis, C. P., *et al.*, 1953. "Social Status and Communication in Costa Rican Rural Communities." In Leonard, O. E., and Loomis, C. P., 1953. *Latin American Social Organization and Institutions*. E. Lansing: Michigan State College Press. Table, p. 283.

Miller, D. C., 1945. "A Research Note on Mass Communication." *Am. Soc. Rev.*, 10:691–694. Table, p. 59.

Mood, A. McF., 1950. *Introduction to the Theory of Statistics*. New York: McGraw-Hill. P. 1.

National Resources Committee, 1939. "The Structure of Controls." In Bendix, R., and Lipset, S. M., eds., 1953. *Class, Status, and Power*. Glencoe: Free Press. (Original title: *The Structure of the American Economy*, Washington: Govt. Prtg. Office.) Table, p. 145.

Porterfield, A. L., and Talbert, R. H., 1954. "Crime in Southern Cities." In Vance, R. B., and Demerath, N. J., eds., 1954. *The Urban South*. Chapel Hill: University of North Carolina Press. Table, p. 117.

Rossi, P. H., 1955. *Why Families Move*. Glencoe: Free Press. Tables, p. 150.

Shaw, C. L., and McKay, H. D., 1931. *Social Factors in Juvenile Delinquency*. Washington: Govt. Prtg. Office. Table, p. 31.

Siegel, S., 1956. *Nonparametric Statistics for the Behavioral Sciences*. New York: McGraw-Hill. Tables, pp. 324, 338.

Snedecor, G. W., 1946. *Statistical Methods*, 4th ed. Ames: Iowa State College Press. Table, p. 247.

Sogge, T. M., 1954. "Industrial Classes in the United States, 1870–1950." *Jour. Am. Stat. Assn.*, 49:251–253. Table, p. 144.

Stouffer, S. A., 1955. *Communism, Conformity, and Civil Liberties*. New York: Doubleday. © 1955 by S. A. Stouffer. Table, p. 146; p. 179.

Stouffer, S. A., *et al.*, 1950. *Measurement and Prediction*. Princeton: Princeton University Press. Tables, p. 136.

Thibaut, J., 1950. "An Experimental Study of the Cohesiveness of Underprivileged Groups." *Human Relations*, 3:251–278. Table, p. 265; p. 266.

U. S. Bureau of the Census. *Statistical Abstract of the United States: 1951, 1952,* and *1955*. Washington: Govt. Prtg. Office. *1951:* Table, p. 5; *1952:* Table, p. 145; *1955:* Tables, pp. 143, 144.

World Almanac and Book of Facts for 1956, 1956. New York: New York World-Telegram and Sun. Tables, pp. 118, 356.

Yule, G. U., and Kendall, M. G., 1950. *An Introduction to the Theory of Statistics*, 14th ed. New York: Hafner; London: Charles Griffin & Co., Ltd. Table, p. 103.

Zeisel, H., 1957. *Say It with Figures*, 4th ed. New York: Harper. Table, p. 210.

Zetterberg, H. L., 1952. "Cohesiveness as a Unitary Concept." Unpublished Ms. Table, p. 239.

Contents

CHAPTER 1 **Some Basic Concepts**   1

A Simple Statistical Investigation, *1*
A Note on the Next Two Sections, *3*
Types of Populations, *3*
Types of Characteristics, *4*
Where We Stand, *9*

WORKBOOK EXERCISES, 11

CHAPTER 2 **Organizing Univariate Measurement Data**   15

The Array, *15*
The Function of Symbols, *16*
Grouping, *17*
Intervals, Limits, and Midpoints, *19*
Types of Distributions, *21*
Where We Stand, *27*

WORKBOOK EXERCISES, 29
The Histogram, *29*
The Frequency Polygon, *30*

CHAPTER 3 **Measures of Central Tendency**   41

The Mean, *41*

The Median, *45*

    Computation design for mean of grouped data, using coding shortcuts, for Type III characteristics having k class intervals, *46*

    Computation design for median of grouped data for Type III characteristics having k class intervals, *50*

The Mode, *51*

Summary of Appropriate Applications of Mean, Median, and Mode, *52*

Where We Stand, *53*

WORKBOOK EXERCISES, *55*

CHAPTER 4   **Measures of Dispersion**   67

The Range, *67*

Deviations from the Mean, *68*

    Computation design for variance and standard deviation of grouped data, using coding shortcuts, for Type III data having k class intervals, *74*

Location-based Measures of Dispersion, *75*

Where We Stand, *77*

A Note on the Table of the Normal Curve, *78*

WORKBOOK EXERCISES, *81*

CHAPTER 5   **The Relationship of Two Variables**   93

Simple Regression Problems, *94*

Negative Linear Relationships, *95*

Estimating Regression Constants from Fallible Data, *96*

Correlation, *100*

    Computation of the product-moment correlation coefficient r from grouped observations of two Type III variables of k and m classes respectively, *106*

Where We Stand, *109*

    Computation of regression constants and error variance from grouped data, *110*

WORKBOOK EXERCISES, *113*

CHAPTER 6 **Introduction to Attributes** 125

Ratios, Proportions, and Percentages, *127*
The Cross-classification of Two Attributes, *131*
Where We Stand, *141*

**CONTINGENCY TABLES FOR USE WITH WORKBOOK
EXERCISES, CHAPTERS 6, 7, 8,** *143*

WORKBOOK EXERCISES, *153*

CHAPTER 7 **The Association of Attributes and Orders** 163

The Percentage Difference as a Measure of Association, *163*
  Detailed treatment of asymmetrical $r \times s$ tables: ϵ, *166*

Measures of Associates Based on the Definition of Independence, *167*
The Special Treatment of Fourfold Tables, *168*
Association in the General $r \times s$ Table, *171*
  Computation of Q and the phi coefficient from fourfold tables, *172*
  Computation of lambda measures of association for cross-classified mani-
  fold classifications having r and s classes, *178*

The Interpretation of, and Choice Among, Lambda, Gamma, Q, and
  Phi, *183*
  Computation of gamma for the association of two cross-classified orders
  having r and s classes, *184*

A Note on r-Based Measures for Attributes, *186*
Where We Stand, *187*

WORKBOOK EXERCISES, *189*

CHAPTER 8 **Multivariate Attributes** 201

General Form of Multivariate Tables, *201*
The Control of Confounding Factors, *203*
Interpreting a Relationship, *208*
Specification of a Relationship, *209*
Where We Stand, *212*
  Steps in multivariate analysis, for attributes having two classes, *213*

WORKBOOK EXERCISES, *215*

CHAPTER 9   **Introduction to Statistical Inference**   **229**

Drawing Random Samples, *229*
Confidence Intervals: Large Sample Theory, *233*
Small-Sample Statistics, *237*
    Confidence intervals for means and proportions for large samples, *238*

Assumptions Underlying the Use of the *t* Test, *244*
    Computation design for *t* test of the difference between two means, for two
     independent samples, *245*

Interpretation of Significance Tests, *248*
Where We Stand, *249*
WORKBOOK EXERCISES, 251

CHAPTER 10   **Binomial and Chi-square Tests**   **271**

Tests of Significance for Proportions, *271*
    Computation of exact binomial probabilities of obtaining *r* *A*'s in samples
     of size *N*, *277*

Independence in 2×2 Tables, *283*
Application of χ^2 to the General $r \times s$ Table, *288*
    Computation design for χ^2 for testing significance of association between
     two attributes; for general $r \times s$ case and for the special 2×2, *290*

Where We Stand, *291*
WORKBOOK EXERCISES, 293

CHAPTER 11   **The Logic of Nonparametric Methods**   **313**

The Central Limit Theorem and Tchebyscheff's Inequality, *314*
Distribution-free and Nonparametric Methods, *315*
Confidence Intervals for Order Statistics, *317*
    Computation of confidence intervals for the median, *321*

Rank Correlation Methods, *322*
    Computation design for Spearman rank correlation coefficient, r_s, *326*

The Difference Between r_s and γ, *327*

Replacing Variates with Signs Instead of Ranks, *327*

The General Utility of Ranks, Signs, and Orders, *329*

   Computation design for the median test for two independent samples, *330*

Where We Stand, *331*

WORKBOOK EXERCISES, *333*

Bibliography and References   353

Appendix   357

Table 1. Table of Squares and Square Roots, 358
Table 2. Probabilities That Given Values of z Will Be Exceeded, 365
Table 3. Table of Critical Values of t, 366
Table 4. Table of Critical Values of Chi Square, 366

Index   367

Chapter 1

Some Basic Concepts

I T HAS proved troublesome to define the term "statistics," and we will not try to give a precise definition of the field here. Even in the most elegant and advanced treatises a very clumsy and unappealing definition is usually given. So instead we borrow a phrase from Mood: "The statistician is . . . engaged in producing tools for research workers." (1950, p. 4.)* The purpose of this text is to convey as simply as possible some idea of how these tools are to be used.

A Simple Statistical Investigation

Assume for the moment that we are interested in finding out how many people in New York City watched the Republican National Convention on television, what they thought about it, and perhaps why. We do not ordinarily think of questioning every person in New York City. We plan, possibly, to question only 2000. We call these 2000 persons a *sample* and we call the eight million or so whom they represent a *population* or a *universe*.

* We shall follow the practice of citing sources by giving name of author, date, and page or table number. The full citation will be found in the section on "Bibliography and References" at the end of the text.

A *population* (or *universe*) is any collection of persons, or objects, or events in which we may be interested.

A *sample* is a selection of observations or members from the population.

If we follow certain rules in selecting our sample it is possible to make some general statement about the eight million in the population on the basis of the 2000 persons representing them. We grant at the outset the fallibility of our data. The consequence is the uncertainty of our conclusions. We will not be able to make perfectly precise or certain statements, but we *will* be able to state very exactly just *how* precise our statement is, and just *how* certain our conclusion is (always remembering that we assume the sample was chosen in certain ways, which we will describe in Chapter 9).

Suppose that we ask the members of our sample the following questions: What is your age (to the nearest birthday)? About how much money did the head of your household make this year? Did you watch the Republican National Convention on TV? How long would you say you watched (for those who say "Yes" to the previous question)?

We will call the answers a set of observations. A statistical treatment of our information usually begins with a set of such observations. The peculiar characteristic of these observations is that they can be converted into numbers of some sort. We have ages, incomes, units of time, number who say "yes." In sociological research, of course, the conversion of observations into numbers is sometimes difficult. This may be true even when the original observations appear to be numerical. Ecologists, for instance, are interested in "place of residence," which may come in the form of an address or census tract number. But if you add up all the numbers in the addresses of 2000 persons and find the "average" address, the result is meaningless. We can, however, convert an address into "distance from city center," and this can be treated meaningfully by statistical procedures. The researcher's first problem, then, may be to transform observations into quantitative form to permit statistical analysis.

Let us suppose that we have made a set of such observations. Now the problem is, what shall we do with them? It is with this kind of problem that statistics is directly concerned. We usually go through at least the following steps:

1. We summarize the set of observations in some simple and convenient form. This is the purpose of a field customarily referred to as *descriptive statistics*. We also examine the relationship of our three pieces of information to one another. This is simply an extension of descriptive statistics to data of a more complex form. It is called the examination of *association* or *correlation*.

2. We want to make some statement about the population from which we have drawn the sample, and about this sample compared to other samples, either from the same or different populations. A field known as *statistical inference*, built on the theory of probability, is capable of telling us how much in error we may be in generalizing beyond the immediate set of observations we have drawn, *if* we have conformed to certain assumptions in the way we originally collected the data.

It is evident that a first broad division of the field of statistics is into descriptive statistics and statistical inference.

A Note on the Next Two Sections

The next two sections are crucial for anyone who wants to get beyond the most elementary stage with statistics. Because their general context is lost, however, the importance of these sections is easily overlooked by the beginner. The only purpose of *this* section is to comment on why we emphasize the next two sections.

The preface to this book is a general comment on the problem of application. (The student who makes a practice of avoiding prefaces is advised to stop now and read the preface before going on.) Theoretical statistics consists of a number of precisely formulated mathematical models; the central problem of application is to understand the relation of these models to a given practical situation. We have expressed, in the preface, a concern that the student shall learn how to decide when a particular method is appropriate. Computation designs can be filed away, and pulled out when they are needed. The more immediate issue is to learn how to ask, and how to answer, the question "To what kind of problem do I apply this design, and what assumptions must I make in using it?"

The next two sections are decisive in answering the first part of this question. They define the kind of problem for which you must choose the appropriate method.

Types of Populations

We take a simple aspect of the question first. We can easily distinguish populations according to the number of characteristics we measure on each member (age, income, sex, place of residence, etc., are all "characteristics" in this sense). Elaborating this, we have, for instance:

1. *A univariate population* is one in which we consider only one characteristic at a time; e.g., respondent's age, or income, or sex, or TV-listening time, each separately.

This conception requires some abstract thinking. It does not mean, for instance, that the population *has* only one characteristic. But if you treat only one you must be careful not to assume anything about any other characteristic in that population. It is safer, actually, to think of "populations" of ages, or incomes, or listening times, or "populations" of prices of television sets, or of car accidents, than of a population of concrete persons. Then it is always clear exactly about *what* population you can safely generalize.

2. *A bivariate population* is one in which we consider two characteristics measured simultaneously on each member; e.g., age and listening time of respondent 001, age and listening time of respondent 002, etc.

3. *A multivariate population* is one in which we consider observations on three or more characteristics simultaneously; e.g., age, income, and listening time of each member, all at the same time.

The same terms are used for samples taken from these populations. Data from each type pose their own special problems of investigation, and for each there is a special body of methods appropriate to its treatment. (Note, for instance, that Chapters 2, 3, and 4 deal with univariate samples; Chapter 5 deals with bivariate samples.)

Types of Characteristics

We divide characteristics into three rough classes:

1. *An attribute* is a characteristic which is either present or absent, either is or is not. (E.g., a respondent did or did not say "yes" when you asked if he watched the convention.) There is no question of the degree to which an object or person has the attribute, only of whether he does or does not have it. The numerical picture we get is simply the frequencies with which the attribute occurs or does not occur, and we call these frequencies *enumeration data*. We get them by counting the number of persons who have or do not have the attribute. (We will sometimes call this *Type I data*.) Attributes, in turn, fall into two classes:

    a. *A dichotomy* is a classification of all members into two and only two classes; each sample member is either male or female; either blind or not blind; either has TV or does not have TV; etc. This gives a result which in its most general form looks like this:

A	Not-A	
n_A	$n_{\text{not-}A}$	N

    where A and Not-A designate the two classes of the dichotomy; n_A designates the number of members of the population falling in the class A; and $n_{\text{not-}A}$ the number falling in the class Not-A. N designates the total number of members of the sample and is the sum of n_A and $n_{\text{not-}A}$.

As an example we might be interested in something like the information in the following table.

TABLE 1-1.

Employment Status of the Civilian Male Labor Force,

March 1950 (Numbers in thousands)

Employed	*Unemployed*	*Total*
40,877	3002	43,879

Source: Statistical Abstract, 1951, Table 204, p. 173.

Data like these can be conveniently obtained from the annual *Statistical Abstract of the United States*, published by the Bureau of the Census.

b. *A manifold classification*, or a *polytomy*, is obtained when we classify members into more than two classes, although there is still no question of the degree to which any sample or population member falls in or out of the class. This is one of the most frequent forms of sociological data; examples include the familiar occupational classifications, regional classifications, etc. The essential feature of a manifold classification is that it has no intrinsic order.* In general form it looks like this:

A_1	A_2	A_3	A_4 $\cdots$	A_k	
n_{A_1}	n_{A_2}	n_{A_3}	n_{A_4} $\cdots$	n_{A_k}	N

A typical example of a manifold classification is shown in Table 1-2. The regional classification along the stub (the identifying information on the left side of the table is called the *stub*) of this table is a manifold classification. Note that the entries are rates, rather than absolute numbers, and do not conform exactly to the general form above; actually any entry in the "cells" of the table is possible. A *rate* is the number having the attribute during a specified period of time *per* some specified number of the population; e.g., in East South Central United States the number who are convicted of murder is 12.45 per 100,000 in the population. (See Chapter 6 for further discussion of rates.)

2. *Order*, or *quasi-variable*, is a term we shall use for data that can be ordered, in a sense that attributes cannot, but cannot be precisely coordinated to the conventions of the number

---

* The term *manifold classification* originates with Yule and Kendall (1950), who, however, use the term differently. Here we restrict its usage to unordered classifications, but Yule and Kendall use it for *any* classification, ordered or not, having more than two classes. *Polytomy*, a more recent term, also has this more general usage, which we do not follow in this text.

TABLE 1-2.

Urban Rates of Murder and Aggravated Assault by
Geographic Divisions of the United States, 1951
(Rate per 100,000)

Geographic Division	Murder Rate	Aggravated Assault
East South Central	12.45	102.6
South Atlantic	10.30	214.9
West South Central	9.11	75.9
East North Central	4.33	66.4
Pacific	3.21	49.7
West North Central	3.05	52.3
Mountain	2.76	36.3
Middle Atlantic	2.56	34.9
New England	1.24	12.1

Source: Henry and Short, 1954, p. 83.

scheme. (We will also call these *Type II data*.) This is another form in which sociological data frequently appear. As a general form, we can give something approximately like this:

High A Medium A Low A

n_h	n_m	n_l	N

Since the problem presented by this kind of data arises so frequently, for sociologists, we will try to spell this out a little more, and to contrast it with a manifold classification so that the difference is clear.

Take another frequently recurring manifold classification:

white collar   blue collar   farmer

Now rearrange it in this form:

blue collar   white collar   farmer

When we say that this classification has no intrinsic order, we mean that the second arrangement does nothing essential to the presentation of the data that is not done in the first arrangement. We sometimes feel that there *is* an intrinsic order to these data, because there is an implicit ranking in terms of the prestige of occupations in our society. The order, however, is at best a difficult assumption to justify; not that the items do not have different prestige, but the classification ought to be one of prestige itself if that is the basis of the order.

Suppose now that we take a classification of the condition of housing in a given area as,

good   fair   poor

Now rearrange it in this form,

poor   fair   good

You should feel intuitively that in the first case the data are arranged so that they increase from right to left (poor to good), and that in the second they increase from left to right (poor to good). Furthermore, we also feel intuitively that we would violate the nature of the data to arrange them in the form,

poor   good   fair

You should be able to see that this characteristic has an intrinsic order, and that the third arrangement violates this intrinsic order.

The quasi-variable has an order but does *not* have certain features of our number scheme which would make it a true *variable* in the sense in which we will use that term below. An elementary text is no place to analyze the number system, but we need to grasp two aspects of it in order to understand the problems involved in dealing with many forms of sociological data.

Look at the following set of integers (i.e., whole numbers):

0 1 2 3 4 5 6 7 8 9

With this set of numbers we can make certain familiar statements, such as:

4 is twice as large as 2
6 is twice as large as 3
9 is three times as large as 3

Without analyzing the reasons for this very rigorously, we can say that two essential properties of the number scheme are that *it has a zero-point* and *it has equal intervals between consecutive pairs of points*. This means, for instance, that the interval between 1 and 2 is equal to the interval between 2 and 3, and both intervals are assigned a constant numerical value equal to 1; the interval between 1 and 4 is the same as the interval between 3 and 6 and has a numerical value of 3. It is precisely these two properties which the quasi-variable does not have. We cannot, consequently, make statements such as:

Good is twice as good as fair
Fair is twice as good as poor
Good is three times (or four times, or any times)
    as good as poor

All we know is that good is better than fair, and fair is better than poor. One of the most useful and common sociological examples of this kind of characteristic is the *rank order*, and we can frequently give a fairly refined treatment to data that are ranked. (See Chapter 11.)

3. *Variable* is a term used for characteristics having intrinsic order, a zero-point, and equal intervals.* Examples are age, income, number of children ever born, etc.; i.e., anything that is conveniently represented by the conventional number scheme. Within the limits of the accuracy of our measurement we can say exactly the degree to which each object or person has the variable property, and for this reason we call the resulting set of observations *measurement data*.

It is also common to use the term "variable" for the more general statement "such and such is the variable in which we are interested"; in this sense, sex, which is a dichotomous attribute, is a variable in many investigations. To keep the two meanings clear, therefore, we will frequently use the term *measurement data* to refer to this type of characteristic; we may also use the term *Type III data* for this purpose. A third convenient way to distinguish the two is to specify the kind of variable (in the Type III sense) involved; we make a basic distinction between two types of variables:

    a. *Discrete variables* cannot take every possible value in the number scheme; frequently they are confined to the whole numbers 1, 2, 3, 4, etc. Examples: number of children ever born, family size, etc. You can have 1 child, or 2 children, or 10 children, but not 1.4 children. Although all discrete variables are not confined to integers, they always have a gap between possible values.

    b. *Continuous variables* can take every possible value, depending only on the degree of precision with which you can measure them. Examples: age, weight, height, time. If you want to be facetious, for instance, you can try to measure age to the nearest day, to the nearest hour, to the nearest minute, etc.; the limits are set by the accuracy of your measurement, but not by the inherent features of the variable.

It should be fairly clear that it is possible to conceive a measuring instrument that would turn one of our examples of a quasi-variable (good . . . fair . . . poor) into a con-

---

* Measurement scales having equal intervals but *no* zero point exist (called *interval scales*), but we will not speak of these as "variables" in this sense; they should be treated as quasi-variables.

tinuous variable some day. This can also be said of attributes. Some physical anthropologists have started to measure the degree of masculine component in their subjects, converting male *vs* female into *degree* of masculinity. There are also frequent occasions, particularly in sociological monographs, when a potentially continuous variable is for one or another reason converted into a quasi-variable (particularly into high, medium, low, or a rank order). We shall discuss some reasons for doing this later. It is not, therefore, always the inherent nature of the characteristic that we are here classifying, but rather the way in which the set of observations has been recorded.

Where We Stand

Let us review the purpose of this chapter. We have asserted that the principal difficulty in applying statistics is that of choosing from among many available techniques the one best suited to a given problem; and we have implied that we grasp the essential features of a given problem when we have made certain basic distinctions: (1) between sample and population; (2) between questions of description and inference; (3) among univariate, bivariate, and multivariate observations; and (4) among attributes, orders (quasi-variables), and variables. Of these, perhaps the last distinction is the most important. Frequently, for example, sociologists are well trained in the use of techniques dealing with measurement data (variables) but are helpless in the face of a problem concerning attributes or orders. Even worse, they sometimes do not recognize that any difference in treatment is needed. But the differences are fundamental, and failure to understand how the characteristics themselves differ leads to great confusion.

The remaining ten chapters illustrate the differences we have so vaguely referred to; and the table of contents shows that the organization of the text is based principally on these distinctions.

Chapter 1

WORKBOOK EXERCISES

Where a blank line occurs, complete the sentence. Where **T   O   F** occurs, in parentheses, circle **T** if the statement is true; **F** if it is false; and **O** if not enough information is given to decide.

1. Marsh and Coleman (1956) report the following investigation. 393 farm operators, in 13 neighborhoods of Washington County, Kentucky, were interviewed on the extent to which each of the operators had tried and was using 21 farm practices recommended by agricultural agencies.

a. Each respondent was given an adoption score in the following way: First the investigator determined how many of the 21 practices *could* be applied on the respondent's farm. Then he determined how many *had* been adopted. The percentage adopted of those applicable was the adoption score. If the first respondent used 9 recommended practices out of an 18 possible, his score is $100(9/18) = 50$; if the second used 10 and could have used

14, his score is $100(10/14) = 71.4$, etc. A set of such scores is Type .... data,

because ....

....

....

....

....

b. In order to manage the analysis of their data the investigators divided the 13 neighborhoods into "low-adoption areas," "medium-adoption areas," and "high-adoption areas," with 156, 139, and 98 cases respectively.   These are Type .... data, because ....

....

....

    c. Marsh and Coleman then compared the three types of neighborhoods on several indicators of socioeconomic status, including education of the respondents and value of products sold.   In dealing with education, they divided respondents into those who had 8 or less years of schooling and those who had more than 8 years.   These are Type ....

data, because ....

....

....

    d. It was found that socioeconomic factors do not completely account for differences in adoption scores.   Some or all of the differences between neighborhoods must be explained by differences in norms and expectations with respect to innovations and "scientific" practices, which differ from neighborhood to neighborhood.

    The investigators compared the three kinds of neighborhoods on the means by which residents of each sought out information about farm practices.   First they examined exposure to information from the following sources: radio, farm magazines, newspapers, farm meetings, farm bulletins, circular letters from the county agent, friends and neighbors, salesmen,

etc.   This is a .... classification, because ....

....

....

    e. The investigators also compared the neighborhoods on whether or not respondents had talked with a representative of the agricultural agency during the two years preceding the interview.   They divided respondents into those who had and those who had not.   This

is an example of Type .... data, because ....

....

....

f. How would you describe the difference between the characteristic referred to in paragraph (e) and the characteristic referred to in paragraph (d)? ....

....

....

....

g. One of the most interesting aspects of the investigation concerns the behavior of leaders in high- and low-adoption neighborhoods. Previous reports had produced contradictory evidence about the adoption practices of leaders compared to others in their neighborhoods; one study shows leaders far out in front in accepting new practices, but an equally competent study shows them to be quite conservative in their "innovating" behavior. A leader is defined as a man to whom other farmers frequently go to talk about farming; e.g., for Marsh and Coleman he is a man mentioned by two or more farmers as a source of information. Respondents are then divided into *those mentioned by two or more* (the "leaders") and *those mentioned by less than two* ("nonleaders"). These are Type .... data, because

....

....

....

This part of the investigation showed that in high-adoption areas, where the norms favor innovators, leaders are far ahead of others in adopting new practices; in low-adoption areas, where norms favor traditional practices, leaders are about the same as other farmers in their adoption rates.

2. Katz and Hyman (1947) report the following investigation. During a period of great alarm about absenteeism from war plants, the Surveys Division of the OWI designed a study of 18 war plants, covering six war industries, to investigate the relation of absenteeism to both community and plant conditions.

a. One hundred workers were interviewed in each plant. They were chosen by taking every *n*th name from the files in the office of the plant (every 5th, every 10th, etc.; depending on the size of the plant). The 1800 workers, taken altogether, are called a *population*.

(**T O F**)

b. The research team collected information on absenteeism from plant time cards, classifying workers who had been absent for more than 3% of the time over a 3-month period as "absentees." Absenteeism defined in this way is *univariate* data. (**T O F**)

For the same workers they collected "morale" data also (e.g., satisfaction with job, satisfaction with plant, promotion policies, etc.). For each worker, then, they had simultaneous information on absenteeism and morale, which is *bivariate* information. (**T O F**)

Finally, they collected data on conditions not directly related to the plant itself, such as the length of travel time from home to plant, and housing conditions. In other words they had *multivariate* data for each worker. **(T   O   F)**

      c. From the way absenteeism is defined, obviously all workers are either absentees or not absentees. This is what we call a *manifold classification*. **(T   O   F)**

A moderate relation was found between absenteeism and several of the community conditions, including the time it took to travel from home to plant. Travel time is an example of a *discrete variable*. **(T   O   F)**

      d. The survey showed a complex interaction of inplant and outplant factors in relation to absenteeism. Substandard housing, for instance, was correlated with absenteeism in four plants in which morale was low; but in two plants with high morale there was low absenteeism in spite of substandard housing. In order to investigate systematically such relationships, several community factors were combined into one index: "number of bad community factors," ranging from "no bad community factors" to "two or more bad community factors." This is a *quasi-variable*. **(T   O   F)**

Chapter 2

Organizing Univariate Measurement Data

THE FIRST step in dealing with a set of observations is to summarize and condense the information it contains. Even with the simplest set of observations we have to do something to it in order to make it yield information. Procedures for summarizing data are called descriptive statistics. We will take the description of univariate measurement data first. There are three basic elements in the description of data of this kind: we need to discover the *form* of their distribution; the *central tendency* (or average value) of their distribution; and the *dispersion* (or variability) of their distribution. We will discuss these three elements in this and the following two chapters.

The Array

Before we can describe and summarize our observations, however, we take certain steps in order to organize them conveniently. The most primitive form in which information comes to us is called an *ungrouped* set; this is simply a number of individual observations. The following numbers, for instance, form a set of ungrouped observations:

2, 2, 1, 1, 3, 5, 7, 8, 3, 0, 2, 0, 0, 1, 3, 2, 3, 4, 5, 6, 3, 2, 6, 1

These numbers come from an actual investigation (Gorden, 1952), and represent the number of times each of 24 members in a cooperative living project agreed in his private opinion with what he perceived to be the opinion of his group on 12 questionnaire items. The set of observations is in order by the interview number of the individual case (i.e., case no. 1 is first, case no. 2 is second, etc.). Examination of even this simple set of observations is facilitated by arranging them in a somewhat different order. We may, for instance, arrange them as follows:

$$0, 0, 0, 1, 1, 1, 1, 2, 2, 2, 2, 2, 3, 3, 3, 3, 3, 4, 5, 5, 6, 6, 7, 8$$

This is called an *array*. The observations are in order from the lowest to the highest value. We can see readily from this array, for instance, that the observations tend to fall largely in the 0, 1, 2, 3 values. The observations are still ungrouped; all we have done is to rearrange them. An array, therefore, can be defined as *an ordered set of ungrouped observations*.

The Function of Symbols

In order to have some way of talking about the general case, rather than always referring to this particular investigation, we introduce certain conventional symbols. In the first place, we will almost always refer to the measurements we have made as "observations" and to the whole of them as a "set of observations," just as we have up until now. One of these observations is customarily represented by the letter X (in its capital form), and subscripts are used if we wish to refer to a particular one of the observations. X_1 is the first observation, X_2 the second, etc. (these symbols are read "X-one," "X-two," etc.). We use the symbol X_i when we want to talk about a single, but general, observation. "The ith observation" means *any* one observation in the set. When we want to refer specifically to the last observation, as we do quite frequently, we designate it X_N. The number of observations in the set, finally, is represented by a capital N (e.g., in the set above $N = 24$).

Symbols have the double purpose of being general and—once you understand them —of making life easy by condensing expression. For instance, when we arrange observations in an array, we can precisely and at the same time very generally represent what we have said as follows:

To make an array, set

$$X_1 \leq X_2 \leq X_3 \leq \cdots \leq X_N, \qquad \text{for } N \text{ observations}$$

where $\leq$ has a conventional meaning, "equal to or less than"
   $\cdots$ means "and so on up to."

This can be read: order the observations in such a way that the smallest in value is first and that every observation is either equal to or less than its successor in the order.

On a piece of scratch paper, the student may now form an array of the following observations from Gorden. They represent the amount by which each member of the group *changed* his opinion in the direction of his estimate of group opinion, when he was asked to give his opinion in the presence of the group.

4, 9, 0, 11, 5, 7, 6, 9, 7, 2, 4, 5, 5, 10, 5, 5, 3, 2, 13, 7, 8, 5, 8, 3

Grouping

With ungrouped data we are given, and preserve, each observation's exact value. We can, however, proceed somewhat differently. Instead of making an array, we can summarize by noting that there are three 0's, four 1's, five 2's, etc., up to one 8. This sort of summary is called *grouping*, and usually we show the grouping in the following form:

X_i Number of Agreements	f Frequency
0	3
1	4
2	5
3	5
4	1
5	2
6	2
7	1
8	1
9	0
	$N = 24$

These are the same data as before, but now they are *grouped;* the "frequency" column shows the number of times each value of X occurred. The i subscript now designates, or names, the *class* of X rather than a particular observation.*

This is a frequency distribution. What we have done is to list at the left all the potential values of our variable, which is "number of agreements," and then we *tabulated* the number of times they show up in our set of observations. Every time we get a 0, for instance, we make a tab mark / beside the zero; every time we get a 1 we make a tab mark / beside the one, etc.; the worksheet will look like the example shown at the top of page 18.

* Throughout the text we will comment on formulas, examples, figures, etc., in material set off from the text and adjacent to features that we desire to emphasize. These comments will serve several purposes: frequently they will summarize text material, sometimes they will simply emphasize text material, and very infrequently they will add to text material. They are not to be regarded as text material in themselves, and are of more importance in reviewing than during the first reading.

X_i	f
0	///
1	////
2	/////
3	/////
4	/
5	//
6	//
7	/
8	/
9	

In the case of the grouped data, we call the value the variate may take the *class*, and the distance between the boundaries of the class is the *class interval*. The sum of the tab marks for a given class is the *class frequency*, or simply *frequency* (*f*). The sum of the frequencies must equal *N*, the total number of observations. The result is a *frequency distribution*.

TABLE 2-1.

Socioeconomic Scores of 909
Southern Farm Families

X_i	f
35–39	3
40–44	33
45–49	191
50–54	229
55–59	169
60–64	90
65–69	56
70–74	54
75–79	52
80–84	26
85–89	5
90–94	1

Source: Adapted from Anderson and Bancroft, 1952, p. 161. The scores are based on possessions, such as radio, TV, telephone, cars, and education and church attendance. The original scores range from 39 to 91.

The class interval is 5. The "real limits" extend 0.5 above and below the actually recorded limits in order to give precise and unambiguous boundaries to the interval. It is assumed that all the observations are concentrated at the "midpoint" or "midmark" of the class interval.

Actually, we gain very little from tabulating this particular set of observations. But when we have a large number of observations and a wide range of values, a frequency distribution is not only convenient, it is imperative. At the same time, we do lose something

TABLE 2-2.

Distribution of the Socioeconomic Scores of 909 Southern Farm Families, with Intervals and Midpoints

X_i	f	Midpoint
35–39	3	37, which is $34.5 + 2.5$
40–44	33	42, which is $39.5 + 2.5$
45–49	191	47, which is $44.5 + 2.5$
50–54	229	
55–59	169	
60–64	90	
65–69	56	
70–74	54	
75–79	52	
80–84	26	
85–89	5	
90–94	1	

Types of Distributions

One of the first steps in examining a set of observations, after they have been grouped or ordered, is to discover their general form. We do this for two reasons: In the first place, the information is intrinsically interesting; we will find it useful in discussing and presenting the data. In the second place, the use of a large number of statistical techniques depends on what we call "distribution assumptions," or some form of the question: "What is the shape of this distribution?" The choice between the several different "averages" in the next chapter, for instance, will depend in part on the answer to this question.

We may distinguish between a "rough" description of the form of a distribution and a relatively precise mathematical description. In this chapter we will deal mostly with "rough" descriptive terms. We will try first to give a rough description of the distribution of socio-economic scores.

The easiest way to begin is to convert a frequency distribution into some simple visual form. There are several ways to do this, but we will describe only the two most common ways. One way is to make a *histogram* of the scores. The histogram represents the frequencies in each class interval by a rectangular bar, the area of which is proportional to the frequency. A histogram of the socioeconomic scores of Table 2-2 is shown in Figure 2-1.

To make a histogram the class intervals are marked off along the baseline (the X-axis, or "abscissa," in analytic geometry) and the frequencies are marked off along the side of the figure (the Y-axis, or "ordinate," in analytic geometry). A rectangular bar is constructed for

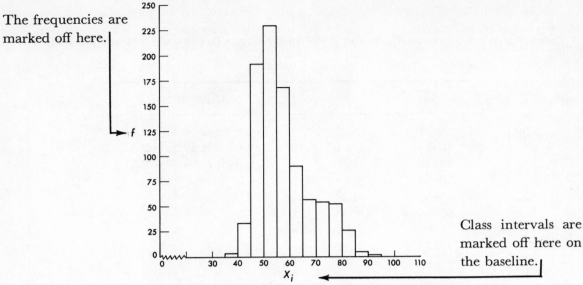

The frequencies are marked off here.

Class intervals are marked off here on the baseline.

Figure 2-1. Histogram of socioeconomic scores of 909 southern farm families.

each interval. The height of the bar is determined by the frequency in the interval and the width by the size of the interval. Detailed instructions are given in the exercises.

The second common visual representation of a distribution is the *frequency polygon*. The frequency polygon represents the frequencies with a dot, or point, placed above the midpoint of the class interval; again the point indicates the size of the frequency by its height above the baseline. A frequency polygon of the socioeconomic scores is shown in Figure 2-2.

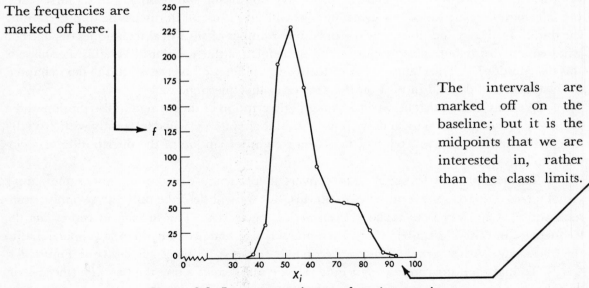

The frequencies are marked off here.

The intervals are marked off on the baseline; but it is the midpoints that we are interested in, rather than the class limits.

Figure 2-2. Frequency polygon of socioeconomic scores of 909 southern farm families.

In the frequency polygon the points are connected by straight lines. Frequently the next step taken, particularly if there are a large number of observations and the underlying variable is continuous, is to "smooth" the curve. We will not describe the curve-fitter's art in this text—in many cases "smoothing" is a quite dubious procedure—but a smooth, or fitted, curve of the distribution of socioeconomic scores is shown in Figure 2-3a. Just as in the frequency polygon, the height of the ordinate above a point on the baseline represents the frequency at that point. The area under the curve between two points represents the frequency in that interval. Now, however, the curve is smooth and it is assumed that we have plotted every point on an infinitely dense variable.

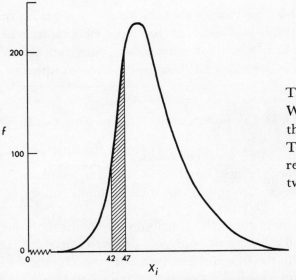

The class intervals are along the baseline. We have erected two "ordinates" from the baseline, at $X = 42$ and $X = 47$. The area between the two ordinates represents the frequency between these two points.

Figure 2-3a. Fitted curve of socioeconomic scores of 909 southern farm families.

Now we want to describe this frequency distribution in a rough but serviceable fashion. Notice, first, that the curve representing the distribution is not symmetrical. If you were to fold the figure at the middle, for example, the two halves of the distribution would not correspond with each other. A curve which is not symmetrical we call a *skewed* curve. This particular example happens to be *positively skewed*. A curve is positively skewed when the longer tail of the distribution (the portions of the curve that approach the baseline are the *tails*) is to the right.* If the longer tail is to the left, we call this a *negatively skewed* distribution. In general:

* Technically, skewness is measured by a quantity known as the "third moment" of a distribution. The notion of positive and negative skewness arises from the positive or negative sign that this quantity may have. *Usually* a distribution with a positive (or negative) third moment will look like the curve described here, but it is technically possible that it will not. The exception is not likely to occur sufficiently often to worry the beginning student. Incidentally, if the curve is symmetrical the third moment will usually be 0, but again it is technically possible that it will not.

1. The top of the peak, or hump, of the curve is called a maximum of the curve. If you drop a line from the maximum of a *symmetrical* curve, it will fall at the exact middle of the distribution.

2. If you drop a line from the maximum of a skewed curve, more than half the area will lie on one side and less than half will lie on the other; the curve, in other words is *asymmetrical*, or *skewed*.

    a. If the bulk of the area lies to the left, and the trailing tail is to the right, the curve is *positively skewed*.

    b. If the bulk of the area is to the right, and the trailing tail is to the left, the curve is *negatively skewed*.

Returning to the curve in Figure 2-3a, we can see that the second obvious feature is that it has only *one* hump or peak. We call this a *unimodal* distribution. We can, in general, describe any curve by the number of peaks it has. Some have two peaks and are called *bimodal*. Some have even more peaks, and we can call these *multimodal*. Adding to our descriptive vocabulary, then,

3. A curve with only one maximum is a *unimodal* curve. Curves with two or more maxima are *multimodal*.

    a. If there are only two maxima, the curve is called *bimodal*.

    b. If there are three or more, the curve is most simply referred to as *multimodal*.

    c. If every frequency is a maximum (all are equal), the distribution is *rectangular*.

It is important to understand that the form of the distribution remains the same (is *invariant*) regardless of the scale to which the histogram, polygon, or fitted curve is drawn, and regardless of the location of the curve on the baseline (i.e., farther to the left or right of a given position on the baseline). The curves may *look* different, but the crucial issue is what *proportion of the area*, that is, what *relative amount* of it, lies between any two points under the curve. Figure 2-3b, for instance, shows the 909 socioeconomic scores again. We have

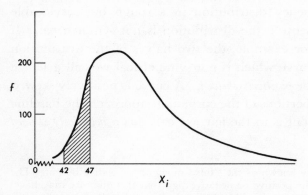

Although we have altered the scale of measurement on both the X- and Y-axes, making the distribution look shorter and fatter, the essential form is unchanged. The area in the shaded portion is the same, in proportion to the total area, as the shaded area in Figure 2-3a.

Figure 2-3b. Fitted curve of socioeconomic scores of 909 southern farm families, with X-scale stretched and Y-scale compressed.

stretched the scale along the baseline and compressed the scale on the Y-axis. (The curve is at the same location on the baseline, however; we could have moved it by subtracting some constant number from every X without altering the form of the distribution.) We have shaded in the area under the curve representing the frequency in the interval from 42 to 47 again. The curve may look different, but the shaded area in Figure 2-3b is the *same proportion of the total area* under the curve as the shaded area in Figure 2-3a.

THE NORMAL DISTRIBUTION CURVE

One class of symmetrical, unimodal curves has played a historically important part in the development of theoretical statistics; these are the so-called *normal* curves. Not only has this distribution been theoretically important, but it was once thought that the normal curve was among the most frequently *observed* distributions as well. In the study of errors of measurement in physics; in the study of biometric distributions (height, length of arm); in agricultural investigations (weight gains in pigs, for example); and in the study of intelligence quotients, the normal curve turned up sufficiently often to earn its name "normal." A normal curve is shown in Figure 2-4.

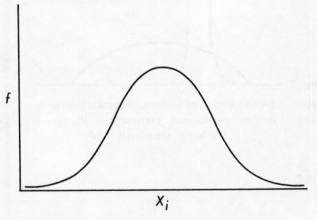

The normal curve has been historically the most important distribution curve in theoretical statistics. In Chapter 4 we will be able to give a more precise description of the normal curve.

Figure 2-4. An example of the normal curve.

Without a technical mathematical description there is little one can add about the normal curve after one has said that it is symmetrical and unimodal. Yet it is more than just symmetrical and unimodal. One whole group of curves, for instance, is symmetrical and unimodal but has a taller, narrower peak than the normal, or a flatter, peak and shortened tails. (The degree of "peakedness" of a curve is called the *kurtosis*. Curves that are taller and narrower than the normal curve are called *leptokurtic*. Curves that are flatter and fatter than the normal are called *platykurtic*. You will find very little use for these terms in what follows, but illustrations will be found in the accompanying figures.)

Some Types of Distribution Curves

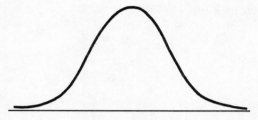

A normal distribution curve.

Two skewed distributions. Most continuous distributions of interest to sociologists are more or less skewed. The curve with the hump to the left is *positively* skewed. The other is *negatively* skewed.

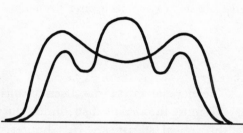

A bimodal and a trimodal distribution. A sociological example is found in the exercises.

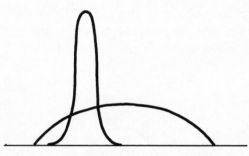

Two examples of kurtosis. *Leptokurtosis* (tall, narrow peak) and *platykurtosis* (flattened out hump, shortened tails).

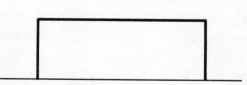

A rectangular distribution. Here every class has the same frequency. An example will be found in the sampling experiments in Chapter 9.

A symmetrical, unimodal discrete distribution.

The normal curve is usually roughly described as a bell-shaped curve. But all normal distributions, regardless of scale or location, have the same mathematical form; thus when we say a distribution is normal, we mean something very exact: namely, its frequencies are related to the values of the variable, X, by the formula that describes the normal curve. What we have said before about invariance of form—that the form of a distribution is unchanged when the scale on which the axes are measured is changed—is true, of course, of the normal curve. There is, then, a whole family of normal curves all having essentially the same form. (We will give more details of this form in Chapter 4.)

So far we have mostly discussed continuous variables. A symmetrical and unimodal *discrete* variable is often said to "approximate" the normal curve if the intervals are made small enough and the number of observations is large enough. (The desire to approximate the normal arises partly because of the convenience, for many computations, of statistical tables which already exist for the normal curve.) If the number of observations is too small or the size of the interval too large, discrete observations may still be distributed symmetrically and more or less in a bell-shaped form, but they will not describe a smooth curve.

Where We Stand

We are now in a position to do two things: we can organize our data in a manner that will facilitate their examination and manipulation; and we can roughly describe the shape of their distribution. With a small number of observations an *array* is useful as a tool of organization; this means simply that we arrange our set of observations in order from highest to lowest value. With a large number of observations, *grouping* becomes useful; we combine a range of values into class intervals—for example, we assign the values 0, 1, 2, 3, 4 to the interval 0–4—and tabulate the number of observations in each interval, treating the observations as if they all had the value of the midpoint of the interval.

Having obtained a frequency distribution, we may then attempt to describe it as a whole. It may be symmetrical or skewed, unimodal or bimodal, etc. These descriptive terms are useful in two ways: they give us some intuitive sense of the pattern of our data, and they provide—as we shall discover later—an additional guide in choosing the statistical methods appropriate for our data.

In the next two chapters we continue with the description of univariate measurement data, facing the following problem: in the frequency distribution as a whole there are N observations, and we desire a smaller set of numbers that will give an economical yet precise description of the distribution's salient features. The two most important features are: (1) the distribution's central or typical value, called an *average*, which we take up in Chapter 3; and (2) the distribution's concentration or spread around this central value, called the *dispersion*, which we take up in Chapter 4.

Chapter 2

WORKBOOK EXERCISES

In the following exercises you will be asked not only to tabulate frequency distributions but also to represent them graphically, so that you may better visualize them. There are many forms of graphic presentation, but for variables the two simplest methods are the *histogram* and the *frequency polygon*. We will describe briefly how to construct each of these.

The Histogram

The histogram represents frequencies by a rectangular bar, the area of which is proportional to the frequency. If the class intervals are all equal, the height is sufficient to indicate the frequency in the interval. A histogram of an approximately normal distribution looks something like this:

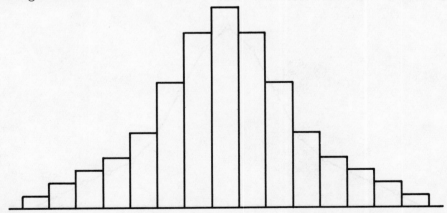

To make a histogram you must mark the class intervals off along the baseline; we have done this for you in the following problems. Your problem then reduces to finding the right height for each rectangular bar. We have marked off frequencies along a line perpendicular to and at the left of the baseline. This serves as a ruler. For the first interval suppose the frequency is 10. To represent this you find 10 on the perpendicular rule and this is the height of the first bar. The sides of the bar are drawn at the boundaries of the class interval, indicated on the baseline, e.g.:

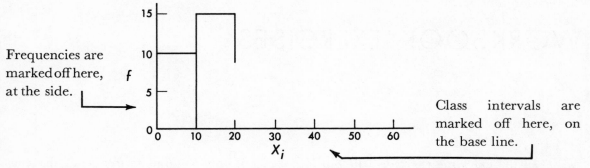

To find the height of the second interval, with a frequency of, say, 15, find approximately where 15 is on the perpendicular rule (you will have to estimate when frequencies fall between marked points).

The Frequency Polygon

Instead of rectangular bars, the frequency polygon uses dots connected by lines. The dots, or, more elegantly, points, are placed at heights representing the frequency, as before, and directly above the *midpoint* of the class intervals on the baseline. A frequency polygon of the distribution shown above looks like this:

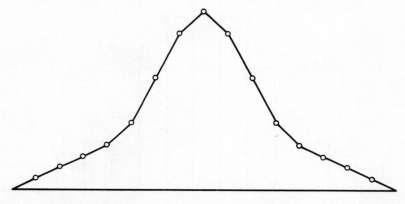

To make a frequency polygon you can use the same kind of baseline and perpendicular rule, provided below. (To make your own polygon, of course, you first make your own

X- and *Y*-axes.) The only new steps are that you must find and mark off the *midpoints* of each interval, as described on page 20; and you must finish off the polygon by touching the baseline on the two ends of the distribution. For the first interval, for instance, suppose the class boundaries are 0 to 10. The midpoint is therefore 5. Mark the point on the baseline. The frequency is 10, as before. Find 10 at the side. A point is placed at $X = 5, f = 10$. Follow this procedure for the second interval, also. It will have a midpoint of 15 and a height of 15 (using the same illustration as in the histogram), and a point is put at 15, 15; and so on. You connect the points by a straight line. The first two steps are shown below:

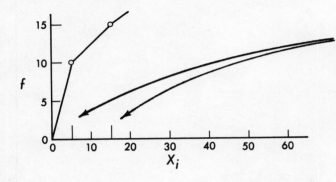

The midpoints are marked on the baseline; actually the class boundaries are not necessary, except to find the midpoints.

1. One of the classic studies of delinquency is Shaw and McKay's *Social Factors in Juvenile Delinquency* (Shaw and McKay, 1931); and one of their basic sources of data is the 1926 police series (records of offenses known to the police) from Chicago, showing rates of delinquency in 113 ecological subareas of the city. The rates, in order by area number, are as follows (there are 112 rates; one is missing):

0.0	1.3	0.5	0.3	0.0	9.8	21.5	1.0	2.1	5.1
0.2	1.2	1.6	0.9	0.4	6.9	7.2	13.1	26.6	2.2
0.3	2.3	1.6	1.1	1.4	2.2	7.3	8.0	14.2	8.0
1.6	0.9	1.0	0.8	1.1	26.1	9.2	7.4	4.6	14.9
1.9	3.0	3.0	0.7	0.3	17.2	23.0	6.0	17.6	18.8
1.5	2.4	4.1	8.0	4.4	18.9	8.9	9.2	5.2	10.9
1.4	0.7	0.7	1.7	4.9	16.1	10.5	1.8	1.3	0.4
7.7	14.3	4.9	0.0	1.6	1.5	2.3	3.8	1.7	1.7
1.8	4.6	10.2	14.0	22.5	1.0	1.3	3.4	2.8	1.5
0.8	3.2	2.9	3.6	8.2	3.1	4.4	8.8	1.7	3.1
4.9	9.0	8.7	4.5	9.3	7.0	3.1	8.1	4.6	7.2
					5.2	4.7			

a. Using the following class intervals, tabulate the rates and record the frequency in the table on page 32.

X	Tabulation	Frequency*
0–1.9		
2–3.9		
4–5.9		
6–7.9		
8–9.9		
10–11.9		
12–13.9		
14–15.9		
16–17.9		
18–19.9		
20–21.9		
22–23.9		
24–25.9		
26–27.9		
28–29.9		

* Column three is used for adding up the tab marks.

[*Note:* Before turning in your work transfer your tabulation to Problem 3 on page 83. You will use it again in this problem.]

b. Draw a histogram of the distribution.

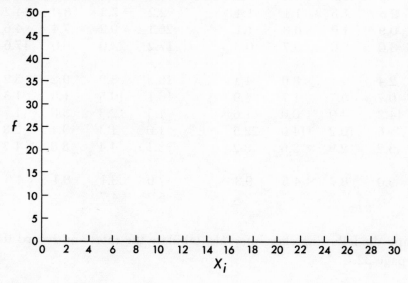

c. This is a .... distribution of a .... variable.

d. Draw a frequency polygon of the distribution.   I can find the midpoints by taking

....

of each interval and adding the result to ....

For the first interval, for instance, this would be .... — .... = ... ,

and .... + ... = ...

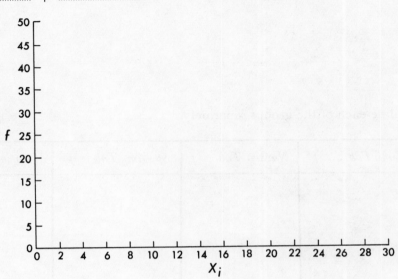

2. The extension of Rorschach testing into other cultures has sometimes provided interesting results, particularly from features of the test that are easily interpreted.   The following results (from Kaplan, 1954) are average response time of subjects in four cultures in the Ramah area of New Mexico, i.e., the total time taken for the test, divided by the number of responses each individual made; time is given in seconds.

Average Individual Response Time: 4 Southwestern Cultures (In Seconds per Response)

	Zuni Time					Navaho Time			
48	117	256	96	43	76	124	23	43	98
54	73	35	109	126	53	67	62	136	131
63	103	54	36	51	241	34	111	127	94
45	41	46	58	52	67	75	180	88	170
30	56				142	110	104	93	22
					67				

	Spanish-American Time			
44	30	179	62	42
60	41	40	100	36
36	26	92	31	81
60	112	20	36	48
64	45	70		

	Rural Mormon Time			
36	25	32	35	29
74	30	33	65	52
37	34	110	78	67
50	45	32	47	27

a. Form an array of the Mormon response time. ....

....

....

....

....

b. Tabulate each of the groups separately.

X	Zuni Tab	f	Navaho Tab	f	Sp.-Am. Tab	f	Mormon Tab	f
0–20								
20–40								
40–60								
60–80								
80–100								
100–120								
120–140								
140–160								
160–180								
180–200								
200–220								
220–240								
240–260								
260–280								
280–300								

[*Note:* Before turning in your work transfer these tabulations to Problem 4, page 60. You will use them again in this problem.]

c. Make a histogram for each group.

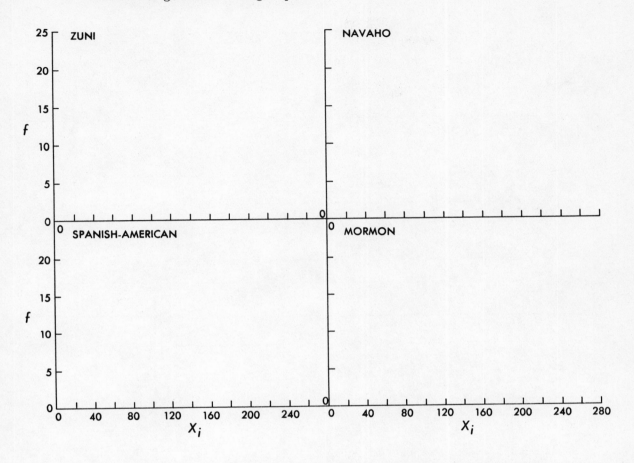

d. Describe the general form of each distribution. Note what they have in common as well as how they differ. ....

....

....

....

....

....

....

....

3. a. Draw a frequency polygon of the following distribution of the ages of ex-husbands of a sample of young divorced mothers (the mothers in this sample were chosen to range from 18 to 38). (See Goode, 1956, for analysis of the data; the original distribution does not appear in this form, in the book.)

X	f
18–20	2
20–22	8
22–24	24
24–26	24
26–28	46
28–30	48
30–32	43
32–34	38
34–36	35
36–38	27
38–40	18
40–42	18
42–44	9
44–46	10
46–48	3
48–50	1
50–52	2
52–54	1

b. How would you describe this distribution? ....

....

....

....

....

....

....

4. a. Draw a histogram of the following distribution of sentences for five serious felonies in Los Angeles County, 1938. (Adapted from Lemert, 1951, p. 322.) The distribution is broken into two parts because of the number of sentences of less than one year.

Sentences in Months	
X	f
Probation	200
0–1	30
1–2	25
2–3	30
3–4	20
4–5	22
5–6	160
6–7	10
7–8	5
8–9	45
9–10	12
10–11	5
11–12	210

Sentences in Years	
X	f
0–1	574
1–2	10
2–3	10
3–4	5
4–5	45
5–6	30
6–7	0
7–8	15
8–9	10
9–10+	15

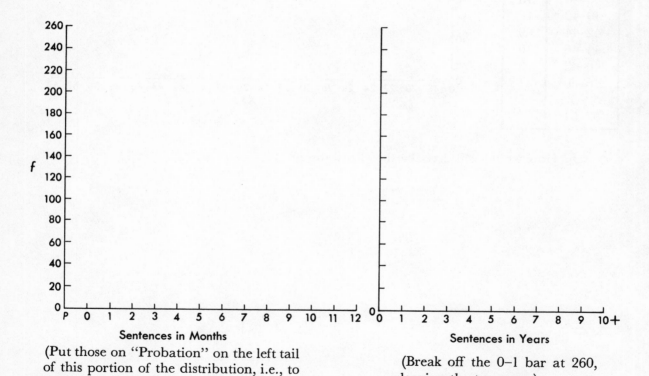

Sentences in Months

(Put those on "Probation" on the left tail of this portion of the distribution, i.e., to the left of "0–1 months.")

Sentences in Years

(Break off the 0–1 bar at 260, leaving the top open.)

b. How would you describe the distribution of sentences in months? ....

....

How would you describe it with probation sentences excluded? ....

c. How would you describe the distribution of sentences in years? ....

Chapter 3

Measures of Central Tendency

AN "AVERAGE" is a measure designed to reduce a set of measurement data to a single representative number. The three most commonly used averages, the *mean*, the *median*, and the *mode*, are all based on the idea that one way to represent a set of observations is to choose the most typically occurring or central value in the set. The three averages differ, however, in the way they define "typical" and in the amount and kind of information they lose in summarizing the observations.

The Mean

The *mean* (sometimes referred to as the *arithmetic mean*) is defined simply enough as the sum of a set of observations divided by the *number* of observations in the set, or

$$\bar{X} = \frac{\sum X_i}{N}$$

A mathematical formula is simply a set of instructions; in this case you are instructed to carry out two operations: (1) add up the observations ($\sum X_i$), and (2) divide the result by the number of observations. The result is called the *mean*. Using a formula to define the mean, rather than a verbal description, results in greater economy and precision.

where $\bar{X}$ is a symbol for the *mean* of the distribution of X_i (read "*X*-bar")

X_i is any observation in the set

$\sum$ means "add up," and is called the summation sign. You will see this sign frequently, so learn it now; it is the Greek capital S, *sigma*, for "sum"

N is the number of observations in the set

If we have a set of 9 observations, say, 8, 12, 14, 3, 4, 6, 8, 12, 5, we add them up and divide by 9, giving

$$\bar{X} = \tfrac{72}{9} = 8$$

COMPUTATION OF THE MEAN FOR GROUPED DATA

For grouped data, the definition of the mean is the same but we apply slightly more complex computational methods.

We will take as an example Table 3-1a (page 43), which shows the adjusted gross income of persons in the United States in 1950 reporting income to the Internal Revenue Service.

In order to find the mean for grouped data we modify the procedure for ungrouped data in the following way. Because we have lost the exact values of the individual observations by grouping, we assume that all the observations in an interval have the value of the midpoint of the interval. For example, in the process of grouping we have lost information concerning the exact values of the 7.77 million individual observations in the first interval (0–0.99) of Table 3.1a, but we assume that they are all equal to 0.50, the value of the midpoint of that interval. In order to recapture the information lost, we estimate the sum of these 7.77 million observations by multiplying the midpoint by the frequency, $(0.50)(7.77)$. We do this for every class, and adding up the products is equivalent to adding up every one of the original 52.39 million observations, except for the error we introduce by being wrong in our assumption that the midpoint represents the interval (i.e. except for *grouping error*). We may then divide by the number of observations to find the mean.

It is possible, however, to simplify this procedure by *coding*.* Coding is any process by which the values of the numbers in a computation are reduced in size. This may be done either by dividing by or subtracting a constant or by carrying out both procedures. We will describe one form of coding in a moment. Before doing this however, we introduce one further simplification: the use of an arbitrarily *guessed* mean (designated X_0) in order to find the true mean. It is possible to compute the mean by using deviations from an arbitrarily chosen starting point and to correct for the error introduced by altering the formula for the mean—the advantage being in the small size of the deviations.† Our coding procedure, therefore, will involve three steps:

---

* This is a simplification if we are computing by hand. If machine computers are available it is simpler not to code.

† The principle on which this procedure is based is that the sum of the deviations around the true mean is zero. If you wish to understand the mathematics of the various shortcuts employed here, see Chapter 4 in Edwards, 1955.

(1) choosing an arbitrary starting point, which we will call the *guessed mean* (X_0).

(2) reducing the numerical values of our computation by subtraction of a constant and/or division by a constant. In the procedure we will describe, we subtract the guessed mean and divide by the size of the class interval.

(3) "uncoding" in the formula with which we compute the true mean.

TABLE 3-1a.

Adjusted Gross Income of Persons Reporting Annual Income of Less Than $15,000 to the Internal Revenue Service, 1950

Income, in Thousands*	Frequency, in Millions*	Coded Midpoint d	Coded Class Sum fd
$0–$0.99	7.77	−3	−23.31
1– 1.99	10.55	−2	−21.10
2– 2.99	11.43	−1	−11.43
3– 3.99	9.84	0	0.0
4– 4.99	5.99	1	5.99
5– 5.99	3.03	2	6.06
6– 6.99	1.52	3	4.56
7– 7.99	.80	4	3.20
8– 8.99	.47	5	2.35
9– 9.99	.30	6	1.80
10–10.99	.22	7	1.54
11–11.99	.16	8	1.28
12–12.99	.13	9	1.17
13–13.99	.10	10	1.00
14–14.99	.08	11	0.88
	52.39		−26.01

Computations

$$\bar{X} = X_0 + \left(\frac{\sum fd}{N} \right) i$$

$$= 3.50 + \left(\frac{-26.01}{52.39} \right)(1.00)$$

$$= 3.50 + (-.4965)(1.00)$$

$$= 3.00$$

$$= \$3,000$$

* In this and in many following tables the numbers have been simplified to make computations less tedious. By converting 7,766,316 into 7.77 million, for example, multiplication and division are made somewhat less difficult. When we do this we make a note, usually after the title of the table, indicating that the table is in 100,000's, or 10,000's, or 1,000's, and so on. In this case we have used two different size-units, millions and thousands, indicated at the head of the appropriate columns. If you want a rough idea of the actual number represented in the table you must take the number actually shown and multiply by the unit in which the table, or column, is expressed; e.g., 7.77 × 1,000,000 = 7,770,000. There will be a "rounding" error introduced because we lose the exact value of the original number in the process of simplifying it, but the number will be approximately correct.

Step (2) may appear complicated and hardly worth the effort, but we use this form of coding because in practice it is exceedingly simple. All it involves is *counting* intervals up and down from the interval containing the guessed mean. For example, suppose that

TABLE 3-1b.

Adjusted Gross Income of Persons
Reporting More Than $15,000
Annual Income to the Internal
Revenue Service, 1950

Income, in Thousands	Frequency, in Millions
$15–$100	0.68
100– 500	.02
500–1000	.006
1000–5000	.002
5000 or more	8 persons

Source: U.S. Treasury, Internal Revenue Service, 1954, Part I.

For persons earning over $15,000, income data are reported with unequal class intervals and an open interval in the top income group (i.e., there is no closing boundary in the class "$5,000,000 or more"). Computation of the mean when unequal intervals are used is possible, but more complex. Computation of the mean when an open-ended interval is used is not usually possible, because the midpoint of an open interval cannot be estimated. (An exception will be explained in the text, p. 47.) We show the data for persons earning over $15,000 for your information, however, and will use them in computing the median.

in Table 3.1a we guess the mean to be 3.50 (i.e., $3500). This is X_0. The *coded* midpoint is 3.50–3.50/1.00, which is 0. The coded midpoint of the next interval down is 4.50–3.50/1.00, which is $+1$; of the second interval down it is 5.50–3.50/1.00, which is $+2$, and so on. In each case we have subtracted the guessed mean from the midpoint of the interval and divided by the size of the class interval; but it is possible simply to *count* down (0, 1, 2, ...) and obtain the equivalent of the coded value. The midpoints coded in this manner are labeled d and are called *step deviations*. Note that as we count *up* from X_0, the step deviations are minus in sign. We always give a minus sign to the values that grow smaller than X_0 (in the sense that the midpoints 2.50, 1.50, etc., are smaller than 3.50) and a plus sign to values that grow larger.

When we have found the value of d for each interval, we now find the sum for each class interval by taking f_i times d_i.* The sum of the $f_i d_i$ column is the sum of its positive

* Note that the letter i is used in two ways in this discussion, both of which follow established conventions. It appears here as a subscript which identifies the class interval of f and d, although in a quite general way. It appears later as a letter designating the size of a class interval; in this second case it is on the same line as f, d, X, etc., and is not a subscript. The two uses must be carefully distinguished and have no necessary relation to each other. Where the context makes clear what is intended, we may omit the use of i as a subscript, and we will frequently do so although it is always implied. Here, however, despite the fact that the sub-i is perfectly general and we could replace it by any number we chose, using the subscript helps make our instructions more precise. It is a general rule that whatever number is chosen to replace i, in the same context i always has the same interpretation; so that in the expression $f_i d_i$ we recognize that the ith class is the *same* class for both f and d. We are, that is, multiplying in every case a frequency in some class by the coded midpoint of the same class. The subscripts help keep this clear.

values minus the sum of its negative values, which we call an *algebraic* sum. The result, of course, can be negative as it is in this case. We then compute the mean according to the formula:

$$\bar{X} = X_0 + \left(\frac{\sum f_i d_i}{N}\right)(i)$$

The "correction" term is added to the guessed mean to give the true mean; i is necessary to uncode the correction term.

where $\bar{X}$ is the mean

X_0 is the guessed mean

d_i is the coded midpoint of the class intervals

f_i is the frequency in each class interval

i is the size of the class interval

$\sum$ is the summation sign

N is the number of observations ($\sum f$)

This formula contains three new features, all of which compensate, in a sense, for the shortcuts we have taken; and a fourth new feature due to grouping. It contains the guessed mean (X_0), the class frequencies (f), the step deviations (d), and the size of the class interval (i). You will note that ($\sum f_i d_i / N$) (i) is called a "correction" term. It rectifies the provisional mean, i.e., adjusts for the error in your guessing. The size of the class interval i is in the formula to "uncode" the d's again. The frequency is there, of course, because the data are grouped.

Use of the computation designs

On page 46 you will find the first in a series of *computation designs*, which are intended to serve three purposes: first, they summarize the steps in computation illustrated in the text; second, they show the most useful way to lay out a problem for computation purposes; and third, they may be pulled out, if desired, and preserved in a file for future reference. Computation designs of this kind will be found in most of the following chapters.

The Median

The mean carries most of the burden in standard statistical discussions, largely because of certain theoretically useful properties. For the sociologist, however, it is frequently an inappropriate statistic. When the mean is computed, each observation contrib-

Computation design for mean of grouped data, using coding shortcuts, for Type III characteristics having k class intervals

(1) Interval X_i	(2) Frequency f_i	(3) Coded Midpoint d_i	(4) Coded Class Sum $f_i d_i$
X_1	f_1	d_1	$f_1 d_1$
X_2	f_2	d_2	$f_2 d_2$
X_3	f_3	d_3	$f_3 d_3$
$\vdots$	$\vdots$	$\vdots$	$\vdots$
X_k	f_k	d_k	$f_k d_k$

$N = \sum f_i =$

1. $X_0 =$
2. $\sum f_i d_i =$
3. $\sum f_i d_i / N =$
4. $(\sum f_i d_i / N)(i) =$
5. $\bar{X} = X_0 + (\sum fd / N)(i)$
   $=$

1. Choose some interval as the one provisionally containing the mean. The midpoint of this interval is X_0. Enter on line 1, at right of table. (Note: unlike d, this is not a coded value; the actual midpoint is used.)

2. Assign the coded midpoints by counting in each direction from X_0; the first interval in each direction is assigned 1, the second 2, the third 3, etc. For the interval containing X_0, $d = 0$. The sign of d is negative for those intervals the midpoints of which are smaller than X_0; otherwise positive. Enter d in column 3 of the table.

3. Multiply the frequency of each class (column 2) by the coded midpoints (in column 3) giving fd. Enter in column 4 of the table.

4. Take the algebraic sum of the fd's (column 4); i.e., add the positive values, then add the negative values and take the difference. If the negative fd's are larger, the sum of the fd's is negative, otherwise the sum is positive. Enter the result on line 2 at the right of the table.

5. Compute the value of the correction term, lines 3 and 4 on the right of the table. Divide $\sum fd$ (line 2) by N, then multiply by the size of the class interval, entering the result on line 4 at the right of the table.

6. Add the result to X_0, giving the true mean. Note that to add implies either addition or subtraction, depending on the sign of the correction term. If the sum of fd is negative, then the correction term will be negative and you will subtract it from X_0.

utes to the result in proportion to its relative size, and the effect is to inflate the influence of a few extreme observations. We understand this intuitively when we try to deal with income data. A few very large incomes can inflate the apparent "average" income of a population, expressed by the mean income, because the mean depends on the *numerical value* of each observation. The extreme incomes, having the largest numerical values, contribute a disproportionate amount to the mean—disproportionate in the sense that relatively few persons have these extreme incomes.

In Table 3-1a we have broken the income distribution at \$15,000; even in this table you can see that the curve of the incomes is *skewed* toward the smaller incomes. But the effect of including the bottom piece of the table is startling. In Table 3-1a the mean income is about \$3000. If the 708,000 persons in Table 3-1b are included in the calculations, the mean income of the combined 53 million jumps to \$3400. Adding 1.3% more persons makes a difference of about 13% in the mean income of the population. (The exact total income reported to the Internal Revenue Service in 1950 was \$179,148,276,000; divide this by 53,060,098, the total number of persons reporting, to get the mean income. Without knowing the exact total income reported we could have only approximately computed the mean, since the last interval in Table 3-1b is "open"—has no closing boundary—and we would have had to guess its midpoint.)

If we do not want to count the extreme values so heavily in summarizing the central tendency of distributions like this one, we must find some measure that does not depend so much on the *amounts* contributed by the extremes. The *median* (designated $\tilde{X}$, which is read "X-tilda") is the measure that serves this purpose. The *median* is a value that neither exceeds nor is exceeded by more than half the observations in an ordered set. This definition leads to somewhat different interpretations for sets with an odd number of observations than it does for those with an even number. If, for example, we have a set of nine observations and have ordered them from highest to lowest values, the fifth observation divides the set in half; four observations are *larger* than the fifth and four are *smaller*. In this sense the median is the "middle" observation. For an even number of observations, on the other hand, the so-called "middle" observation does not exist, and it is therefore assumed by convention that the median is halfway between the *two* observations in the middle. For 10 observations, for example, the median would be halfway between the fifth and sixth.

The median is one of a larger class of order statistics, all of which depend on *position* within an order rather than on absolute magnitude; it is the *number* of observations on either side of the median, for example, rather than the *values* of the observations, that determines the location of the median.

COMPUTATION OF THE MEDIAN FOR UNGROUPED DATA

To get the median for ungrouped data we arrange the observations in order of magnitude first; this is the only point at which size of the observation makes any difference—once the observations are in order we forget their magnitude. Then,

1. If there is an odd number of observations we simply take the middle one as the median.

$$1, \ 3, \ 4, \ 4, \ 4\left(\!7,\!\right) 7, \ 10, \ 88, \ 88, \ 150$$

There are 11 observations; the sixth observation divides the set in half, since 5 observations fall on either side of the sixth observation. The median is the value of the middle observation, $\tilde{X} = 7$. For the same set of observations the mean is 33.3.

2. If there is an even number of observations, the median is conventionally taken to be halfway between the two middle observations (i.e., their average). If the two middle observations are the same, then this is the median.

$$1, \ 3, \ 4, \ 4, \ 4, \ 7, \ | \ 7, \ 10, \ 88, \ 88, \ 150, \ 150$$

There are now 12 observations; if we take the point between the sixth and the seventh observations we will again divide the set in half, with six observations falling on either side of the middle value. But both the 6th and 7th observations have the same value, so $\tilde{X} = 7$ again.

$$4, \ 4, \ 7, \ 10$$

Suppose that the set consists of the four observations shown above; now the median lies between 4 and 7. To find it we take $(4 + 7)/2 = 5.5$.

COMPUTATION OF THE MEDIAN FOR GROUPED DATA

If the data are grouped we have to interpolate within the class interval which contains the middle value of the distribution in order to give an exact figure for the median. The formula looks something like the formula for the mean from coded, grouped data, but in fact it is considerably different:

$$\tilde{X} = l_{\tilde{x}} + \left[\frac{N/2 - \text{cum} f_{\tilde{x}}}{f_{\tilde{x}}} \right](i)$$

This is the *interpolation* term. It serves to locate the median *within* the interval that contains it.

where $\tilde{X}$ designates the median

$l_{\tilde{x}}$ is the lower limit of the interval containing the median

N is the number of observations in the set

cum $f_{\tilde{x}}$ is the cumulative sum of the frequencies up to but not including the interval containing the median

$f_{\tilde{x}}$ is the frequency in the interval containing the median

i is the size of the class interval

In this formula, the term to the right of the plus sign is called the *interpolation* term. This term serves to locate the value of the median *within* the interval which contains it. We will use our income data again to illustrate its use.

TABLE 3-1c.

Adjusted Gross Income, 1950, with Computation of Median for Grouped Data

Income in Thousands	Frequency in Millions	Cumulative Frequency		Computations
$0–$0.99	7.77	7.77		$$\tilde{X} = l_{\bar{x}} + \left[\frac{N/2 - \text{cum} f_{\bar{x}}}{f_{\bar{x}}} \right] (i)$$
1– 1.99	10.55	18.32		
2– 2.99	11.43	29.75		$$= 2.00 + \left[\frac{26.55 - 18.32}{11.43} \right] (1.00)$$
3– 3.99	9.84	39.59		
4– 4.99	5.99	45.58		$$= 2.00 + (.72)(1.00)$$
5– 5.99	3.03	48.61		$$= 2.72$$
6– 6.99	1.52	50.13		
7– 7.99	.80	50.93		
8– 8.99	.47	51.40		
9– 9.99	.30	51.70		
10–10.99	.22	51.92		
11–11.99	.16	52.08		
12–12.99	.13	52.21		
13–13.99	.10	52.31		
14–14.99	.08	52.39		
15 and over	.71	53.10		

For ungrouped data the first operation was to order the observations. For grouped data the equivalent of ordering the observations is the cumulation of the class frequencies in the third column of Table 3-1c. The cumulative frequencies are found by adding successive class frequencies. You can start from either the top or the bottom, whichever appeals to you, without affecting the calculation of the median. Here we have started from the top. To the first frequency, 7.77, we have added the second, 10.55, to get 18.32. To the result, 18.32, we have added the third frequency, 11.43, to get 29.75. To this result we have added the fourth frequency to get 39.59, and so on. Now we want to find which observation is the middle one; so we divide N by 2, obtaining 26.55 (N is 53.10, the largest cumulative frequency). The middle value, then, lies somewhere in the third interval, 2–2.99; that is, it lies somewhere between 18.32 million observations and 29.75 million. We have to interpolate within the interval to find just where it lies. In this case we must take an additional 8.32 million observations (26.55–18.32) out of the 11.43 million in the interval, to find the middle observation; and the value of the interpolation term, $(8.23/11.43)(1.00)$, is added to the lower limit of the interval to find the median.

Note one convenient property of the median, illustrated in this computation. Whereas to compute the mean you must know both the upper and lower bounds of the distribution,

(1)	(2)	(3)
Interval	*Frequency*	*Cumulative Frequency*
X_i	f_i	cum f_i
X_1	f_1	f_1
X_2	f_2	$f_1 + f_2$
X_3	f_3	$f_1 + f_2 + f_3$
$\vdots$	$\vdots$	$\vdots$
X_k	f_k	$f_1 + f_2 + f_3 + \cdots + f_k$

$$N = \Sigma f_i =$$

1. $N/2 =$

2. $l_{\tilde{X}} =$

3. $f_{\tilde{X}} =$

4. cum $f_{\tilde{X}} =$

5. $\tilde{X} = l_{\tilde{X}} + \left[\dfrac{N/2 - \text{cum} f_{\tilde{X}}}{f_{\tilde{X}}} \right] (i)$

$=$

Steps in Computation

1. Obtain the cumulative frequency distribution. Start with the frequency of the lowest interval (representing the smallest value of X). Add the frequency of the adjacent interval, giving the result $f_1 + f_2$. Add the succeeding interval f_3 to this result, giving $f_1 + f_2 + f_3$, and so forth, until the frequencies are all added. The final result should equal N. Enter the distribution in column 3 of the table.

2. Find the middle observation. Divide N by 2 and find, by inspection, which interval contains the middle observation. Enter on line 1, at the right of the table, the result of the division.

3. Find the lower limit and the frequency in the class containing $\tilde{X}$. Enter on lines 2 and 3 at the right.

4. Find the cumulative frequency up to the lower limit of the interval containing the median. Enter on line 4 at the right of the table.

5. Compute $\tilde{X}$, following the instructions in the formula, on line 5. Subtract cum $f_{\tilde{X}}$ from $N/2$, divide by $f_{\tilde{X}}$ and multiply by i. This gives the interpolation term. Then add to $l_{\tilde{X}}$ to give $\tilde{X}$.

6. The median may also be found by starting with the highest interval (representing the largest value of X). In this case, cumulate in the other direction, find the *upper* limit of the interval containing the median, and *subtract* the interpolation term from the value of the upper limit, i.e., $\tilde{X} = u_{\tilde{X}} - \left[\dfrac{N/2 - \text{cum} f_{\tilde{X}}}{f_{\tilde{X}}} \right] (i)$.

with the median you can deal also with *open-ended classes*. An open-ended class is an interval that looks like the bottom interval in Table 3-1c, "15 and over." The upper bound of this interval is unknown (8 persons in the original source are listed as earning $5 million or over; how much over is unknown). We could not find the mean of a distribution reported in this fashion unless we were willing to make some assumption about the midpoint of this un-bounded class. Sociologists frequently make computations on data reported in census sources or statistical abstracts which have such open classes at one or both ends of a distribu-tion (e.g., age distributions are almost always reported with "65 and over" as the bottom class). For such purposes the median or the mode (which follows below) are the only possi-bilities, and of these two the median is the more suitable.

The Mode

The mode is a measure of central tendency which sacrifices even more information than the median, gives a much cruder result, and is thus only occasionally useful. By defini-tion it is the value of that observation which occurs most frequently. If, for instance, we have the following set of ungrouped observations:

$$6, \ 5, \ 7, \ 8, \ 10, \ 6, \ 6, \ 8, \ 6, \ 5$$

the mode is 6; i.e., 6 is the number that occurs most often. This gives a rough and ready measure and is sometimes the simplest immediate summary of a set of data since it can be determined simply by inspection. Note that neither the size *nor* the location of the number is necessary to define the mode.

For grouped data, however, to define the mode *exactly* is no simpler than computing any other measure. If a very rough estimate is sufficient for your purposes you can simply determine by inspection the class the mode is in—the one with the highest frequency—and let that suffice. Otherwise one must interpolate, as with the median.

Perhaps the most useful purpose of the mode comes in the case where more than one mode exists. This happens in *bimodal* or *trimodal* distributions, i.e., double or triple humped curves, as described in Chapter 2. With distributions of this type both median and mean may conceal essential features of the data, and consequently should not be used. To calculate only one mode, of course, would also be an inept treatment of the data, but to say roughly that it is bimodal (giving the two modal classes) may be useful information. In general the calculation of the exact mode is not justified, but if you ever need it, you can find the formula in most elementary texts (e.g., Hagood and Price, 1952, p. 113).

Summary of Appropriate Applications
of Mean, Median, and Mode

The choice among the mean, median, and mode depends primarily on the purpose a measure is to serve. Our purpose might, for example, be to *describe* the central tendency of a sample we have obtained or of a population we have enumerated. If this is our purpose, it should be evident that choice among the three depends largely on the *form of the distribution* which they are to summarize. The mean is suited to symmetrical distributions. For skewed distributions, however, the median is more suitable. It will not be distorted by extreme observations in one tail of a distribution. Finally, if a distribution has more than one peak, a single measure conceals interesting properties; therefore it is best to report the two (or more) modes of the distribution, at least roughly. If a distribution is perfectly symmetrical and unimodal, incidentally, the three measures will be exactly the same in value.

We may, however, be primarily interested in *inferring* the central tendency of a population from a sample value. For this purpose, the mean is more suitable because it fluctuates less on repeated sampling than the median or mode—it is more stable.*

There are, in addition, a number of more specific considerations—more specific in the sense that they are relevant to special cases and special purposes rather than to such general purposes as description or inference. We have pointed out, for example, that the mean cannot be computed from distributions with open ends (unless the source also gives the total value $\sum X$, as well as N), whereas the median or mode can be. On the other hand, the mode cannot be obtained from continuously varying, ungrouped data, because no value would occur more than once. Nor is the median generally considered suitable when the variable to be described can take only a few values. Two medians or two modes, finally, cannot be simply averaged together to obtain the average value of two combined samples, whereas with appropriate weighting, means can easily be combined, even without knowledge of the original distribution.†

---

* A third general purpose is to *predict* the value of an individual observation to be obtained from the population, on the basis of a sample already obtained from the population. The best prediction, for measurement data, will be based on the central tendency of the sample. The decision among the three measures of central tendency, however, depends on the kind of error in prediction we are willing to make. For an excellent elementary discussion, see Freund, 1952, pp. 235–245; in Chapter 7 we will discuss this problem from the point of view of enumeration data.

† To combine means you cannot simply add and then divide by the number of the means to be averaged. You must weight each mean by the number of observations on which it is based; for example, to combine two means, say 4 and 5, from two samples, one of 10 observations, one of 20 observations, you take

$$\frac{(10)(4) + (20)(5)}{10 + 20} = 4.67, \text{ or, in general, } \frac{N_1\bar{X}_1 + N_2\bar{X}_2}{N_1 + N_2}.$$

The values of the larger sample thus receive more weight. To combine samples and compute the median or mode, however, you would need to begin again with the original sets of observations.

Where We Stand

Let us review the purpose of the methods presented in this chapter. We have a distribution of N observations. We want to choose that single number—the *average*—which will best represent one important feature of this distribution—its central tendency. The average is in some sense "typical" of the distribution as a whole, although the particular sense in which it is typical depends on which average—mean, median, or mode—is chosen.

In the next chapter we consider a single number that best represents another descriptive aspect of the frequency distribution: the degree to which the values are concentrated about the central value. Here, too, we will find that there are several different ways to determine such a number.

Chapter 3

WORKBOOK EXERCISES

1. One of the classic studies in the genesis of prejudice is Horowitz's investigation of grade school children (Horowitz, 1936). Horowitz's data come from children in the urban North, and the urban and rural South. The table we shall use is from one of three tests used to measure prejudice; this one is called the "ranks" test. Each child was asked to rank 12 pictures, eight of Negroes and four of whites (presented in random order), in order of preference. The scores are the sum of the white ranks (e.g., if S places whites in ranks 1, 2, 3, 4, then his score is $1 + 2 + 3 + 4 = 10$). If all the white pictures are placed first, this is the minimum score; and if the pictures are placed in order purely at random, with no preference for either Negro or white, the score expected would be about 26.

Compute the means of the four groups. Assume that all the grades have the same number of children. (Use the space at the right in each table to make your computations; show the results, $\bar{X}$, clearly labeled, in the margin.) What conclusions do you come to after comparing the means? (Additional space is provided on page 65.)..........................

....

....

....

We have assumed that all the grades have the same number of children, in order to simplify the example; what would be necessary if they were *not* equal in size? (See the footnote on page 52.) ....

....

....

....

TABLE 1a.

Results of Ranks Test for New York City
Grade School Children, 1936
(Mean Scores per Grade)

Grade	Score
Kindergarten	17.4
1B	13.0
2B	13.5
3B	17.1
4B	14.0
5B	14.9
6B	14.5
7B	15.8
8B	15.4

TABLE 1b.

Results of Ranks Test for Grade School
Children in Urban Tennessee
(Mean Scores per Grade)

Grade	Score
Kindergarten	24.8
2nd	18.0
4th	10.1
5th	11.1
6th	20.5
7th	13.9

TABLE 1c.

Results of Ranks Test for Grade School
Children in Urban Georgia
(Mean Scores per Grade)

Grade	Score
2nd	17.8
4th	16.3
6th	13.2

TABLE 1d.

Results of Ranks Test for Grade School
Children in Rural Georgia
(Mean Scores per Grade)

Grade	Score
2nd	15.9
4th	17.4
6th	14.1

2. An "urbanized area," in the census definition, includes both the population of central cities and the urban fringe areas which are socially and economically dependent on them. Altogether 157 urbanized areas have been defined, accounting for virtually every city of 50,000 or more in the United States. One quarter of the United States population is

concentrated in the 12 largest of these urbanized areas, each of which has a million inhabitants or more.

The relation of the central city and fringe areas, and also of central city and satellite cities (i.e., cities according to their boundaries and charters, but dependent on the central city), is of considerable current interest to urban sociologists. The two following distributions give some basic background information about this relationship.

TABLE 2.

Percentage of the Populations of 157 Urbanized Areas That are Contained *Inside* Central Cities, U. S., 1950

%	f	Computations for $\bar{X}$	Computations for $\tilde{X}$
0–10	0		
10–20	0		
20–30	1		
30–40	1		
40–50	5		
50–60	14		
60–70	24		
70–80	33		
80–90	46		
90–100	33		

Source: Hatt and Reiss, 1951, pp. 64–66.

a. The mean is .... The median is .... The modal class is

.... In this particular case the .... would be the best measure of the

central tendency of this distribution, because ....

....

....

TABLE 3.

Percentage Growth of the Population of the U. S. as a Whole, Metropolitan Areas, Central Cities, and Satellite Cities, 1900–1950

Decade	U. S.	Metropolitan Areas	Central Cities	Satellites
1900–1910	21.0	34.6	33.6	38.2
1910–1920	14.9	26.9	25.2	32.0
1920–1930	16.1	28.3	22.3	44.0
1930–1940	7.2	8.1	5.1	15.1
1940–1950	14.5	22.0	13.9	35.6

Source: Hawley, 1956, p. 2.

b. Compute the mean for each column. (Note that the data are ungrouped, despite their appearance.) What conclusions do you draw from comparing these means? ....

....

....

....

....

....

....

....

....

....

....

....

NAME..

SECTION...DATE..

3. A study of 143 Kent State students (Miller, 1945) shows how the message of President Roosevelt's death diffused in the student community. Like many other studies of the mass media, this study shows the importance of personal contacts as an intermediate step in the spread of messages received from such initial sources as radio.

a. Only 16 students in the sample reported hearing the message first on radio; these 16, however, told a total of 111 other students the news by word of mouth. This is a mean of about .... told by each informant. They, in turn, told others. A total of 122 in the sample, who first heard the news by word of mouth, informed 172 others; in other words, they told about .... each, on the average.

The message was first flashed at 4:50 P.M.; each student was asked when he first heard about Roosevelt's death. The following distribution resulted.

TABLE 4.

Time at Which Students Reported Hearing of President's Death, Regardless of Source of Information*

Time	f
4:10–4:39	7
4:40–4:59	28
5:00–5:19	72
5:20–5:39	19
5:40–5:59	4
6:00–6:19	7
6:20–6:39	1
6:40–6:59	0
7:00–7:19	1

$\bar{X} =$ $\tilde{X} =$ Modal interval ....

* No time was reported by 4 subjects.

b. Find the mean time, median time, and modal time interval for the spread of the information. (Note that some students report hearing the message before it was actually announced.)   Which average is most appropriate here?   Why? ....

....

....

....

      4. Transfer the tabulation of the Rorschach time, Problem 2 of Chapter 2, to the following 4 tables, and calculate the mean and median response time for each culture.   What does the comparison of these averages show? ....

....

....

....

....

....

....

....

a. Zuni Time

X	f
0–	
20–	
40–	
60–	
80–	
100–	
120–	
140–	
160–	
180–	
200–	
220–	
240–	
260–	
280–	

$\bar{X} =$ $\tilde{X} =$

b. Navaho Time

X	f
0–	
20–	
40–	
60–	
80–	
100–	
120–	
140–	
160–	
180–	
200–	
240–	
260–	
280–	

$\bar{X} =$ $\tilde{X} =$

c. Spanish-American Time

X	f
0–	
20–	
40–	
60–	
80–	
100–	
120–	
140–	
160–	
180–	
200–	
220–	
240–	
260–	
280–	

$\bar{X} =$ $\tilde{X} =$

d. Mormon Time

X	f
0–	
20–	
40–	
60–	
80–	
100–	
120–	
140–	
160–	
180–	
200–	
220–	
240–	
260–	
280–	

$\bar{X} =$ $\tilde{X} =$

Problem I

Chapter 4

Measures of Dispersion

AN AVERAGE is useful because it is the single most representative figure in a distribution. But *all* the observations are not concentrated at the average value, and distributions with the same average may differ significantly in how closely they are concentrated around a given central point. We represent the idea of closeness of concentration by measures of *dispersion*, or variability. Here again we choose some single number which summarizes for us a distinctive feature of the distribution we want to describe.

The Range

The crudest measure of dispersion is the *range*. The range is simply the difference between the highest and lowest values in the set of observations $(h - l)$. If, for instance, we have the following five observations,

$$5, 8, 7, 9, 11$$

the range is equal to

$$11 - 5 = 6.$$

For a number of reasons we say that the range is crude. First, it sacrifices a great deal of information. It uses only two observations to describe the distribution, losing $N - 2$ pieces of information. At the same time it is especially sensitive to extreme values. In a set of 100 observations, with a range of, say, 5 to 80, it may happen that 99 observations are between 20 and 80 and only one of them is as low as 5. This has an important bearing on what we call the sampling fluctuation of the range. If further samples are drawn from the same population, the range may differ greatly each time the sample is drawn. Because it is so sensitive to extreme values the range may be both misleading and unstable. Yet for quick, rough work, where there is no premium on efficiency over the long run, the range is very useful despite these drawbacks.

Deviations from the Mean

Suppose that the following set of observations represents the number of children born to the first 10 mothers sampled in a low-rent residential area of a large city:

$$5, \ 3, \ 2, \ 5, \ 6, \ 8, \ 5, \ 1, \ 4, \ 3$$

We can say that the mean number of children per family is 4.2. Furthermore, we can say that the range is from 1 to 8, or $R = 7$. How can we arrive at a better, i.e., more precise and more stable, description of the dispersion of these values?

One way is to use the *deviations* from the mean value. This uses all the observations and it gives us what we want, namely, some measure of the closeness of the observations to the mean. There is some problem, however, in deciding how we should use them. We might take *their* mean, which would give us some single number describing the average amount of

X_i	x_i
5	.8
3	−1.2
2	−2.2
5	.8
6	1.8
8	3.8
5	.8
1	−3.2
4	− .2
3	−1.2
42	0.0

The sum of the deviations taken in the usual way is 0. This is always the case when the algebraic sum is used, simply because of the way the deviations and the mean are defined.

deviation from the mean. As usual, the mean of the deviations is equal to their sum divided by their number.

It is customary to represent the deviations from the mean by a lower case letter, x_i. If our observation is represented by X_i and mean of the set is $\bar{X}$ then $X_i - \bar{X} = x_i$. ("The deviation of the ith observation from the mean is x_i," this says.) The mean of the deviations, in turn, would be $\bar{x} = \sum x_i / N$. Try this once and see what you get...

Obviously some method has to be chosen to get around this particular property of the deviations, or else we have to sacrifice what looked like a promising measure of dispersion. In fact, two methods have been developed to accomplish this, leading to two different measures of dispersion.

THE AVERAGE DEVIATION

One method, called the *average deviation* (A.D.), involves ignoring the signs and taking the sum of the *absolute* values of the deviations. (The absolute value of a signed quantity is the value without the sign, e.g., -4 has the absolute value of 4). For the above set, for instance, the absolute sum of the deviations is 16. The *average deviation* is defined as this sum divided by N, giving 1.6 in this case. In general,

$$\text{A.D.} = \frac{\sum |x_i|}{N}$$

where A.D. means average deviation

    $|x_i|$ designates the absolute value of the ith deviation from $\bar{X}$

  $\sum$ and N, as usual, are the summation sign and number of observations

THE VARIANCE AND THE STANDARD DEVIATION

The alternative method is not so simple but is mathematically preferable to the A.D. This does not usually suffice to recommend it to a beginning student, but the *variance*, and its square root, which is called the *standard deviation*, have nevertheless almost completely replaced the A.D. in current literature. The variance sacrifices the least information of any measure of dispersion; is mathematically the most useful and elegant (because of its algebraic properties); and for certain forms of distribution it has an easily grasped intuitive meaning. Its behavior in samples drawn from theoretically known populations, furthermore, has been rather thoroughly investigated.

Computation of the variance and standard deviation involves squaring the deviations from the mean, in order to eliminate minus signs. The sum of the squared deviations, divided by N, gives a mean squared deviation representing the amount of variability, or dispersion, in the observations. By definition, the variance is $\sum x_i^2 / N$, where again x_i represents a deviation from the mean, $X_i - \bar{X}$. It happens that if our purpose is to estimate the actual *population* variance, and not simply to describe this particular set of observations, this formula for the variance gives a *biased* estimate of the population variance (in this case, an estimate that is systematically smaller than the population value). This bias is corrected by dividing $\sum x_i^2$ by $N - 1$ instead of N. The correction is *not* necessary for purposes purely of description, but we will nevertheless begin to employ it now simply to economize on the number of ways we will talk about the variance. The usage we employ, then, is

$$s^2 = \frac{\sum x_i^2}{N - 1}$$

This is the *sum of squares*, an expression that is important in more advanced treatment of measurement data. To get the *variance*, we divide the sum of squares by $N - 1$, rather than by N itself, because this gives a better estimate of the true population variance than dividing by N will give.

where s^2 designates the variance
x_i are the deviations from the mean, $X_i - \bar{X}$

The standard deviation, s, is simply the square root of the variance,

$$s = \sqrt{\frac{\sum x_i^2}{N - 1}}$$

COMPUTATION OF s AND s^2 FROM UNGROUPED DATA

The definition of the variance, although it gives exact instructions for computation, is not the most convenient formula for this purpose. This is frequently the case in statistics, and explains the sometimes bewildering variety of formulas given for the same concept in many texts. There are usually two ways, and often more, of mathematically expressing the same notion. At least one of these will be theoretically useful; that is, it will be the most concise and will illuminate the skeletal structure, the components, the origin, etc., of the concept. To be concise from the theoretical point of view, however, often entails tedious labor in computation. In addition to the theoretically most useful expression, therefore, there are one or more formulas that are convenient for computation. All these formulas are mathematically equivalent, and many texts try to take the student through the derivations leading from one to another. The several different computation formulas themselves exist because some are better for hand operations, some better for grouped observations, some better for machine calculators, etc. The following formula is probably the most useful for calculating the variance from ungrouped data, by hand:

$$s^2 = \frac{\sum X^2 - \frac{(\sum X)^2}{N}}{N-1}$$

Note that this formula is in terms of the *original observations* X_i, rather than deviations x_i; this saves a great deal of labor in computation.

where s^2 is again the variance

$\sum X^2$ is the sum of the original observations squared

With this formula we do not need to find $X_i - \bar{X}$, for every X_i; we simply square each X_i itself;* for the same 10 observations we have already used, the computations look like this:

X_i	X_i^2
5	25
3	9
2	4
5	25
6	36
8	64
5	25
1	1
4	16
3	9
42	214

$$s^2 = \frac{\sum X^2 - \frac{(\sum X)^2}{N}}{N-1}$$

$$= \frac{214 - \frac{(42)^2}{10}}{9}$$

$$= \frac{214 - 176.40}{9}$$

$$= 37.60/9$$

$$= 4.18$$

$$s = 2.04 \text{ children}$$

In these computations we deal with the original observations in the first column, and their squares in the second column; we add each column and of course count the number of observations, N, and we have all we need to find the variance from ungrouped data. We square the sum of X; divide by N; and subtract the result from the sum of the X^2 column; this happens to be mathematically the same as adding the squared deviations from $\bar{X}$ and saves us the steps required to calculate the deviations. We now have our sum of squares term. We divide this, in turn, by $N - 1$, and we have the variance; we take the square root of the variance and we have the standard deviation.

COMPUTATION OF s AND s^2 FROM GROUPED DATA

Dealing with grouped data, we use the same kinds of shortcuts we used in finding the mean, and usually $\bar{X}$, s^2, and s are computed at the same time. Using the income data of Chapter 3 again, the simple extension of the procedure will be evident.

Up to a point our procedure is exactly the same as in the computation of the mean. A guessed mean is chosen and we assign d by counting, stepwise, up and down from X_0;

* A table of squares and square roots will be found in the Appendix.

TABLE 4-1.

Adjusted Gross Income of Persons Reporting Annual Income of Less

Than $15,000 to the Internal Revenue Service, 1950

(Illustrating Computation of the Variance)

Income, in Thousands, X_i	Frequency, in Millions f_i	Coded Midpoint d_i	Coded Class Sum $f_i d_i$	Coded Sum Squared $f_i d_i^2$
$0–$0.99	7.77	−3	−23.31	69.93
1– 1.99	10.55	−2	−21.10	42.20
2– 2.99	11.43	−1	−11.43	11.43
3– 3.99	9.84	0	0.0	0.0
4– 4.99	5.99	1	5.99	5.99
5– 5.99	3.03	2	6.06	12.12
6– 6.99	1.52	3	4.56	13.68
7– 7.99	.80	4	3.20	12.80
8– 8.99	.47	5	2.35	11.75
9– 9.99	.30	6	1.80	10.80
10–10.99	.22	7	1.54	10.78
11–11.99	.16	8	1.28	10.24
12–12.99	.13	9	1.17	10.53
13–13.99	.10	10	1.00	10.00
14–14.99	.08	11	0.88	9.68
	52.39		−26.01	241.93

$$s^2 = i^2 \left[\frac{\sum f_i d_i^2 - \frac{(\sum f_i d_i)^2}{N}}{N-1} \right]$$

$$= 1.00 \left[\frac{241.93 - \frac{(-26.01)^2}{52.39}}{52.39^*} \right]$$

$$= 1.00 \left[\frac{241.93 - 12.91}{52.39} \right]$$

$$= 4.37$$

$$s = 2.09$$

* Because the frequencies in this example are in millions, to subtract 1 from the denominator would have no material effect on the computation. We have therefore left the denominator unchanged.

Source: U. S. Treasury, Internal Revenue Service, 1954, Part I.

we compute the frequency times the deviation, $f_i d_i$, entering it in column 4. We add a new column, now, which is the coded, grouped version of X^2. We find it by multiplying each $f_i d_i$ again by d_i, giving $f_i d_i^2$, which we enter in column 5. We adapt our computation formula as follows:

$$s^2 = i^2 \left[\frac{\sum f_i d_i^2 - \frac{(\sum f_i d_i)^2}{N}}{N-1} \right]$$

This is the computation formula for the variance from grouped observations; the standard deviation, as usual, is the square root of this quantity.

where s^2 designates the variance

f_i designates the class frequencies

d_i designates the coded deviations

N designates the number of observations

$\sum$ is the summation sign

For the normal distribution, at least, the standard deviation *s* has a very precise interpretation. We can visualize this by looking at the following figure:

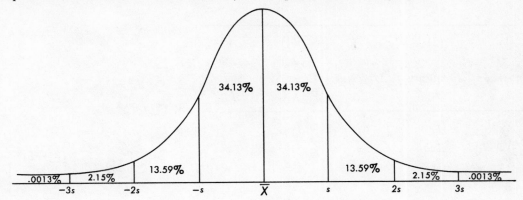

Figure 4-1. Area under the normal curve.

The area under the curve is interpreted as the proportion of observations in the distribution, the total adding to 1.00, or 100%. Between $\bar{X} \pm s$ lie about 68% of the observations (or area) in a normal distribution. Between $\bar{X} \pm 2s$ lie about 95%, and between $\bar{X} \pm 3s$ lie over 99% of the observations.

The mean of a normal distribution exactly divides the distribution in half. If we go one standard deviation to the right of the mean, we will include approximately 34% of the observations between lines marked off at the two points. If we go one standard deviation to the left we include another 34% of the observations. Altogether, a little over two thirds of our distribution is included within $\bar{X} \pm s$. Within $2s$ on either side of the mean, about 95% of the distribution is contained; *almost* all the observations lie within $\pm 3s$.

This information is useful in many ways, *if* (and only if) a distribution actually approximates a normal curve. A distribution that departs from the normal in form will *not*, obviously, be interpreted in the same way. For instance, in the example we have used for computation, about 43% of the incomes are between $\bar{X}$ and $\bar{X} - s$, rather than 34%, and about 24% are between $\bar{X}$ and $\bar{X} + s$. To interpret the standard deviation in terms of the distribution of areas under the normal curve would obviously be inappropriate in this case. Either some other measure, or some other way of interpreting the standard deviation, would be required, in order not to mislead those who make use of these income statistics.*

* We should distinguish between the formal mathematical meaning of the standard deviation—which is simply $\sqrt{\dfrac{\sum x_i^2}{N-1}}$—and the kind of interpretation which tries to make the concept *intuitively* meaningful. The standard deviation always has an appropriate interpretation of the first kind, and it is only with its intuitive meaning that difficulties arise. Note in addition that in the particular example we have used 67% of the observations fall within the range $\bar{X} \pm s$, only differing from the normal curve interpretation by 1%. The principal error in interpretation, in this case, would be in thinking of the area $\bar{X} \pm s$ as symmetrically distributed around $\bar{X}$, rather than in estimating the percentage of observations within the interval.

Computation design for variance and standard deviation of grouped data, using coding shortcuts, for Type III data having k class intervals

(1)	(2)	(3)	(4)	(5)
		Coded	*Coded*	*Sum*
Interval	*Frequency*	*Midpoint*	*Class Sum*	*Squared*
X_i	f_i	d_i	$f_i d_i$	$f_i d_i^2$
X_1	f_1	d_1	$f_1 d_1$	$f_1 d_1^2$
X_2	f_2	d_2	$f_2 d_2$	$f_2 d_2^2$
X_3	f_3	d_3	$f_3 d_3$	$f_3 d_3^2$
$\vdots$	$\vdots$	$\vdots$	$\vdots$	$\vdots$
X_k	f_k	d_k	$f_k d_k$	$f_k d_k^2$

1. $\sum f_i d_i =$

2. $\sum f_i d_i^2 =$

3. $(\sum f_i d_i)^2 =$

4. $(\sum f_i d_i)^2 / N =$

5. $s^2 = i^2 \left[\dfrac{\sum f_i d_i^2 - \dfrac{(\sum f_i d_i)^2}{N}}{N-1} \right]$

6. $s = \sqrt{s^2}$

1. Choose X_0, the guessed mean, and count off the step deviations d, entering in column 3; you will not need the guessed mean itself.

2. Multiply the frequency of each class (in column 2) by the coded midpoints (deviations, in column 3) giving $f_i d_i$.   Enter in column 4.

3. Multiply each $f_i d_i$ by d_i again, and enter in column 5.

4. Take the algebraic sum of the $f_i d_i$'s (column 4) and enter the result on line 1 at the right.

5. Take the sum of the $f_i d_i^2$ (column 5) and enter the result on line 2 at the right.

6. Square the sum of the $f_i d_i$'s (line 1) and enter the result on line 3.

7. Divide this quantity by N, entering the result on line 4.

8. Compute the variance, inserting the quantities on lines 3 and 4 into the computation formula on line 5; be sure to multiply by the *square* of the class interval (to uncode the result), and not just the interval itself.

9. Find the standard deviation by taking the square root of the result on line 5.

Location-based Measures of Dispersion

Most sociologically significant distributions are not normal. Because this is true we need some measure of dispersion that we can interpret clearly even when a distribution is not normal. This takes us again to *order statistics* (such as the median). Two measures frequently used are the range between the first and third *quartiles* of a distribution, and a measure based on this range called the *semi-interquartile range*. These measures, like the median, are based on a positional or locational argument.

The first quartile, Q_1, is that *point* below which one-fourth of the observations lie and above which three-fourths of the observations lie. The second quartile, Q_2, is the median, the point below which one-half of the observations lie and above which one-half of them lie. The third quartile, Q_3, is the point *below* which three-fourths of the observations fall; obviously the remaining one-fourth lie above Q_3. The value of the observations, you will recall from Chapter 3, does not affect these location-based measures, except that the observations must be arranged in order of magnitude.

COMPUTATION OF QUARTILES FROM UNGROUPED DATA

For the time being, in order to make computations simple we will just add two observations to the fictitious set of 10 mothers' progeny given above. We choose two more mothers and they have 6 and 5 children respectively. We now take our set and arrange the observations in an array:

$$Q_3 \quad Q_2 = \bar{X} \quad Q_1$$

8, 6, 6/, 5, 5, 5/, 5, 4, 3/, 3, 2, 1

Q_1 is $\frac{1}{4}N$ from the bottom of the array. Q_3 is $\frac{3}{4}N$ from the bottom or $\frac{1}{4}N$ from the top. Q_2 is the median.

and, by definition, to find Q_1 we have to find the point below which one-fourth of the observations fall. There are 12 observations, so that we need to count up $12/4 = 3$ from the bottom to get Q_1. The value of Q_1 is 3 in this set. (This is purely a coincidence; counting up 3 observations does not always make Q_1 equal 3.) In other words, we have taken $N/4$ of the observations. To get Q_3 we can count $N/4$ down from the top or $3N/4$ up from the bottom. Here it happens that Q_3 lies between two different numbers, 6 and 5, instead of between two similar numbers (3 and 3); in this case we want the point halfway between them, so we take 5.5 as Q_3. Q_2, the median, is 5.

Now the interquartile range is simply $Q_3 - Q_1$, which in this case is $5.5 - 3 = 2.5$. The semi-interquartile range is half this, or 1.25. More generally the semi-interquartile range is:

$$Q_s = \frac{Q_3 - Q_1}{2}$$

This is the interquartile range.

where Q_s designates the semi-interquartile range

Q_3 designates the 3rd quartile

Q_1 designates the 1st quartile

COMPUTATION OF QUARTILES FROM GROUPED DATA

We adapt our computations for grouped data in the same way as for the median. The formula for Q_1, for instance, is:

$$Q_1 = l_1 + \left[\frac{N/4 - \operatorname{cum} f_1}{f_1} \right] i$$

where Q_1 is the 1st quartile

l_1 is the lower bound of the interval containing the 1st quartile

$\operatorname{cum} f_1$ is the cumulative frequency up to this interval

f_1 is the class frequency in this interval

i is the size of the interval

N is the number of observations

For Q_3 simply substitute $3N/4$ in the same formula, take the cumulative frequency up to the interval containing the $3N/4$th observation, etc., as above. Then, to give the interquartile and semi-interquartile ranges, the same formulas are used as for ungrouped data.

No computation design is given for quartiles since they are essentially the same as that for the median, using $N/4$ and $3N/4$ instead of $N/2$ and identical otherwise. For the income data used as an example above, Q_1 is 1.52 and Q_3 is 4.04 (including the portion of the population over \$15,000 in the distribution). The student can try the computations on scratch paper.

INTERPRETATION OF THE INTERQUARTILE AND SEMI-INTERQUARTILE RANGES

Ranges based on the quartiles can be interpreted in two ways. Frequently, for instance, the semi-interquartile range is used with the median and interpreted by analogy to the standard deviation; that is, Q_s is computed and it is assumed that one half the distribution lies between $\tilde{X} \pm Q_s$. But this is true, actually, only if the distribution is symmetrical, and usually we are interested most in medians and quartiles when our distribution is *not* symmetrical. In other words, this interpretation of the semi-interquartile range, Q_s, though common enough, defeats the only purpose for which it is really suited. It *is* true to say that 50% of the distribution lies between Q_3 and Q_1, however, regardless of how the observations are distributed; but we cannot assume that they fall *symmetrically* around the *median* taken as a fixed point.

This bears spelling out a little. If Q_s is treated like s, in the sense that we talk about

$\bar{X} \pm Q_s$, we are saying that 25% of the distribution lies within Q_s on each side of $\tilde{X}$; $\tilde{X} \pm Q_s$ then encloses 50% of the distribution. But in the 12 observations on page 75, for example, 58% of the observations lie between $\tilde{X} \pm Q_s$, not 50% of them. What this erroneous interpretation of Q_s does is to "adjust" the interquartile range $Q_3 - Q_1$ so that it falls symmetrically about $\tilde{X}$. If the distribution is skewed this is exactly what we do not want. Therefore, although Q_s is commonly enough used this way, its meaning can be misinterpreted very easily. The range $Q_3 - Q_1$ is to be preferred for asymmetrical distributions; and the student should not fall into the trap of fixing $\tilde{X}$ somewhere in the middle of this range except in purely positional terms—the *value* of $\tilde{X}$ is not necessarily halfway, nor any consistent distance, between the quartiles.

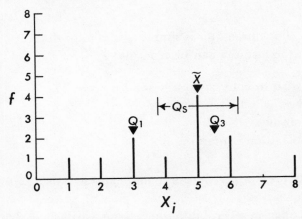

Figure 4-2. Distribution of children ever born to a sample of 12 mothers, showing interpretation of Q_s. (Data are fictitious.)

$$Q_s = \frac{5.5 - 3}{2} = 1.25$$

$$\tilde{X} \pm Q_s = 5 \pm 1.25 = 3.75 \text{ to } 6.25$$

This range contains $\frac{7}{12} = 58\%$ of the observations; what Q_s does is to take the range $Q_3 - Q_1$, split it in half, and redistribute it symmetrically around $\tilde{X}$. This is to be avoided unless the distribution is in fact symmetrical. Note that Q_3 and Q_1 themselves are not equidistant from $\tilde{X}$.

Where We Stand

This completes our treatment of the description of univariate measurement data. In the last three chapters we have seen how: (1) to organize measurement data into arrays and frequency distributions; (2) to describe the shape, or form, of these distributions; (3) to replace N observations with one number that best describes the central tendency of the distribution; and (4) to replace the same observations with one number that best describes the dispersion of the values around the central value. We are now able, in other words, to give a compact but clear description of *uni*variate measurement data.

The natural extension of this kind of procedure is discussed in the next chapter, in which we consider the summary description of the *relations* between observations when we are given *bivariate* measurement data—that is, when we are given two sets of observations made simultaneously on the same individuals.

A Note on the Table of the Normal Curve

Figure 4-1 (p. 73) gives you the basic distribution of area under the normal curve between the mean and the one, two, and three standard deviation points. You will not, in this book, have much use for more knowledge of the normal curve than this figure conveys. However, at the discretion of your instructor, you may wish to read a table of the normal curve, since it is frequently used in more advanced work. The table is constructed as follows.

First the values of X_i are converted to *standard deviation units*, sometimes called *standard scores*, or *standard normal variables*. This means that we express X_i in terms of the number of standard deviations it departs from its mean. We use the letter z_i to designate this transformed value of X_i.

$$z_i = \frac{X_i - \bar{X}}{s}$$

The numerator is simply x_i again, so that the formula can be read also $z_i = x_i/s$.

where X_i is some value of the variable X we wish to convert to a standard score so that we can use the table of the normal curve, which is in standard form

$\bar{X}$ is the mean of the distribution containing X_i

s is the standard deviation of the distribution containing X_i

Class frequencies are represented by an area under the curve and expressed as a proportion of the total area. The total area equals 1.00.

The table of the normal curve, which comes in several different versions, will show the areas under the curve in one or more of the following three ways:

1. It may show the area from $\bar{X}$ to z (area a in the figure at the right). If $z = 1.00$, for instance—i.e., you go out one standard deviation from the mean—the table shows 0.3413; in other words, about 34% of the total area is between $\bar{X}$ and an ordinate erected at a point one standard deviation out from $\bar{X}$.

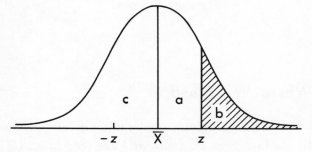

2. It may show the area in the smaller portion of the curve cut off by z (area b). This is the case, for instance, with Table 2 in the Appendix to this book. If $z = 1.00$ the area to the right of z is 0.1587, or about 16% of the total area. If $z = -1.00$ instead of 1.00, the area in the smaller portion is again 0.1587, although it is the tail on the left side of the curve that is involved. The area to the right of z_i will equal the area to the left of $-z_i$ since the curve is perfectly symmetrical.

3. A complete table may also show the area in the larger portion of the curve cut off by z. (This would be the area c in the figure above, plus the area a.) If z is 1.00, for instance, the area to the left of z would be 0.8413. If z is -1.00, the area in the larger portion is now

to the right of z, but is still 84% of the total area. If the table does not give the area in the larger portion you can find it simply by taking $1 -$ the area in b, since the area as a whole is equal to 1.00. You can also find it by taking 0.5000 plus the area in a. (Do you see why?)

Now look at a portion of a table of the normal curve.

TABLE 4-2.

Portion of Table of the Normal Curve

(1) $z_i = x_i/s$	(2) Area from $\bar{X}$ to z_i	(3) Area in Larger Portion	(4) Area in Smaller Portion
0.00	0.0000	0.5000	0.5000
0.50	0.1915	0.6915	0.3085
1.00	0.3413	0.8413	0.1587
1.96	0.4750	0.9750	0.0250
2.00	0.4772	0.9772	0.0228
2.58	0.4951	0.9951	0.0049
3.00	0.4987	0.9987	0.0013

Source: Adapted from Edwards, 1955, Appendix, Table III. The full table shows, of course, many more values of z.

The only other information you might want from the table is the area between two values of z. This is found simply enough with the aid of column 3. In this column you find the area up to the *larger* of the two z values for the interval you are obtaining and subtract from it the area up to the *smaller* of the two z values. In other words, take

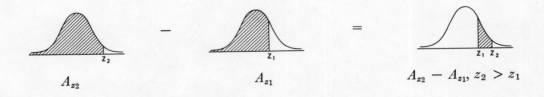

$$A_{z2} \qquad A_{z1} \qquad A_{z2} - A_{z1},\ z_2 > z_1$$

For example, to find the area between the second and third standard deviations from the mean in Figure 4-1—this area is not given in the table itself—we take the area up to $z = 3.00$, which is 0.9987, and subtract from it the area up to $z = 2.00$, which is 0.9772, giving 0.0215. (Do you see why z is 3 if we go out $3s$ from the mean and 2 if we go out $2s$ from the mean? If you do not, study the formula for z again.)

The only values of z you will see much of in this book are 1.96 and 2.58 in column 1 above; they are the more exact versions of the $2s$ and $3s$ ranges, and are very important in statistical inference. (See Chapters 9, 10, and 11.)

Chapter 4

WORKBOOK EXERCISES

1. An author of a monograph reports a mean, $\bar{X}$, and a standard deviation, s, for some distribution in his study. Nothing else is reported about the distribution. A common interpretation of $\bar{X} \pm 2s$ would be that ....

....

Would you accept such an interpretation in this case? ....

....

Explain your decision: ....

....

....

2. French (1951) reports a study of the relation of sociometric status to illness and deviance at a naval recruit training station. The lower the sociometric status the more likely a recruit is to go to sick bay or to be disciplined for some infraction of the rules. (Sociometric status means the number of choices received from others when they are asked such questions as, with whom would you like to go on liberty, or on a dangerous mission, or who would you like to have as top recruit leader.)

A by-product of the study is some evidence on the stability and consistency of status in the recruit companies. Each company was given a sociometric test early in the study and again at the end of the study. Out of the total of 12 companies, 4 were given the initial test in the *first* week, 4 in the *second* week, and 4 in the *fifth* week of their training period. The training period lasted 10 weeks. French computed the correlation between the choices for each company on the initial test and the final test. This means he measured the degree of relationship between the two tests. (Computing correlations is discussed in Chapter 5.)

In the correlations between the tests, shown in the table below, the higher the correlation the closer the relationship between the initial and final tests. In other words, the higher the correlation the more the choices made on the initial and final tests are the same; the lower the correlation, the more the recruits *change* in status from the initial to final tests.

TABLE 1.

Relation of Sociometric Status on Initial Test to Sociometric Status on Final Test

Companies Having Initial Test in 1st Week	*Companies Having Initial Test in 2nd Week*	*Companies Having Initial Test in 5th Week*
0.54	0.56	0.86
0.43	0.41	0.86
0.83	0.71	0.84
0.27	0.75	0.93

Source: French, 1951, p. 521.

a. In the space below, show your computations of the mean, variance, and standard deviation of each column.

b. Now discuss, in terms of the meaning of the mean and standard deviation, the results obtained in the study. First report the conclusion in statistical terms; what happens to the mean correlation over time? What happens to the dispersion over time? Try to draw more general implications, showing what these statistics mean for an analysis of the development of a status structure over time. ....

....

....

....

....

....

....

....

3. Transfer the tabulation of the Shaw and McKay delinquency rates from page 32 to the following table:

X_i	f_i
0–	
2–	
4–	
6–	
8–	
10–	
12–	
14–	
16–	
18–	
20–	
22–	
24–	
26–	
28–	

a. Compute the mean, variance, and standard deviation of the series. Use the table above to fill in d, fd, fd^2, etc. (Allow space for cum f, however); show the rest of your computations below.

Would you make the common interpretation of the standard deviation in this case?

....

....

b. Find the first and third quartiles, and the median of the series (putting in the cumulative frequency). Additional space for computation is provided on page 90.

What interpretation can you make of these measures? ....

....

....

....

....

How does this differ from the interpretation of s? ....

....

....

....

....

c. Compute Q_s (the semi-interquartile range) for the distribution. ....

....

What interpretation do you make of this measure? ....

....

....

d. Which measure of dispersion would you choose to describe these data?   Why?.........

....

....

e. A crucial point in Shaw and McKay's argument (which is that high delinquency rates are not distributed randomly throughout the city but are concentrated in a relatively few areas where they are supported by a traditionally delinquent culture) is based on the following evidence.

TABLE 2.

Percentage of Delinquents, of Population 10–16 Years Old, and City Area,

When 113 Districts are Divided into Quarters on the Basis of Their Delinquency Rates

Quarter*	% Total Delinquents	% Total Population 10–16	% Total City Area
4th Q	54.9	21.8	22.4
3rd Q	30.4	27.1	26.6
2nd Q	10.9	26.2	19.2
1st Q	3.8	24.9	31.8

* A *quarter* in this sense means the interval from quartile point to quartile point; e.g., the 1st quarter is the interval from the lowest value in the distribution to Q_1, the 2nd quarter is the interval from Q_1 to the median, etc.

How would you interpret this table?   (Note: consider again what a quartile is and what it means when you divide the 113 districts into quarters on the basis of their delinquency rates.) ....

....

....

....

....

....

4. The following distribution demonstrates a frequently observed fact about people who marry—that they live fairly close to each other before marriage (this is called "residential propinquity"). The variable X is a "standard city block," i.e., it represents the number of blocks apart the married couple lived at the time they met. Additional space for computation is provided on page 91.

TABLE 3.

Distance (in Standard City Blocks) between Homes of 281 Couples at the Time They Met

X	f
0–8	105
8–16	48
16–24	29
24–32	33
32–40	24
40–48	19
48–56	9
56–64	10
64–72	3
72–80	1

Source: Clarke, 1952, p. 18.

a. Find the mean, variance, and standard deviation of the distribution.

b. Find the median and quartiles of the distribution.

c. Compare the interpretations of the two kinds of measure. Which is the better measure of dispersion in this case? Why?...

....

....

....

....

....

....

5. Kaufman (1944) obtained prestige ratings of 418 families in a rural community in upstate New York, using a panel of 14 raters from the community. Raters were instructed to rank families in terms of general reputation in the community. Kaufman used the mean rank given as the prestige score for a family.

The distributions in Table 4 (page 88) show the prestige scores of individuals of the two basic ethnic stocks, the "Yankees" and the "Oldlanders" (the latter are of more recent European origin than the Yankees).

The "high prestige" families have the low scores (0.75 is high; 5.74 is low). Now briefly summarize the central tendency and variability of the two distributions, comparing them to each other as follows:

a. With the mean and standard deviation.

TABLE 4.

Prestige Scores of Two Ethnic Stocks, Rural New York Community

Prestige Score	Yankees	Oldlanders
0.75–1.24	25	0
1.25–1.74	47	4
1.75–2.24	40	4
2.25–2.74	63	5
2.75–3.24	160	39
3.25–3.74	257	67
3.75–4.24	188	101
4.25–4.74	83	25
4.75–5.24	73	14
5.25–5.74	40	0

Source: Kaufman, 1944, p. 192.

The comparison shows that ....

....

....

....

b. With the median and quartiles.

The comparison shows that ....

....

....

....

c. How much could you say simply with the range alone? ....

....

....

....

....

....

Problem 3b

Problem 4

Chapter 5

The Relationship of Two Variables

THE descriptive techniques that we have encountered so far are designed for observations made of a single characteristic, such as age, or income, or education; now we need to extend them to deal with samples from *bivariate* populations. We will now have two simultaneous observations for each individual. We will have, for instance, both the age and the income of Mr. J., the age and the income of Mr. K., etc. And if we have enough such joint observations we may inquire how age and income are related in this set of observations.

The bivariate problem arises for any of the three types of characteristics defined in Chapter 1. In this chapter we deal with measurement data, for which we employ the techniques of *regression* and *correlation*. Regression techniques are used to *predict* the values of one variable when the values of the other are known. Correlation describes the *degree* to which the two variables are related and indicates to a certain extent *how* they are related. The two techniques are intimately linked, and it will be obvious that the ability to predict one variable when another is known depends on the degree to which the two are correlated. The goals of the two techniques, however, differ and this is indicated by the differences in their end results. Analysis of regression results in what is known as a *regression equation*, which is simply an empirically determined prediction equation. Analysis of correlation results in a *correlation coefficient*, r, which by its magnitude and sign tells you how two variables X and Y are related.

Simple Regression Problems

We will investigate the simplest regression problems first. We begin by examining the idea of a "positive linear relationship" between two variables X and Y.

Suppose that we have the following 10 (fictitious) observations. Note that they are in pairs, i.e., we can identify the individual on whom each observation is made and can say, therefore, that X_1 and Y_1 go together, that they measure the same individual.

X	Y
5	10
4	8
3	6
8	16
7	14
2	4
6	12
5	10
4	8
3	6

Y is obviously equal to $2X$; for example, $(2)(5) = 10$, $(2)(4) = 8$, etc. All you have to do to determine Y for a given individual, then, is to know X. In the equation which defines the relation of Y to X we call X the *independent* variable and Y the *dependent* variable, because X determines Y. In its general form, this equation is:

$$Y = bX$$

This is a simple regression equation; the b is a constant, called the *regression coefficient*, which tells us by how much to multiply X to get Y. For this case b is 2.

When these values are plotted on a graph they form a straight line which increases positively, i.e., goes upwards toward the right. We call this relationship *positive*, and because the line is straight we call it *linear*.

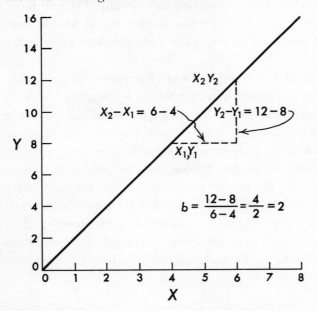

To find b, we find what is called in analytic geometry the "slope" of the line. For any two points on the line, we can find the *rate of change* of Y for a change in X. This is given by:

$$\text{Slope} = \frac{Y_2 - Y_1}{X_2 - X_1}$$

This example happens to involve a line which passes through the 0-point (origin) of both the *X*- and *Y*-axes. This is not always the case, however, and the line can intercept the *Y*-axis at any point. The effect will be to introduce an additive constant into the formula $Y = bX$, which is denoted by the letter *a* and is called the *Y-intercept*.

X	Y
5	12
4	10
3	8
8	18
7	16
2	6
6	14
5	12
4	10
3	8

This relationship is still a positive linear one. But now *Y* is two times *X* plus 2; e.g., for $X = 5$, *Y* is $(2)(5) + 2 = 12$. This gives us *two* constants, and the relation is described in general by the equation:

$$Y = a + bX$$

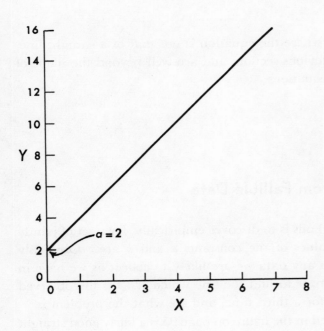

In the general equation of a positive linear relationship, the *a* constant indicates where the line cuts the *Y*-axis; the *b* constant indicates the rate of change of *Y* with respect to *X*. For each value of *X* we find the corresponding value of *Y* by multiplying *X* by *b* and adding the constant *a*. When the line of the equation passes through the origin of both axes, the *a* constant vanishes (equals 0) and only *b* is left, as in our first example.

Negative Linear Relationships

Relationships between *X* and *Y* are frequently neither positive nor linear. The idea of a *negative* linear relationship is simple and means only that the sign of *b* is negative and the line representing the regression slopes downward from right to left rather than upward from left to right; for example:

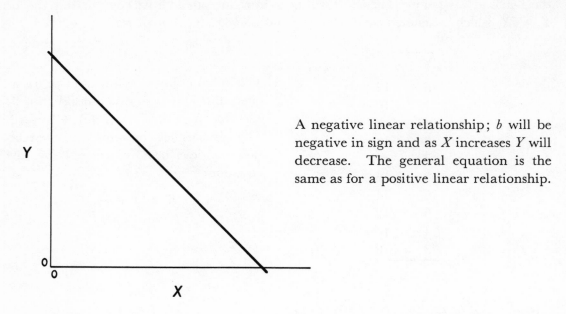

A negative linear relationship; b will be negative in sign and as X increases Y will decrease. The general equation is the same as for a positive linear relationship.

Curvilinear relationships, however, where the equation is not that of a straight line, are not equally simple extensions of the previous section, and are well beyond the scope of this book. We will deal only with linear equations.

Estimating Regression Constants from Fallible Data

The purpose of linear regression methods is to discover empirically, for a set of jointly observed values of X and Y, what the values of the constants a and b are. Obviously we will not find such perfect predictions in any data we are likely to collect as we have in the previous examples. Our problem, then, is to find the line which *best* fits the observed values. Let us take the same values of X, for a third time, and see what the problem is.

The general tendency of points plotted in the figure on page 95 is a fairly good straight line. By inspection we have drawn a line through these points. Can we be more precise? Actually, the line we have drawn is *not* the best fitting line, but how may we know this? The criterion usually chosen, in dealing with this question, is that the sum of the squared deviations from the line be minimized. Note that from the line we have drawn there is a perpendicular to each observed value of Y; these perpendiculars represent the deviation between the predicted values of Y (our regression line) and the observed values

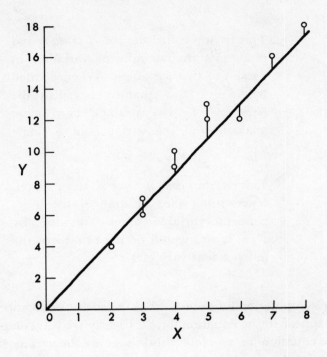

X	Y
5	13
4	9
3	6
8	18
7	16
2	4
6	12
5	12
4	10
3	7

of Y. Now, roughly speaking, we want to make the total length of these perpendiculars as *small* as we can. The algebraically most suitable method for doing this is known as the *least-squares method* which involves minimizing the quantity

$$\sum(Y - \hat{Y})^2$$

where Y denotes the observed values of the dependent variable

$\hat{Y}$ denotes the estimated values of the dependent variable given by the equation

$\hat{Y} = a + bX$

COMPUTATION OF a AND b FROM UNGROUPED DATA

Convenient computation formulas have been derived which satisfy this condition. For a, we have:

$$a = \frac{\sum Y - b\sum X}{N}$$

Note that this is equivalent to saying
$a = \bar{Y} - b\bar{X}$

and for b we have:

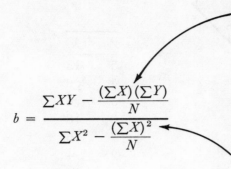

This term is called the *sum of products* and represents the amount of variation in *common* of two variables. When divided by $N - 1$, this quantity is called the *covariance* of two variables, in a sense analogous to the variance of a single variable.

$$b = \frac{\sum XY - \frac{(\sum X)(\sum Y)}{N}}{\sum X^2 - \frac{(\sum X)^2}{N}}$$

This is the *sum of squares* term again, representing the variation of the independent variable alone (divided by $N - 1$, this would be the *variance* of the independent variable).

Notice that we have set up the computation formulas so that the coefficient b appears in the equation for a, but a does not appear in the equation for b. Clearly we will compute b first, and substitute our result in the equation for a. Notice also that only the variance for the *independent* variable X appears in the denominator of the equation for the b constant. Let us practice first on the simple set of 10 observations we have given before. Our set-up looks like this.

X	Y	X^2	Y^2	XY
5	13	25	169	65
4	9	16	81	36
3	6	9	36	18
8	18	64	324	144
7	16	49	256	112
2	4	4	16	8
6	12	36	144	72
5	12	25	144	60
4	10	16	100	40
3	7	9	49	21
47	107	253	1319	576

$$b = \frac{576 - \frac{(47)(107)}{10}}{253 - \frac{(47)^2}{10}}$$

$$= \frac{73.10}{32.10}$$

$$= 2.28$$

$$a = \frac{107 - (2.28)(47)}{10}$$

$$= -0.02$$

(The Y^2 column is not needed now, but we will use it below.) Our prediction for Y, given X, then, is

$$\hat{Y} = -0.02 + 2.28X$$

The error variance

The least-squares method, we have said, is a method of minimizing $\sum(Y - \hat{Y})^2$, where this quantity represents the errors of prediction. Unless the relationship between X and Y is perfect the method cannot reduce this quantity to zero; obviously also, the larger this quantity is, the worse our predictions are. The name for this quantity is *the residual sum of squares*. If we divide by $N - 2$, we have a result which we call the *error variance*; i.e.:

$$s_e^{\,2} = \frac{\sum(Y - \hat{Y})^2}{N - 2}$$

This is the residual sum of squares, i.e., the error of prediction.

where $s_e^{\,2}$ denotes the error variance, or residual variance

Y denotes the observed values of Y

$\hat{Y}$ denotes the estimated values of Y

$N - 2$ is the number of observations, corrected for a bias in the estimation of the population value of the error variance

The square root of the error variance $\sqrt{\sum(Y - \hat{Y})^2/(N - 2)}$ is called the *standard error of estimate*, s_e. This corresponds to the standard deviation of a univariate distribution, and represents the dispersion of the observed values of Y around the estimated regression line, Y on X. If the distribution of the Y values about the regression line is normal, then about two-thirds of the observed values are within plus or minus one s_e of the line.

There is a technical way of talking about the error variance that is rather useful in thinking about both statistical and sociological problems. If the relationship of X and Y is perfect the error variance will be equal to 0; there will be no errors of prediction, or no residual variance left over after Y is predicted from X. In this case, we say that *X accounts for all the variance in Y*. Where the relationship is less than perfect, then we say that X does not account for all the variance in Y, and some other source of variation is present in our data—perhaps pure measurement error, perhaps some other variable that we have not measured, or both. The larger the error variance, the larger is this unaccounted for, or "unexplained," variance. We will expand on this interpretation in the next sections.

Computation of $s_e^{\,2}$ and s_e

It is possible to get the error variance by actually taking the residual sum of squares from the estimated and observed Y's, but the labor involved is unnecessary. It is simpler to use a computation design that does not require the extra work of subtracting each $\hat{Y}$ from each Y; and all we need to do this is the Y^2 column we have shown in the table on page 98. The computation formula itself looks quite fearsome written out, but essentially it involves only elements with which you are already familiar:

$$s_e{}^2 = \frac{\left(\sum Y^2 - \frac{(\sum Y)^2}{N}\right) - b\left(\sum XY - \frac{(\sum X)(\sum Y)}{N}\right)}{N - 2}$$

The elements of this equation are (1) the *sum of squares* of the Y distribution, $\sum Y^2 - (\sum Y)^2/N$, representing the variation of the *dependent* variable; (2) the regression coefficient b; and (3) the *sum of products* of the X and Y distributions, $\sum XY - (\sum X)(\sum Y)/N$, representing the amount of variation X and Y have in common. This formula gives a good idea, actually, of what the error variance is. It consists in the *total variance* of the Y's *minus* that part of the total variance which is accounted for by the relation of the Y's to X. The closer the relationship, the more of the variance X accounts for. Obviously, the more of the variance X accounts for the less is left over as "residual" variance, and the smaller the error variance becomes.

We already have b and the sum of products and we see that the sum of the Y^2 column is 1319, so that the sum of squares of the Y distribution is $1319 - 107^2/10 = 174.10$. The error variance, then, is

$$s_e{}^2 = \frac{174.10 - (2.28)(73.10)}{8} = 0.93$$

and the standard error of estimate is

$$s_e = \sqrt{0.93} = 0.97$$

Correlation

We have so far assumed that Y is dependent on X and that our problem is to find the equation which tells us what Y will be when we know X. The error variance gives us some idea of how much of the variance in Y is explained by X and suggests, therefore, how closely X and Y are related. The error variance of the line relating Y to X, however, is not usually the same as the error variance relating X to Y. When we are *not* willing to say which variable depends on which, we do not have an unambiguous estimate of the degree of relationship between X and Y. We have, instead, two error variances, one for Y predicted from a knowledge of X and one for X predicted from a knowledge of Y. To distinguish the two error variances, when we wish to designate the error variance for Y as a dependent variable we use $s_{y \cdot x}{}^2$ (which is read, "the error variance of Y on X") and when we wish to designate the error variance for X as a dependent variable we use $s_{x \cdot y}{}^2$ (which is read "the error variance of X on Y"). It happens frequently in sociology that we are interested in the *association* of two variables without any assumption about which variable is independent and which is dependent; and even where we are willing to guess, the custom is to measure the degree of *mutual* relationship between two variables by a *correlation coefficient*.

For two Type III characteristics the correlation coefficient usually used is called the *product-moment correlation coefficient*, always symbolized by r. This coefficient takes any value between 1.00 and -1.00. When r is 0 we say there is "no correlation" between X and Y. When r is -1.00 there is a perfect negative correlation; i.e., when X increases, Y decreases. When r is 1.00 there is a perfect positive correlation; when X increases, Y increases.

As in the case of the regression problem we have two simultaneous observations on the same individual, for each individual in the set. We are interested again, essentially, in the variance of each distribution, X and Y, and in their covariance, the amount of variance they have in common. These are the three elements of our definition of r:

$$r = \frac{\sum xy}{\sqrt{\sum x^2 \sum y^2}}$$

This is a commonly cited expression for r. In the numerator you have the sum of products again; in the denominator the two sums-of-squares terms.

where r denotes the correlation coefficient

x represents the deviations of X from $\bar{X}$

y represents the deviations of Y from $\bar{Y}$

$\sum x^2$ is the sum of squares of the deviations of the X distribution

$\sum y^2$ is the sum of squares of the deviations of the Y distribution

This formula is in terms of deviations from the mean (x and y rather than X and Y), but you will see that its essentials are the sum of products (expressing the *joint* variability of X and Y) and the sums of squares of the two distributions (expressing their *independent* variability).

COMPUTATION OF r FROM UNGROUPED DATA

Using the same observations that we have invented for the regression problem, we can illustrate the calculation and interpretation of the correlation coefficient.

X	Y	X^2	Y^2	XY
5	13	25	169	65
4	9	16	81	36
3	6	9	36	18
8	18	64	324	144
7	16	49	256	112
2	4	4	16	8
6	12	36	144	72
5	12	25	144	60
4	10	16	100	40
3	7	9	49	21
47	107	253	1319	576

We use exactly the same set-up that we did for the regression problem; for each member of the sample we have two simultaneous observations, X and Y, and we want to know in what degree and in what way X and Y are related.

A convenient computation formula for r for ungrouped data is:

$$r = \frac{\sum XY - \frac{(\sum X)(\sum Y)}{N}}{\sqrt{\left[\sum X^2 - \frac{(\sum X)^2}{N}\right]\left[\sum Y^2 - \frac{(\sum Y)^2}{N}\right]}}$$

Again you should recognize familiar elements in this equation. Let us review them before computing r. In the numerator we have a familiar formula from which we compute the sum of products; this represents the covariance,* measuring the amount of variance of X and Y together. In the denominator are two more familiar terms, the sums of squares of the X and Y distributions, respectively, in their most convenient forms for computation. Each sum of squares represents the variance of these distributions; i.e., these terms measure the amount each set of observations varies about its *own* mean, or the amount they vary *alone*. The coefficient r, then, is a way of expressing the *ratio* of covariation to independent variation.

In the above illustration,

$$r = \frac{576 - \frac{(47)(107)}{10}}{\sqrt{\left(253 - \frac{(47)^2}{10}\right)\left(1319 - \frac{(107)^2}{10}\right)}}$$

$$= \frac{73.10}{\sqrt{5588.61}}$$

$$= 0.98$$

COMPUTATION OF r FROM GROUPED DATA

For any large number of observations computation of r without a machine calculator can become quite tedious, but basically the procedures are adaptations of those for finding the mean and variance. The only new step introduced, other than the use of a different formula, of course, is the computation of the sum of products term, which is carried out in two stages.

We will illustrate the computation with some data, taken from Yule and Kendall (1950), on the ages of husbands and wives in England and Wales in 1933.

First, look at the set-up of Table 5-1 (page 103). This is a joint frequency table of the two variables, age of husband and age of wife. Look at the number in the lower left-hand corner (you should be looking at a 33). This number represents the frequency of the joint

---

* Covariance is actually defined as the sum of products *divided* by $N - 1$, just as the variance is defined as the sum of squares divided by $N - 1$. We do not, however, require $N - 1$ to appear anywhere in the formula.

TABLE 5-1.

Correlation Between Age of Husband and Age of Wife in Marriages in England and Wales, 1933

Age of Wife						Age of Husband								(1) f_y	(2) d_y	(3) $f_y d_y$	(4) $f_y d_y^2$
	15–19	20–24	25–29	30–34	35–39	40–44	45–49	50–54	55–59	60–64	65–69	70–74	75–79				
70–74											1	1	1	3	9	27	243
65–69									1	1	3	2	1	8	8	64	512
60–64								1	1	4	3	2		11	7	77	539
55–59						1	1	3	5	4	3	1		17	6	102	612
50–54					3	5	3	7	6	5	3	1		26	5	130	650
45–49				1	9	14	9	9	7	4	3	1		42	4	168	672
40–44			1	5	28	19	12	10	6	4	2	1		64	3	192	576
35–39		2	10	24	42	20	13	8	5	2	1			112	2	224	448
30–34		11	75	101	40	14	10	5	2	1	1			268	1	268	268
25–29	1	140	511	179	19	5	6	3	1	1				896	0	0	0
20–24	18	682	585	106	2		2	1						1418	−1	−1418	1418
15–19	33	189	56	8										288	−2	−576	1152
(1) f_x	52	1024	1238	424	143	78	56	47	34	26	20	9	2	3153		−742	7090
(2) d_x	−2	−1	0	1	2	3	4	5	6	7	8	9	10				
(3) $f_x d_x$	−104	−1024	0	424	286	234	224	235	204	182	160	81	20	922			
(4) $f_x d_x^2$	208	1024	0	424	572	702	896	1175	1224	1274	1280	729	200	9708			
(5) $\sum f_{xy} d_y$	−84	−1045	46	46	125	102	127	146	133	118	108	57	17	6224			
(6) $\sum f_{xy} d_x d_y$	168	1045	0	46	250	306	508	730	798	826	864	513	170				

Source: Yule and Kendall, 1950, p. 201.

occurrence of a husband who is between 15 and 19 and a wife who is also between 15 and 19. Each cell of the table similarly contains the frequency of the joint occurrence of the value of X in the column containing the cell and the value of Y in the row containing the cell. Take the number to the right of 33, but in the same row. There are 189 cases in which a husband was between 20 and 24 and his wife was between 15 and 19. If we use X_i to refer to some general class of X and Y_j to refer to the general class of Y, then each cell or box in the table represents those persons who are simultaneously X_iY_j.

At the bottom we have extended the table by adding a series of rows that represent much the same worksheet features that we have used before. In row 1 at the bottom we find the frequencies of the X distribution (without regard to Y). In the second row we have the coded step deviations d_x, for the X distribution. In row 3 we have $f_x d_x$ and in row 4 $f_x d_x^2$. All these represent the univariate X distribution.

On the right of the table we have also added a series of columns, giving the same information for the univariate Y distribution; we have the frequency distribution of Y in column 1; the step deviations in column 2; $f_y d_y$ and $f_y d_y^2$ in columns 3 and 4.

Now we come to the part that is new. What we need is the sum of products, Σxy. Rows 5 and 6 at the bottom of the table are both devoted to finding it. To illustrate the procedure, which is somewhat complicated, we are going to lift a column out of the table.

	30–34	d_y	$d_y f_{xy}$
	$\vdots$	$\vdots$	$\vdots$
	1	4	4
	5	3	15
	24	2	48
	101	1	101
	179	0	0
	106	−1	−106
	8	−2	−16
(1) f_x	424		
(2) d_x	1		168
(3) $f_x d_x$	424		−122
(4) $f_x d_x^2$	424		46
(5) $\Sigma f_{xy} d_y$	46		
(6) $\Sigma f_{xy} d_x d_y$	46		

We have taken the 30–34 column out of the table; next to it we have placed the d_y column, also from the table. The sum of products is now obtained in two steps: (1) The entry in row 5 ($\Sigma f_{xy} d_y$) is obtained by multiplying the cells in the 30–34 column by the d_y in each row [e.g. (1)(4), (5)(3) . . .], and algebraically summing the result (the work for this step is exhibited in the third column of the excerpt on the left, labeled $d_y f_{xy}$); (2) the result in row 5 is multiplied by the d_x for the column, giving row 6 [in this case (1)(46)]. The $d_y f_{xy}$ column frequently appears on the worksheet as a notation in the upper-right corner of the cells of the table.

Let us examine what we have done for the last cell in this column. The frequency is 8. In the row corresponding to this cell the value of d_y is −2. We have multiplied the two to get −16. With the cell above this the frequency is 106, d_y is −1, so we have −106. Each cell is multiplied by d_y in the row containing the cell.

Because there is no other convenient way to enter the results of this first step in the table, many writers recommend placing the result in the upper-right corner of the cell. You would have something like this:

30–34

106	−106
8	−16

or in general

$f_{x_iy_j}$	$d_{y_j}f_{x_iy_j}$

When we have done this for the column as a whole we add up the little notations in the corners, and we enter the result in row 5 at the bottom of the table. (The sum is algebraic, i.e., the signs are not ignored.) Now to get the entries for row 6 we multiply the cells in row 5 by their corresponding d_x, from row 2. For our 30–34 column d_x is 1 and $f_{xy}d_y$ is 46; in row 6 we enter $(1)(46) = 46$.

The same procedure can be followed in the other direction if we care to, and the result would be a useful check of our computations. The sum of products is the same whether computed one way or the other.

We are now in a position to compute r. The formula for grouped data is:

$$r = \frac{\sum f_{xy}d_xd_y - \frac{(\sum f_xd_x)(\sum f_yd_y)}{N}}{\sqrt{\left(\sum f_xd_x{}^2 - \frac{(\sum f_xd_x)^2}{N}\right)\left(\sum f_yd_y{}^2 - \frac{(\sum f_yd_y)^2}{N}\right)}}$$

Substituting in this formula we have:

$$r = \frac{6224 - \frac{(-742)(922)}{3153}}{\sqrt{\left(7090 - \frac{(-742)^2}{3153}\right)\left(9078 - \frac{(922)^2}{3153}\right)}}$$

$$= \frac{6224 - 216.98}{\sqrt{(7090 - 174.62)(9708 - 269.61)}}$$

$$= \frac{6007}{\sqrt{65,270,053}}$$

$$= \frac{6007}{8079}$$

$$= 0.74$$

Computation of the product-moment correlation coefficient *r* from grouped observations of two Type III variables of *k* and *m* classes respectively

	X_1	X_2	X_3	...	X_k	(1) f_y	(2) d_y	(3) $f_y d_y$	(4) $f_y d_y^2$
Y_1	f_{11}	f_{12}	f_{13}	...	f_{1k}	$f_{1\cdot}$	$d_{1\cdot}$	$fd_{1\cdot}$	$fd_{1\cdot}^2$
Y_2	f_{21}	f_{22}	f_{23}	...	f_{2k}	$f_{2\cdot}$	$d_{2\cdot}$	$fd_{2\cdot}$	$fd_{2\cdot}^2$
Y_3	f_{31}	f_{32}	f_{33}	...	f_{3k}	$f_{3\cdot}$	$d_{3\cdot}$	$fd_{3\cdot}$	$fd_{3\cdot}^2$
$\vdots$	$\vdots$	$\vdots$	$\vdots$		$\vdots$	$\vdots$	$\vdots$	$\vdots$	$\vdots$
Y_m	f_{m1}	f_{m2}	f_{m3}	...	f_{mk}	$f_{m\cdot}$	$d_{m\cdot}$	$fd_{m\cdot}$	$fd_{m\cdot}^2$
(1) f_x	$f_{\cdot1}$	$f_{\cdot2}$	$f_{\cdot3}$	...	$f_{\cdot k}$	N		$\sum f_y d_y$	$\sum f_y d_y^2$
(2) d_x	$d_{\cdot1}$	$d_{\cdot2}$	$d_{\cdot3}$	...	$d_{\cdot k}$				
(3) $f_x d_x$	$fd_{\cdot1}$	$fd_{\cdot2}$	$fd_{\cdot3}$	...	$fd_{\cdot k}$	$\sum f_x d_x$			
(4) $f_x d_x^2$	$fd_{\cdot1}^2$	$fd_{\cdot2}^2$	$fd_{\cdot3}^2$	...	$fd_{\cdot k}^2$	$\sum f_x d_x^2$			
(5) $\sum f_{xy} d_y$	$\sum f_{\cdot1} d_y$	$\sum f_{\cdot2} d_y$	$\sum f_{\cdot3} d_y$	...	$\sum f_{\cdot k} d_y$				
(6) $\sum f_{xy} d_x d_y$	$\sum f_{\cdot1} d_{\cdot1} d_y$	$\sum f_{\cdot2} d_{\cdot2} d_y$	$\sum f_{\cdot3} d_{\cdot3} d_y$	...	$\sum f_{\cdot k} d_{\cdot k} d_y$	$\sum f_{xy} d_x d_y$			

$$r = \frac{\sum f_{xy} d_x d_y - \dfrac{(\sum_x f_x d)(\sum f_y d_y)}{N}}{\sqrt{\left[\sum f_x d_x^2 - \dfrac{(\sum f_x d_x)^2}{N}\right]\left[\sum f_y d_y^2 - \dfrac{(\sum f_y d_y)^2}{N}\right]}}$$

If you have trouble with the notation see the opposite page.

Steps in the computation

1. Choose some provisional mean for both the *X* and *Y* distributions. Enter the step deviations from the means in column 2 and row 2 (at the bottom of the table you will find the "rows" referred to), respectively. You will not need X_0 or Y_0 themselves.

2. Compute $f_x d_x$ and $f_y d_y$, entering the results in column 3 and row 3, respectively.

3. Compute $f_x d_x^2$ and $f_y d_y^2$ as before, entering the results in column 4 and row 4 at the bottom, respectively.

4. Now find the sum of products, as follows:

   a. In the corner of each cell of the table record the product of the cell frequency times the value of d_y in the row containing the cell, giving $d_i.f_{ij}$.

   b. Take the algebraic sum of $d_i.f_{ij}$ for each column and enter in row 5 at the bottom of the table.

   c. Multiply each figure in row 5 by the corresponding d_x in that column (from row 2), and enter in row 6.

5. Take the algebraic sum of columns 3 and 4, and of rows 3, 4, and 6.

6. Substitute these sums in the formula for r and carry out the calculation of r.

7. If you wish to check the computation of the sum of products you can follow steps 4 and 5 again, but for d_y read d_x and for d_x read d_y. The results are entered in additional columns added at the right of the table. (This would give you a column 5 and a column 6.) If you do this, the following quantities should check:

$$\sum f_{xy}d_y = \sum f_y d_y \qquad \text{(col. 3 and row 5)}$$

$$\sum f_{xy}d_x = \sum f_x d_x \qquad \text{(col. 5 and row 3)}$$

$$\sum f_{xy}d_x d_y = \sum f_{xy}d_x d_y \qquad \text{(col. 6 and row 6)}$$

How to read the dot notation

To show the general form of a correlation table with exact detail involves too many subscripts. We have introduced in this table a new form of notation which we have not used in the body of the chapter. We will, however, use it later and it helps here to reduce the confusion of subscripts a little.

In the text we have indicated the joint frequency of a given X and a given Y by $X_i Y_j$. Some economy is achieved by using f_{ij} instead. In this usage the subscripts have a conventionally fixed position. The first position always indicates the *row* and the second position always indicates the *column* in which the frequency is found.

Now when we come to the columns and rows on the margins of the table, we use dots to reduce the subscripts. The secret of the dots is their position; they follow the conventions we have just described. When we are dealing with a bivariate distribution and want to refer to *one* of the two variables we have to use something like f_{x1} or f_{y1} or else we will be ambiguous in our reference. It is slightly less clumsy to use $f_1.$ and $f_{.1}$. The dot fills the *vacant* position, and therefore shows which variable the subscript denotes. The row is always shown in the first position; $f_1.$ means that the 1 is in first position and the second position is vacant. It follows that the 1 means Y_1. The column is always shown in the second position: $f_{.1}$ means that the 1 is in the second position and the first position is vacant. It follows that the 1 means X_1.

There are four essential principles in the interpretation of the correlation coefficient. The first is that it measures association but can tell you nothing about cause and effect, no matter how long you stare at it. The association may be sheer accident. It may be due entirely or largely to the correlation of each variable with some third unmeasured or unknown variable (this problem is considered in detail in Chapter 8). In any case, the concept of cause depends on some idea of a time order of the variables, and correlation itself does not depict this time relation. In order to make an interpretation of *cause*, even for a *perfect* correlation between two variables, you must have some additional piece of information which is not involved at any point in the computation of r itself.

The second principle is that r does not itself tell you how much variation in X and Y is accounted for by their mutual relationship. This is given by r^2. If we have a correlation of 0.90 between X and Y, then only $0.90^2 = 0.81$, or 81%, of the total variation in X and Y is explained by their common variation, or mutual relationship. We call r^2 the *coefficient of determination*. It tells us the proportion of variation "explained" by the relationship of X and Y. The correlation coefficient, r, is a more customary quantity to cite, perhaps because for many people it is difficult to think in terms of squared quantities; but except for the habitual significance accorded r—which varies in different fields—it is very difficult to interpret r itself.

The third essential principle in the interpretation of r is that it measures only the *linear* relationship between two variables. A number of important relationships in sociology are not linear. Bernard Lander, for instance, shows that in Baltimore the relationship between the proportion of Negroes in a census tract and its delinquency rate is curvilinear (Lander, 1954). The delinquency rate is low in all-white neighborhoods in general; as the proportion of Negroes in the neighborhood increases the delinquency rate increases also, which has been known for some time. But as the proportion of Negroes passes 50% the relationship to delinquency changes; it begins, in fact, to reverse itself. And in all-Negro neighborhoods, or in almost all-Negro neighborhoods, the delinquency rate is again low. His regression line would look something like this:

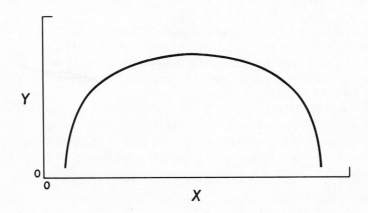

If r is used to measure this relationship it will underestimate the degree of the relationship, and if interpreted without examining the original data it may mislead you. It will tell *only* the amount of *straight line* relationship between X and Y.

A fourth principle is one of special interest to sociologists. This principle concerns the interpretation of correlations between properties of areas or groups, which are known as *ecological* correlations. Such correlations are frequent in sociology; an example is the correlation we have just examined, between the proportion of Negroes and the delinquency rate in a census tract. A correlation between the median income of a tract and its delinquency rate would be another example. The unit in such cases is some aggregate of individuals rather than the individuals themselves, and in fact we may have no information on whether *individual* Negroes are delinquent or whether *individuals* with low income are delinquents. It is frequently assumed that such ecological correlations may be used *in place of* correlations based on individuals. W. S. Robinson has shown that this is not a legitimate use of ecological correlations (Robinson, 1950). Indeed, the error in employing them in this way may be extremely large. Robinson shows, for example, that the correlation between the percentage of Negroes and the percentage of illiterates in a region in the United States is very high, $r = .946$. The correlation between race and illiteracy when individual Negroes and whites and individual literates and illiterates are identified, however, is only .203. The inflation of the ecological correlation between race and literacy is due largely to the fact that the more Negroes in a region the more illiterate whites there are in the same region.

We may think of an ecological correlation as arising in the following way. For each unit area we imagine a correlation table. An ecological correlation is computed essentially on the basis of the univariate frequencies (the two margins) of these tables. Knowledge about the *individuals* in the unit areas, given in the bivariate cells inside the tables, is lost by this procedure. (The computation is made this way usually only because the individual data are unknown to the investigator.) Ecological correlations, therefore, must always be used with extreme care and can only be interpreted as indicating the relationship of group or areal properties to each other. (See Menzel, 1950, for a discussion of some legitimate uses of the ecological correlation.) When they are interpreted as correlations of the properties of individuals, we call this the *ecological fallacy*.

Where We Stand

Chapter 5 completes our discussion of the description of measurement data. We have learned to describe, successively: (1) the shape of a univariate distribution, (2) the central value and dispersion of a univariate distribution, and (3) the relationship between sets of joint measurements made simultaneously on the same individuals. The description of bivariate measurement data has been made from two points of view; we have considered first the problem of *predicting* one set of observations, given our knowledge of the other, which

As we have remarked, the techniques of correlation and regression are intimately related. The same elements, in fact, are involved in the computation of either r or the regression constants and error variance. In the following design we assume that the computations for r are performed first. During these computations you should save the following quantities, entering them on the appropriate lines:

1. $\sum f_{xy} d_x d_y - \dfrac{(\sum f_x d_x)(\sum f_y d_y)}{N} =$

2. $\sum f_x d_x{}^2 - \dfrac{(\sum f_x d_x)^2}{N} =$

3. $\sum f_y d_y{}^2 - \dfrac{(\sum f_y d_y)^2}{N} =$

4. $r =$

In addition, during the computations you should save and record the quantities necessary to compute the means of the X and Y distributions:

5. a. $X_0 =$
   b. $\sum f_x d_x =$ $\bar{X} = X_0 + \dfrac{(\sum f_x d_x)}{N} (i_x) =$
   c. $i_x =$

6. a. $Y_0 =$
   b. $\sum f_y d_y =$ $\bar{Y} = Y_0 + \dfrac{(\sum f_y d_y)}{N} (i_y) =$
   c. $i_y =$

Now the regression constants and error variance may be found as follows:

For the line of Y on X:

$b_{y \cdot x} =$
$$\left[\frac{\sum f_{xy} d_x d_y - \dfrac{(\sum f_x d_x)(\sum f_y d_y)}{N}}{\sum f_x d_x{}^2 - \dfrac{(\sum f_x d_x)^2}{N}} \right] \left(\frac{i_y}{i_x} \right)$$

$a_{y \cdot x} = \bar{Y} - b_{y \cdot x} \bar{X}$

$$s_{y \cdot x}{}^2 = i_y{}^2 (1 - r^2) \left[\frac{\sum f_y d_y{}^2 - \dfrac{(\sum f_y d_y)^2}{N}}{N - 2} \right]$$

For the line of X on Y:

$b_{x \cdot y} =$
$$\left[\frac{\sum f_{xy} d_x d_y - \dfrac{(\sum f_x d_x)(\sum f_y d_y)}{N}}{\sum f_y d_y{}^2 - \dfrac{(\sum f_y d_y)^2}{N}} \right] \left(\frac{i_x}{i_y} \right)$$

$a_{x \cdot y} = \bar{X} - b_{x \cdot y} \bar{Y}$

$$s_{x \cdot y}{}^2 = i_x{}^2 (1 - r^2) \left[\frac{\sum f_x d_x{}^2 - \dfrac{(\sum f_x d_x)^2}{N}}{N - 2} \right]$$

The standard error of estimate, of course, is the square root of the error variance. Note carefully the crucial subscripts in these formulas or you will easily get lost.

is the problem of regression techniques; and, second, we have considered the problem of *describing* the relationship between two variables when we do not assume that knowledge of either of them is prior, which is the problem of correlation techniques.

So far, however, we have usually dealt with measurement data. When we have considered order statistics it has generally been because we have been given measurement data with special distribution problems, not because we have been given data in the original form of an order. And we have not introduced the problem of dealing with attributes at all. In the next three chapters we must now start over again, considering this time the descriptive treatment of attributes and orders.

Chapter 5

WORKBOOK EXERCISES

1. Blau (1955) compares scores of competitiveness and productivity in two sections of a state employment agency. In Section A the norms of the group favor competition, despite the fact that the circumstances of the job are such that if you want to make more job placements than do others in your section you have to monopolize available openings so that others are prevented from filling them. The more competitive interviewers, then, hoard openings. In Section B the norms of the group favor cooperation, so that all job openings coming to the section are shared by the 5 interviewers in that section.

Section A		Section B	
Competitiveness (X) *	*Productivity (Y)* †	*Competitiveness (X)* *	*Productivity (Y)* †
3.9	0.70	2.2	0.53
3.1	0.49	1.6	0.71
4.9	0.97	1.5	0.75
3.2	0.71	2.1	0.55
1.8	0.45	2.1	0.97
2.9	0.61		
2.1	0.39		

Source: Blau, 1955, p. 53.

Section B:

$\bar{X} =$

$\bar{Y} =$

$r =$

Section A:

$\bar{X} =$

$\bar{Y} =$

$r =$

* Based on the degree to which each interviewer made more than the expected number of referrals of his own clients to job openings he himself had received; i.e. the degree to which he hoarded job openings as they came in.

† The proportion of actual placements made (client actually gets job) divided by the number of openings per interviewer per section.

a. Compute the mean competitiveness score for each group; the mean productivity score for each group; and the correlation of competitiveness and productivity for each group.

What conclusions do you draw from this analysis? ....
....
....
....
....
....
....

b. Now compute, in the space provided on page 120, the regression constants for the scores in Section A, predicting productivity from the competitiveness scores; show your completed regression equation. Then compute the error variance and standard error of estimate for this equation.

$b =$

$a =$

$\hat{Y} =$

$s_{y \cdot x}^2 =$

$s_{y \cdot x} =$

2. Table 1 represents the consensus scores of 93 informal work groups on two separate items. Item 1 is a question asking the members of the group to name the individual to whom they would go if they wanted information about unions, wages, or other work-relevant matters; the respondents were asked to name a member of their own work group. Item 2 is a question asking them to name the individual they would ask about local politics, or other community affairs. The scores were computed from the proportion of the group who *agreed* on the individual they would ask. A low score means the group did not agree, a high score means that they did. A high correlation of the two items would mean that if the group agrees on whom it would ask in one case, it also agrees in the other; or that disagreement in one case was related to disagreement in the other. Note that this does *not* mean the *same individual* was chosen for both kinds of items; this happened, in fact, less than half the time. A different individual might be named for the two items and yet the group might achieve consensus on whom they name in both cases; the group, in other words, might have differentiated leader, or "expert" roles, with perfect consensus. Does consensus on one kind of leadership correlate with consensus on the other? (Technically this question is answered by examining how much of the total variation is accounted for by the mutual relation of the two variables.) ....

TABLE 1.

Group Consensus Score, Item 1

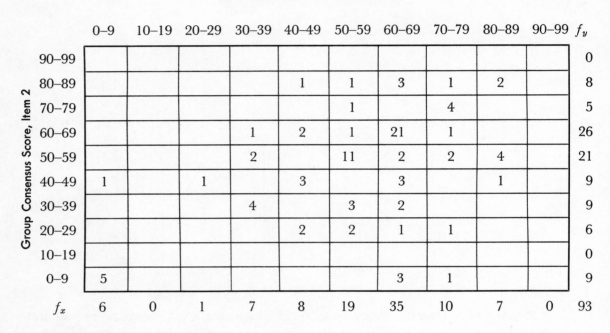

Group Consensus Score, Item 2	0–9	10–19	20–29	30–39	40–49	50–59	60–69	70–79	80–89	90–99	f_y
90–99											0
80–89					1	1	3	1	2		8
70–79						1		4			5
60–69				1	2	1	21	1			26
50–59				2		11	2	2	4		21
40–49	1		1		3		3		1		9
30–39				4		3	2				9
20–29					2	2	1	1			6
10–19											0
0–9	5						3	1			9
f_x	6	0	1	7	8	19	35	10	7	0	93

Source: Original data.

On the blank page provided on page 121, draw your own correlation table for computations.   (Follow the layout in the computation design.)

3. Table 2 represents indices of anomie and crime in 83 cities of the United States, taken from computations reported recently by Porterfield and Talbert (1954, pp. 192–193). What is the correlation between the two indices? How much of the total variation is accounted for by their relationship? ....

....

....

(If you wish, you may also compute the regression of crime, as the dependent variable, on anomie.)

As in question 2, draw your own correlation table in the space provided on page 122.

TABLE 2.

Anomie Scores, 83 U. S. Cities, 1940–1950

Crime Scores (Murder and Burglary), 83 U. S. Cities 1950–1951

Crime Scores	Anomie Scores											f_y
	10–29	30–49	50–69	70–89	90–109	110–129	130–149	150–169	170–189	190–209	210–229	
180–189							1					1
170–179												0
160–169												0
150–159				1				1				2
140–149				1				1				2
130–139				1	2			1				4
120–129		1	1	1	2	1						6
110–119		1	1			1		1				4
100–109		2	5	3	2		5		2		1	20
90–99	1	3	1	2	5	1	1	2				16
80–89	3	5	1	2	2	2	1	1	1			18
70–79		3		1	1							5
60–69	2	3										5
f_x	6	18	9	12	14	5	8	7	3	0	1	83

Source: Porterfield and Talbert, 1954, pp. 192–3.

TABLE 3.

Annual Rate of Divorce, U. S., 1900–1953

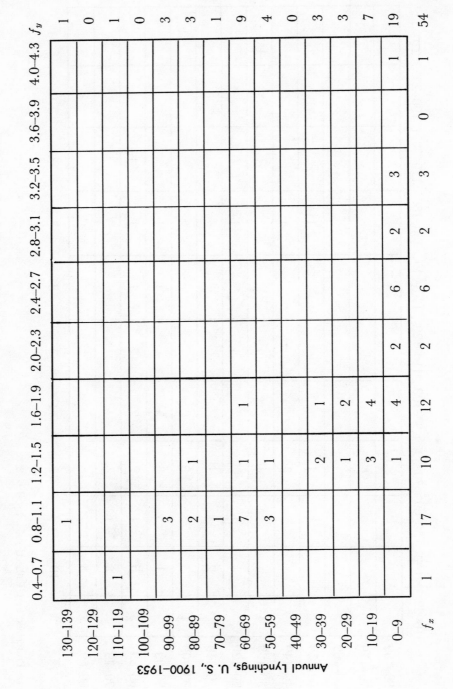

Annual Lynchings, U. S., 1900–1953	0.4–0.7	0.8–1.1	1.2–1.5	1.6–1.9	2.0–2.3	2.4–2.7	2.8–3.1	3.2–3.5	3.6–3.9	4.0–4.3	f_y
130–139		1									1
120–129											0
110–119	1										1
100–109											0
90–99		3									3
80–89		2	1								3
70–79		1									1
60–69		7	1	1							9
50–59		3	1								4
40–49											0
30–39			2	1							3
20–29			1	2							3
10–19			3	4							7
0–9			1	4	2	6	2	3		1	19
f_x	1	17	10	12	2	6	2	3	0	1	54

Source: The World Almanac, 1956, p. 307 and p. 312.

$r =$

4. Table 3 shows annual rates of divorce and annual number of lynchings in the United States for about the first half of the 20th century. The observations are paired by year. Compute the correlation between these two variables. How would you interpret the result? Do you think it represents a genuine relationship? And if not, how do you think such a correlation arises? (Note that the rates are paired measures for the same individual only in the sense that both occur for the same years in the same country.)

As in question 2, draw your own correlation table in the space provided on page 123.

....

....

....

....

....

....

....

....

....

....

5. Faris and Dunham (1939) report that the correlation between the rate of alcoholic psychosis and the percentage of foreign born and Negro in an area, for 68 subareas of Chicago, is .48. They also report that the rate of alcoholic psychosis for Negroes in area number nine, which is predominantly Negro, is one of the lowest for Negroes in the entire city; and in the same area number nine, the rate of alcoholic psychosis for native born whites is one of the highest for native born whites in the entire city. Are these three facts inconsistent?

Explain your answer. ....

....

....

....

....

....

....

Problem 1b

Problem 2

Problem 3

Problem 4

Chapter 6

Introduction to Attributes

AS WE have said, an *attribute* is a characteristic which is counted as either present or absent for any given member of a population; information about the attribute consists in a "yes" or "no," or a plus or a minus, for each sample member drawn. For the sample as a whole we have, as the result of our count, the number that are "yes" and the number that are "no," and we call this *enumeration* data. If the population falls into only two classes, male and female for instance, then we have a dichotomous attribute. If there are more than two classes, then we have a manifold classification.

There are certain logical criteria that define a "good" classification of either kind. In the first place, the categories should be *mutually exclusive*; no member of the sample should be classifiable into more than one category. At the same time, the classification should be *exhaustive;* you should be able to put every member of the sample into some one of the classes. As a corollary to both of these criteria, the classification should be homogeneous (i.e., oranges should not be mixed with apples) and should not shift levels of generality (i.e., white collar, blue collar, farmer, but not white collar, clerical, foreman, farmer). If the two basic rules are met, the corollary automatically follows, so that it is actually redundant; but it is sometimes a help in examining classifications.

It is best to begin now to think about the form of attribute data in terms of the type of the tables in which they may be tabulated. This will allow you to visualize readily the problems and potential treatment of your data. For instance, a dichotomy of a single attribute results in the simplest possible table, one which is seldom shown as a table, the 1×2.

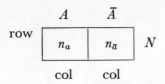

row n_a $n_{\bar{a}}$ N

col   col

This is called a 1×2 table of the dichotomous attribute A and not-A. The table is referred to by the number of rows and columns, with the rows always referred to first and the columns second. The numbers inside are called the cell frequencies.

where A is the attribute A

$\bar{A}$ is the attribute not-A

n_a is the number which are A

$n_{\bar{a}}$ is the number which are not-A

N is the total number in the set of observations and is equal to the sum of n_a and $n_{\bar{a}}$

Note that as long as you can identify A with certainty, this classification is automatically exhaustive and mutually exclusive, because everything that is A falls in the first class and everything else falls in the second. The second class is sometimes called a *residual category*, i.e., it has the left-overs. In certain cases the residual category happens to coincide with a perfect *natural class*, but this is neither necessary nor even frequent. An example, for instance, is male and female. Here, letting A represent male, not-A would be "female," which is itself a positively defined, relatively unambiguous class. This is not always the case with dichotomous classes, or with any other classifications; the logical loopholes are then plugged with such residuals as "all other." (Example: One might classify offenses known to the police into two classes, offenses against the person, and all others.)

A manifold, or polytomous, classification results in a table with more cells, obviously; the number depending on how many classes the attribute gives. Suppose, for instance, there are four classes of the attribute A. Then we have a 1×4 table, like this:

A_1 A_2 A_3 A_4

n_1 n_2 n_3 n_4 N

The 1×4 table has 1 row and 4 columns. The more general case we will call the $r \times s$ table; the letters r, s, or t are frequently used to designate the (general) number of columns and rows in a table.

where each A_i represents a class of A

each n_i represents the number of observations in the ith class of A, and is short for n_{a_i}

N is the total, $\sum n_i$

As in the case of the dichotomy, the classification may be logically completed by a residual class of "other" or A may in fact fall into r natural classes. (Examples: One way of classifying cities is into "production centers, centers of trade and commerce, political capitals, cultural centers, health and recreation resorts, diversified cities," a classification having six natural classes [Gist and Halbert, 1956, p. 6]; a simple classification of races, used frequently by the census, is into "White, Negro, Other," a classification with two positively defined categories and a residual category.)

Ratios, Proportions, and Percentages

You will note that nothing is needed to give a complete description of the 1×2 table except N and n_a. The only remaining piece of information in the table is determined completely by N and n_a (you can find $n_{\bar{a}}$ by subtracting n_a from N). If you were given N and $n_{\bar{a}}$, of course, this would be sufficient to determine n_a.

Absolute numbers, however, turn out to be very difficult to deal with, largely because we usually need information in order to *compare* two numbers, and two absolute numbers are frequently not comparable. Suppose, for example, that someone tells you that college girls are terrible, because in University X it was found that 200 girls were drinkers. Ignoring the problem of how to decide whether any given girl is or is not a drinker (and in its general form this is often a fundamental research problem), it would certainly be a useless piece of information without being able to say whether this is more than, less than, or the same as the population at large, females in the population at large, college-age females in the population at large or some other feasible and relevant comparison group. (Choosing the appropriate comparison is another fundamental research problem.)

The descriptive statistics of attributes are designed to give single numbers which can be meaningfully compared without offering every available piece of information in every statement we make about the attribute. Suppose, for instance, that we compare the two populations:

	Males	Females				Males	Females	
I	150	250	400		II	150	50	200

In absolute numbers there are the same number of males in the two populations, but clearly it would be misleading to say simply, "They have equal numbers of males" —not because it is not true, but because we are really interested in the *relative frequency* of males in the two groups. We must, therefore, take into account the different sizes, N, of the two populations.

The fundamental procedure involved in turning absolute frequencies into relative frequencies is to relate them to some common *base*. One way to do this is to compare the *ratio* of males to females in the two populations. This is done simply by dividing the number of males by the number of females, for example:

In population I the "sex ratio" is $150/250 = 0.60$
In population II the "sex ratio" is $150/50 = 3.00$

The base here is, in a sense, a single female; the ratio gives the number of males for each female in the population. In most technical reports using sex ratios, however, the ratio is multiplied by 100 to rid the expression of decimals, so that the above ratios would be 60 and 300, and the common base would be 100 females rather than 1. It is common also with many other ratios to multiply them by some multiple of 10.

The alternative to this procedure is really a special case of the ratio, but instead of using the number of females as a base the number in the population is used. The result is called a *proportion*, i.e., the proportion of the population which is male in the first population is given by dividing the number of males by the total number of persons, and the proportion of males in the second population is given in the same way:

The proportion of population I which is male is $150/400 = 0.375$
The proportion of population II which is male is $150/200 = 0.750$

Like the ratio, the proportion is frequently multiplied by 100, and when we do this we call the resulting figure a *percentage*. It is actually more usual to report percentages than proportions in sociology, and "percentaging" tables is the first step, almost invariably, in examining them.

Summarizing so far, we can give the following three definitions:

A ratio is	*A proportion is*	*A percentage is*
$\dfrac{n_{a_i}}{n_{b_i}}$	$\dfrac{n_{a_i}}{N}$	$(100)\,\dfrac{n_{a_i}}{N}$

where n_{a_i} is the frequency of the attribute A_i

  n_{b_i} is the frequency either of a second attribute B_i or of a second class of attribute A, say A_j or not-A

  N is the total number of observations

  Note: we will use the notation p_i for proportions and $100\,p_i$ for percentages.

For samples of size N, we can say—reversing the procedure, now—that the absolute numbers in the cells of the table will be given by the simple expression:

$$n_i = Np_i$$

where p_i is the proportion of the population which is A_i.

If you grasp this, you will readily understand that the absolute numbers depend on the size of the sample (or population) and that samples (populations) of different sizes give different absolute numbers even where p_i is the same in the two cases. It is useful to know, also, that because of the way they are defined proportions must be less than 1.00 in any given case and must add up to 1.00 when all proportions in a distribution are taken together; and, of course, for percentages the sum is 100.

Percentages, proportions, and ratios cannot be indiscriminately added and averaged, or combined, etc., as if they were simple numbers. They must be weighted by their base or converted back into their original numerical form before they can be manipulated. The only occasion on which percentages or proportions can be added, for instance, occurs when they are computed to the *same* base. Similarly, if you want to combine two proportions (representing the proportions which are A_i in two separate samples, let us say) and get *one* proportion, you cannot simply average them *unless* the two samples happen to be of the same size. Suppose that there are two estimates of the proportion p_i, one of 0.40 and one of 0.49, from two different samples, one of size 100 and one of size 500. To combine the two estimates, you do *not* take $(0.40 + 0.49)/2 = 0.445$; rather, you take $[(0.40)(100) + (0.49)(500)]/600 = 0.475$. Or, in general,

$$\frac{n_i p_i + n_j p_j}{n_i + n_j}, \qquad \text{and } not \; \frac{p_i + p_j}{2}$$

where p_i and p_j represent the two proportions
n_i and n_j represent the sizes of the bases to which they are computed (for percentages the principle is the same, but multiply through by 100).

TIME-BASED MEASURES: RATES

Two frequently used measures, the *rate* and the *percentage change*, are simple adaptations of the ratio and percentage which have a special relation to *time* and change over time. The *rate* is a ratio in which the numerator and denominator are occurrences during a given period of time; *percentage change* is an increment over time taken relative to a base at the beginning of a period.

The most common rates in sociology use an estimate of a midyear population as a base and something that the population did, or something that happened to it, as the numerator. For example, in 1940 some 264,000 persons were divorced in the United States. To compute a crude divorce rate for that year we divide the number divorced by the estimated midyear population in 1940:

$$\text{Crude D.R.}_{1940} = \frac{264,000}{131,669,000} = 0.002$$

Just as with many ratios, it is customary to multiply this by a multiple of 10; a divorce rate is multiplied by 1000, so that the 1940 crude divorce rate is:

$$\text{Crude D.R.}_{1940} = (1000)(0.002) = 2 \text{ per thousand}$$

This is the most commonly cited type of divorce rate, although the base happens to be a poorly chosen one. (We will show why below.)

A rate is computed for two rather different reasons. In the first place, there is frequently no other way to compute a number in which we are interested. Delinquency rates are often computed in order that two or more neighborhoods or census tracts (the United States census divides up most larger cities into small units called *tracts*) may be compared, without any interest in time *per se*; but since delinquent acts occur in a period of time it is necessary to mark off the beginning and end of some one period and say that we will measure the relative delinquency of two tracts by comparing the number of delinquent acts which we count in this particular period of time. On the other hand, we may compute rates for the simple reason that time is itself of interest to us. Here our interest is in trends over a period of time; but instead of simply comparing the *number* of divorces, the number of delinquents, the number of births, the number of deaths, etc., we compare the rates. The rate converts these numbers into comparable observations, enabling us to make a legitimate interpretation of change over a time period.

DIFFICULTIES IN THE CHOICE OF A BASE

Simply computing a rate, however, is not sufficient to ensure comparability unless a *relevant* base is chosen. And the choice of a proper base is not always a simple matter. It is important to see that the base consists of those persons to whom the event which occurs *could* have occurred.

The fundamental problem is that the base itself may shift in composition, and such shifts are frequently relevant to the comparison we wish to make. For delinquency rates, for example, it would be inappropriate to use the midyear population itself, because the age distributions of various census tracts will differ. Delinquency is legally defined within a certain age range—in many states the range is from 6 to 17—and if two census tracts differ in age composition the potentially delinquent populations differ. The effect of this is shown below:

Item of Information	Tract I	Tract II
Number of persons, 6–17, committing offenses known to the police	10	20
Estimated midyear population	1000	2000
Estimated midyear population, 6–17	250	200

If we compute delinquency rates for the two tracts from the first two items of information we get a delinquency rate of 10/1000 = 0.010 for the first tract, and 20/2000 = 0.010 for the second tract also. The two tracts differ considerably in their potentially delinquent populations, however. In the first, 25% of the estimated midyear population is in the age range 6–17 and in the second only 10% are aged 6–17. If we use the base in the third item, the rates for the two tracts are 0.040 for the first and 0.100 for the second. It would be better, therefore, to use the midyear estimates of population aged 6–17 as a base.

The customary manner of computing divorce rates is inept, of course, for this very reason. The estimated midyear population of the United States includes babies, spinsters, widows, already divorced persons, etc., or, in other words, a large number of persons not at the moment potentially divorceable. If the proportions of these single persons shift over time (as they do), then to use the estimated midyear populations at two different periods as a base for comparing their divorce rates is little better than comparing the absolute number divorced in the two periods. A better base, and one that is fortunately becoming more common, is the number of married females in the population at midyear, or the number of married couples (which presumably gives the same result).

TIME-BASED MEASURES: PERCENTAGE CHANGE

Another way to examine change over time, however, is to compute the *percentage change* in some characteristic from the beginning to the end of a given period. The procedure is a simple one. We take the increase (or decrease) for the period, divide by the count or frequency for the beginning of the period, and multiply by 100. For instance, compare the change in farm labor in the United States from 1870 to 1950. In 1870 there were 2,885,996 farm laborers in the United States (Sogge, 1954). In 1950 there were 2,497,637 of them, a decline of 388,359 over the 80-year period. Expressed in the form of percentage change over time, this is a loss of 388,359/2,885,996 = 13%. In general,

$$\% \text{ Change} = 100 \frac{n_2 - n_1}{n_1}, \quad \text{for the period } t_1 \text{ to } t_2$$

where n_1 is the frequency at the beginning of the period
$\quad n_2$ is the frequency at the end of the period

A single percentage change, such as this one, is not in itself meaningful—which is, of course, true of single proportions, percentages, ratios, and rates in general. It must be compared with some other percentage change. A decline of 13% in farm labor from 1870 to 1950, for instance, might be compared with a rise of about 360% in the total number of persons employed and reporting occupations in the United States in the same period of time.

The Cross-classification of Two Attributes

The one-row table, i.e., the distribution of one attribute, is seldom interesting by itself; it is usually the beginning rather than the end of analysis. The first real step in analysis is the cross-classification of *two* attributes. This is equivalent to the bivariate case that we have already discussed in the chapter on correlation and regression. Now, however, we alter our discussion to deal with the special problems of attributes.

In the case of two attributes, as in the case of one, the simplest results are obtained when both are dichotomous. This gives a 2 × 2 table which is perhaps the most frequently discussed example, if not the most frequently used in practice. For instance, the following table, based on a study of the 1948 presidential election in Elmira, New York, shows the relationship between party affiliation of respondents and the party affiliation of the person they report talking to last about politics during the campaign.

TABLE 6-1.

**Person Last Talked to about Politics,
by Party Affiliation of the Respondent**

		Affiliation of Respondent		
		Republican	Democrat	
Person last talked to about politics	R	118	26	144
	D	39	51	90
		157	77	234

Source: Berelson, Lazarsfeld, and McPhee, 1954, p. 105.

The means for examining this table and presenting a discussion of it are already available to you. As much detail as you can possibly obtain is given simply by the use of ratios, proportions, and percentages. You have, in fact, already used the 2 × 2 table; our comparison of the sex ratios of Populations I and II (see page 127) can obviously be seen as a fourfold table (another name for the 2 × 2 table) in which one attribute is the population into which individuals fall and the other is their sex. In order to examine this 2 × 2 table, then, we can begin with the same sort of analysis. Any of the following pieces of information can be utilized:

1. The proportion of Republicans last talking to a Republican about politics is about .75, whereas the proportion of Democrats last talking to a Republican about politics is only .34.

2. The proportion of Democrats last talking to a Democrat about politics is .66, whereas the proportion of Republicans last talking to a Democrat about politics is only .25.

3. Among Republicans the ratio of those who talked to Republicans divided by those who talked to Democrats last is about 3 to 1; among the Democrats the same ratio is about 1 to 2.

4. The proportion of Republicans last talking to a Republican is .75, whereas in the sample as a whole the proportion last talking to a Republican is .62; the proportion of Democrats last talking to a Democrat is .66, whereas in the sample as a whole the proportion last talking to a Democrat is only .38.

You can proceed in the same way, of course, comparing the *ratios* for a given column to the *ratio* in the population as a whole.

There is only one complication with this table that we have not so far encountered (because of the way we have restricted our discussion of sex ratios above); you can see what it is by continuing the list of comparisons we have started, but now take the comparisons *in the other direction.*

5. Among those last talking to a Republican about politics during the 1948 campaign, .82 were Republican; whereas among those last talking to a Democrat, only .43 were Republican.

6. Among those last talking to a Democrat about politics during the 1948 campaign, .57 were Democrat; whereas among those last talking to a Republican, only .18 were Democrats.

7. The ratio of Republicans to Democrats, among those last talking to a Republican, was about $4\frac{1}{2}$ to 1; whereas among those last talking to a Democrat the ratio of Republicans to Democrats was about 4 to 5.

We have, in other words, a problem of deciding which way to make our comparisons, across or down. Usually our first step is to "percentage" a table in order to make the appropriate comparisons, so our problem is, basically, in which direction shall we run our percentages? This decision is frequently critical, in the sense that very different conclusions might be drawn, depending on the direction in which we percentage. Suppose, for example, we study the recruitment of sons of blue-collar workers into the professional class. From a sample of Indianapolis marriage licenses in 1940 we would find that 29% of the professionals represented in the sample were sons of blue-collar workers. On the other hand, we would find that of all sons of blue-collar workers in the sample, only 3% are professionals. (Rogoff, 1953, Table 2, p. 45). Or suppose we investigate the occupations of employed women. We would find that in April 1954 about 12% of employed women were in the class of "professional, technical, and kindred workers." On the other hand, we would find that about 39% of all professional, technical, and kindred workers were women. Similarly, we would probably find that the proportion of women who are nurses is quite small, yet the proportion of nurses who are women is quite large. We shall follow up this problem, after first showing the general form of the $r \times s$ table.

The general $r \times s$ table, for two attributes, is called a *contingency table*. In order to have a few of the appropriate terms to talk about this table later, we show here the general form of this table with an example of the 3×3.

	A_1	A_2	A_3	
B_1	n_{11}	n_{12}	n_{13}	$n_1.$
B_2	n_{21}	n_{22}	n_{23}	$n_2.$
B_3	n_{31}	n_{32}	n_{33}	$n_3.$
	$n._1$	$n._2$	$n._3$	N

A_i represents the classes of the attribute A, B_j the classes of B; the joint frequencies are indicated as in Chapter 5 by two subscripts whose positions are conventionally fixed; generalizing the rule in Chapter 5, the first position always represents the *row*, the second always represents the *column*. The dot notation, again, indicates which positions are *vacant*, for the univariate frequencies (the "marginals"), and thus by its position shows whether A or B is referred to by the remaining subscript. For example, $n._1$ shows that the row position, the subscript for B, is vacant so that the 1 means A_1. (See page 107 if you have forgotten the dot notation.)

The cell frequencies, n_{ij}, are sometimes called the *ultimate* class frequencies. They are also referred to by their *order*, which we will indicate in a moment. The univariate frequencies are very often called the *marginals*, although they also may be referred to by their order. The order terminology can be generalized to the cross-classification of any number of attributes (for instance three attributes, discussed in Chapter 8) and is very convenient as a means of reference.

N, the total, is called the *zero-order* frequency.
$n._i$ and $n_j.$, the marginals, are called the *first-order* frequencies.
n_{ij}, the ultimate class frequencies of the bivariate case, are called the *second-order* frequencies. In other words, the *order* of the frequency is given by the number of subscripts needed to identify it.

Finally, when the attributes are dichotomous we frequently refer to the number in the positively defined class (A as distinct from not-A) in the 1×2 as the positive class frequency, and the conjunction of two positively defined classes (AB as distinct from the other three logical possibilities) as the joint positive frequency in the 2×2.

All this is to give you a little more familiarity with the kind of tables which you will necessarily see very often, if you do any reading or research in sociology. You can, if you wish, draw out for yourself a 4×4, a 5×5, a 3×5, a 2×4, etc., and enter the zero-, first-, and second-order frequencies, so that you are sure that you understand the general nature of these tables.

TWO RULES FOR PERCENTAGING TABLES

Hans Zeisel (1957) gives two rules for percentaging tables, which cover the general ground very well. The first is simply to percentage in the direction of the attribute whose effect you are interested in examining.

In order to clarify this rule we must first distinguish two kinds of cases. We call one a *symmetrical* case and the other an *asymmetrical* case. In the asymmetrical case you are interested in observing what effect A has on B, and not particularly in the effect of B on A. (You may, of course, be interested in B on A and not vice versa, if B rather than A is conceived of as the independent variable.) For example, we are more interested in seeing what effect the *prior political affiliation* of Elmira (N. Y.) respondents has on *whom they talk to* than the reverse; so we are interested in the effect of A on B but not of B on A. We might, alternatively, be interested in the effect of whom they talk to on their *subsequent* political affiliation, but not in the effect of their subsequent affiliation on whom they had talked to. Or suppose we are interested in the effect of sex on labor force participation (working); then we are interested in the effect of sex (A) on working (B), but not particularly in the effect of B on A.

The symmetrical case occurs when we are not prepared to say which factor is "cause" and which is "effect." For instance, we may be interested in the interrelation of response on two attitude items on a questionnaire; say the two F-scale items, "the world is dangerous" and "sex criminals should be publicly whipped, or worse." The *F-scale* is sometimes used to measure "authoritarian" attitudes: each of the component items is intended to represent some aspect of the authoritarian personality structure. There is little point in defining a cause or effect here, but a great deal of point in examining the relation of the two items.

Rules for percentaging tables apply primarily to the asymmetrical case, except that the dividing line between symmetry and asymmetry is not always clear. By this is meant that we frequently *could* be interested in a table from the point of view of the effect of *either* attribute, even though the question of "cause" becomes difficult to handle. To a large extent whether you treat a table as symmetrical or asymmetrical and which attribute you take as "cause" and which as "effect" depend on what the particular problem at hand happens to be.

We shall discuss treatment of the symmetrical case later; let us return now, however, to Zeisel's first rule. This rule presumes that, whatever the justification, you have decided to treat a table asymmetrically and have chosen, let us say, A as the "causal" factor and B as the effect factor. (Since the word "cause" frequently bothers people, whereas "effect" does not seem to give the same trouble, we can talk about the "A-effect" when we discuss

TABLE 6-2a.

Responses of 563 Hospitalized U. S. Army, Psychoneurotic Patients (1944) and Cross-section Sample of 3501 Nonhospitalized White Enlisted Men to the Question: "Do Your Hands Ever Tremble Enough to Bother You?" (An Asymmetrical Table)

	Neurotic Sample	Cross-section	
Never	113	2381	2494
Sometimes	220	875	1095
Often	230	245	475
	563	3501	4064

We are interested here in the effect of psychoneurosis on psychosomatic complaints, rather than the other way around. The table is *asymmetrical* in the sense that we are interested in the effect of A on B but not in the effect of B on A.

Source: Stouffer et al., 1950, p. 535.

TABLE 6-2b.

Relationship of Responses on Two Questions Concerning Psychosomatic Complaints for Psychoneurotic and Cross-section Samples Combined. Item 1: "Are You Ever Bothered by Having Nightmares?" Item 2 is the Question Concerning Trembling of Hands. (A Symmetrical Table)*

		Item 2			
		Often	Sometimes	Never	
	Often	532	313	146	991
Item 1	Sometimes	419	805	711	1935
	Never	53	406	679	1138
		1004	1524	1536	4064

This time we are interested in whether or not two kinds of symptoms are related, but we do not particularly assume that one symptom causes another. By adding more items (symptoms in this case) to the analysis we may isolate general clusters of items that are interrelated. The table is *symmetrical* in the sense that we are interested in both A on B and B on A.

Source: Stouffer et al., 1950, p. 543.

* This table is freely adapted from the original in which the hospitalized and cross-section samples were weighted in the ratio 9 to 1 when the two were combined in the process of correlating the items. After the absolute frequencies are recaptured the marginals of item 1 in Table 6-2b fail to correspond with the marginals in Table 6-2a because of the weighting procedures employed in Table 6-2b.

the effect of A on B—e.g., "age-effect" or "income-effect," etc.) If you are interested in the A-effect, with respect to B,

1. Set up your table so that A is at the head and B is on the stub (i.e., along the side).
2. Divide each cell frequency by the column total (and multiply by 100, i.e., move the decimal to the right two places). You will then be percentaging *down*, i.e., the percentages will run columnwise. This is what we mean by "in the direction of the cause."
3. Compare frequencies *across* the table when you percentage down; you will then be making the appropriate comparison of the proportion of B_i in each subgroup of A.

For example, let us examine the effect of party affiliation on political discussion, i.e., on the affiliation of the last person talked to about politics, in Elmira, 1948.

Affiliation of Respondent

		R	D		
Person last talked to about politics	R	75%	34%	62%	% ↓
	D	25%	66%	38%	
		100%	100%	100%	
		(157)*	(77)	(234)	

compare →

The percentage in each cell consists of the cell frequency, n_{ij}, divided by the first order frequencies of the attribute A, $n_{.j}$ (the A marginals), and multiplied by 100 (which merely shifts the decimal). This table is *percentaged down*; therefore we *compare across* in order to examine the table.

* You do not need both the original cell values and the percentages when you report tables; but you should put the base at the foot of the column so as to allow re-computation if necessary, and particularly to give some idea of the stability of the percentages. The smaller the base, the less stable the percentage, and for columns with less than 10 observations it is customary not to bother computing the percentages.

In a more general sense, the first step in the instructions is unnecessary. You may, if you wish, simply compute percentages across, if you want the effect of B on A; there is no need to rearrange the table with B at the head and A on the stub if it is inconvenient. If you do *percentage across*, of course, you must *compare down* to examine the table, i.e.,

(a) The effect of A on B

	A_j		
B_i	$n_{ij}/n_{.j}$	$n_{i.}$	% ↓
	$n_{.j}$		

compare →

or

(b) The effect of B on A

	A_j		compare
B_i	$n_{ij}/n_{i.}$	$n_{i.}$	↓
	$n_{.j}$		

% →

Zeisel's second rule consists of a limitation on the first one. If one set of marginals is not representative of the population, then you must percentage in the direction in which the sample is *not* representative. This rule has two important implications, and is therefore worth working out. First, let's see what kind of situation he is referring to.

Let us imagine the following kind of hypothetical situation. In Elmira in 1948 it was found that more people than those who actually liked Truman voted Democratic, because of the salience of socioeconomic issues late in the campaign (this part we did not invent). Now suppose that we knew what the population (not the sample) proportions were for party affiliation (Republican and Democratic) and image of Truman (favorable, unfavorable), and in fact knew that our population looked like this:

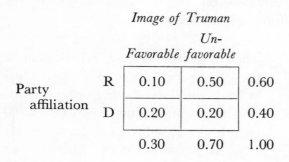

		Favorable	Un-favorable	
Party affiliation	R	0.10	0.50	0.60
	D	0.20	0.20	0.40
		0.30	0.70	1.00

This table is in the form of proportions all the way through; i.e., we have divided through by the zero-order frequency N.

Now say that we draw two samples, each of size 1000, from this population. In one sample, S_1, we draw in such a way that we reproduce the proportions of Democrats and Republicans in the population and also the proportions favorable and unfavorable to Truman; our marginals are "representative" in both directions. In the other sample, S_2, we decide that we need more Democrats to make an adequate analysis, so we choose Democrats and Republicans in equal numbers (this is quite legitimate, if handled properly). We therefore choose 500 of each. However, we choose "randomly" (see Chapter 9) within each group, so that we faithfully reproduce representative marginals of the image of Truman *within* the two groups.

The results are illustrated in the tables on page 139. The row labeled I shows the absolute frequencies obtained in the two samples. Row II shows the tables in row I percentaged down, and row III shows the same tables percentaged across.

This example provides us with two important results. First, the frequencies in row I are clearly sensitive to shifts in the marginal distributions, a point which it is important to remember (compare also the percentaged versions in II). And in addition, the marginals in one direction are sensitive to shifts in the marginals in the other direction; thus, although we adequately represent the strength of Truman within each party, we overestimate it for the sample (population) as a whole by overselecting Democrats in our sample.

Suppose, however, that we are interested neither in how many Democrats there are in Elmira nor in how popular Truman is in the city as a whole; we merely wish to investigate the effect of party affiliation on the image of Truman. In other words, we abandon the goals of a pollster and insist only on the goals of, say, an experimenter. Then the second

I

	F	$\bar{F}$	
R	100	500	600
D	200	200	400
	300	700	1000

	F	$\bar{F}$	
R	83	417	500
D	250	250	500
	333	667	1000

II

	F	$\bar{F}$	% ↓
R	33%	72%	60%
D	67%	28%	40%
	100%	100%	100%

	F	$\bar{F}$	% ↓
R	25%	63%	50%
D	75%	37%	50%
	100%	100%	100%

III

	F	$\bar{F}$	
R	17%	83%	100%
D	50%	50%	100%
	30%	70%	100%

	F	$\bar{F}$	
R	17%	83%	100%
D	50%	50%	100%
	33%	67%	100%

% →　　　　　　　　　　　　% →

important result in this example is the reproduction of the correct *second*-order frequencies in III, the table percentaged *across*, of Sample 2 (compare Sample 1 and Sample 2 on line III). This is, according to Zeisel's second rule, percentaged in the direction in which the marginals are *not* representative. We cannot use the resulting totals, of course, for the marginals in the other direction, since these are clearly affected by the way we have chosen our sample. But the higher-order frequencies are the same as those for Sample 1.

There are many examples of this in research literature. Suppose, for instance, that we are interested in the relation of income to participation in voluntary organizations. We may very well decide, first, that we will not study the effect of belonging to organizations on income, nor will we try to get an accurate accounting of the exact composition of the various voluntary organizations. Second, we decide that we will not try to give an accurate estimate of just how many persons in the population belong to voluntary organizations. We have, in other words, a strictly analytic interest and are willing to restrict our problem considerably. Our third decision may be that in order to make a more penetrating analysis of the income-effect, we should *overrepresent* the higher income group in our sample. We know that joining is highest in this group; now we want to get enough of them to make a more careful and thorough use of other variables that might differentiate high-income joiners from high-income not-joiners. If we select in proportion to their distribution in the population we do not get enough cases to do a very refined analysis. We are perfectly safe in selecting equal groups of low- and high-income sample members, so long as our interest is in comparing and analyzing the relations of variables not affected by the manner of choosing the sample. This means, first, that we must set the number of high- and low-income sample members equal to 100% and percentage in that direction; second, that we must not use the marginals to estimate the proportion in the population actually belonging to voluntary organizations.

THE SYMMETRICAL CASE

We must now consider the treatment of the symmetrical case. Here we must attempt to make a rather tenuous distinction between the symmetrical nature of a table and the symmetrical treatment of a table. Table 6-2b, for example, is symmetrical in the sense that no grounds exist for arguing that either effect is "prior" or can be regarded as a cause of the other. On the other hand, for certain purposes we might wish to treat it *as if* it were asymmetrical. Suppose, for example, we wish to know whether those who are more likely to report nightmares are also more likely to report trembling hands. One way to find out is to percentage the table in one or the other direction. For example, $532/1004 = 53\%$ of those who often have nightmares also report that their hands tremble often, whereas only $313/1524 = 21\%$ of those who report occasional nightmares also report that their hands tremble often. (This is essentially an attempt to measure the association of the two variables, a problem with which we deal in the next chapter.)

Let us compare this with a symmetrical treatment. A symmetrical treatment means percentaging to the base N, i.e. the total number of cases. A formal version of our table would look like this, where $p_{ij} = n_{ij}/N$.

	A_1	A_2	A_3	
B_1	p_{11}	p_{12}	p_{13}	$p_1.$
B_2	p_{21}	p_{22}	p_{23}	$p_2.$
B_3	p_{31}	p_{32}	p_{33}	$p_3.$
	$p._1$	$p._2$	$p._3$	1.00

If our purpose is to examine the relationship between A and B we have defeated our purpose. For this is no more free of the effects of varying marginal frequencies than is the table that has not been percentaged at all. If you divide through by N you do *not* thereby standardize for the effect of differences in marginals. These marginal differences still affect the size of the proportions representing the second-order frequencies, so that division by N is not the same as percentaging in one direction, which we do to rid the second-order frequencies of the effects of differences in column or row totals. For example, in Table 6-2b $p_{11} = 13\%$

and $p_{12} = 8\%$ of the total 4064 cases; the marginals are $p_{.1} = 25\%$ and $p_{.2} = 38\%$. A comparison of 13% with 8% would underestimate the relationship of items 1 and 2, just as a comparison of 532 and 313 would; the appropriate comparison would be between $13\%/25\% = 52\%$ and $8\%/38\% = 21\%$. (The difference between 52% and 53% is only rounding error; in general $p_{ij}/p_{.j} = n_{ij}/n_{.j}$.)

There are occasions, on the other hand, where we might want to treat even an asymmetrical table as if it were symmetrical. We may wish, for example, to compare the proportion p_{ij} from one study with the proportion p_{ij} obtained in another study, when the sample sizes in the two studies differed. More commonly, perhaps, we may wish to make some statement about the proportion p_{ij} in a very general sense, without tying the statement to the specific value of n_{ij} obtained in a given sample with a given N. For example, we might wish to use p_{ij} as an estimate of the population value, in which case we would not want to compensate for varying marginal frequencies unless the marginal frequencies were not representative of the population.

Where We Stand

We now stand at the halfway point in our treatment of the description of attributes. We have examined in some detail the use of ratios, percentages, proportions, rates, and percentage change, all involving the idea of *relative* frequency of occurrence. The principal function of these measures is, we have seen, to compare the frequencies with which a given attribute occurs in several different instances, populations, or samples. In addition, when we must examine the relationship of *two* attributes, cross-classified in a contingency table, these measures facilitate comparisons which are not disturbed by the differences in the absolute magnitude in the marginal row or column totals of the table; in both these cases our problem has been to free our comparisons of the effect of differences in the numbers of observations.

In the next chapter we continue to discuss the description of the relation of cross-classified attributes, introducing in addition the treatment of cross-classified quasi-variables.

CONTINGENCY TABLES

for Use with Workbook Exercises,

Chapters 6, 7, 8

The following contingency tables (Tables A–P) have been selected from the literature for use with the workbook questions of Chapters 6, 7, and 8. You will be asked to refer to the appropriate table in each question. Now turn to the workbook for Chapter 6, page 153.

TABLE A.

Labor Force Status of the Civilian Female Population, 14 Years of Age and Over, by Marital Status, 1954 (in 100,000's)[*]

		Labor Force Status		
		In Labor Force	*Not in Labor Force*	
	Single	5	6	11
Marital Status	Married, husband present	10	27	37
	Other	4	7	11
		19	40	59

Source: Adapted from U. S. *Bureau of the Census: Statistical Abstract of the United States, 1955*, Table 233. Results are from a sample survey.

[*] See again the footnote on page 43, in which we have commented briefly on the simplification of numbers by expressing them in units such as "100,000's," "1000's," etc. The numbers in the following tables are considerably simplified, for ease in computation.

Major Occupation of Employed Persons, by Sex, October 1954 (in 100,000's)

Occupation Group	Male	Female	Total
Professional and kindred workers	37	22	59
Farmers and farm managers	38	1	39
Managers, officials, proprietors (except farm)	54	10	64
Clerical and kindred workers	28	55	83
Sales	24	15	39
Crafts, foremen, and kindred workers	80	2	82
Operatives and kindred workers	86	34	120
Private household workers	—	19	19
Other service workers	25	24	49
Farm laborers and foremen	17	14	31
Laborers, except farm and mine	35	1	36
	424	197	621

Source: Adapted from *Statistical Abstract, 1955*, Table 237. Results are from a sample survey.

TABLE C.

Shifts in Occupational Structure of U. S., 1870–1950 (in 100,000's)

Occupational Group	1870	1900	1950
Professionals, officials, and non-farm proprietors	10	34	110
Other nonfarm occupations	46	130	374
Farm occupations	59	102	68
Unclassified	10	25	24
Total employed and reporting occupation	125	291	576

Source: Adapted from Sogge, 1954.

Interlocking Corporations among 200 Largest Nonfinancial
and 50 Largest Financial Corporations, U. S., 1935

Type of Corporation	Corporation Interlocks with:				
	No Other	One Other	Two Others	Three or More Others	All
Industrial	16	20	11	60	107
Utility	8	12	8	26	54
Railroad	1	2	5	31	39
Bank	0	2	6	22	30
Other financial	0	2	6	12	20
All	25	38	36	151	250

Source: National Resources Committee, 1939.

Number of Divorces and Estimated Midyear Population,
U. S., 1900–1950, by Decades (in 100,000's)

Year	Number of Divorces	Estimated Mid-year Population
1900	6	760
1910	8	920
1920	17	1065
1930	20	1228
1940	26	1317
1950	39	1507

Source: Statistical Abstract, 1952, Table 58.

Tolerance of Nonconformists, by Education, National Cross-Section, 1955 (in 10's)

		Score on Tolerance Scale			
		Low	*Medium*	*High*	
Education	Some college or college graduate	5	21	37	63
	Some high school or high school graduate	19	66	49	134
	Grade school or less	17	49	13	79
		41	136	99	276

Source: Stouffer, 1955, p. 90.

Respondent's Vote Intention by Vote Intention of Three Closest Friends, Elmira, 1948
(Two-Party Vote Only)

		Respondent's Vote Intention		
		Republican	*Democrat*	
Vote intention of three closest friends (R = Republican, D = Democrat)	RRR	216	29	245
	RRD	43	15	58
	RDD	14	15	29
	DDD	12	67	79
		285	126	411

Source: Berelson, Lazarsfeld, and McPhee, 1954, p. 98.

TABLE H.

Length of Engagement by Length of Acquaintance, 425 Divorced Couples, Detroit, 1948

		Length of Engagement		
		Less than 3 Mos.	*3–6 Mos.*	*6 Mos. or More*	
Length of acquaintance	Less than 1 year	72	43	10	125
	1–3 years	46	74	46	166
	3 years or more	35	33	65	133
		153	150	121	424

Source: Goode, 1956, p. 81.

TABLE I.

Present Occupation by Type of Community of Orientation, Oakland, 1949

		Community in Which Respondents Lived Most of the Time from Age 13 to 19		
		Rural Farm	*Rural Non-farm and Small Urban*	*Large Urban*	
Present occupation	Professional, self-employed, and upper white collar	40	93	154	287
	Lower white collar and sales	29	66	128	223
	Skilled, semiskilled, and unskilled	98	138	152	388
		167	297	434	898

Source: Lipset, 1955, p. 222.

TABLE J.

Education by Type of Community of Orientation, Oakland, 1949

Community in Which Respondents Lived
Most of the Time from Age 13 to 19

		Rural Farm	Rural Non-farm and Small Urban	Large Urban	
Years of education	0–11	109	157	182	448
	12	38	65	152	255
	13+	20	75	100	195
		167	297	434	898

Source: Lipset, 1955, p. 224.

TABLE K.*

Occupation by Community of Orientation by Education, Oakland, 1949

Years of Education

Present Occupation	0–11 Years Community of Orientation				12 Years Community of Orientation				13+ Years Community of Orientation			
	RF†	RNF	LU		RF	RNF	LU		RF	RNF	LU	
Nonmanual	57	39	93	189	27	32	109	168	27	45	80	152
Manual	100	69	92	261	28	19	42	89	7	12	17	36
	157	108	185	450	55	51	151	257	34	57	97	188

Source: Adapted from Lipset, 1955, Table 6, p. 225.

* Tables I and J have been altered slightly from the original to make the marginals consistent. Table K is reproduced without change although there are slight inconsistencies between the marginals of this table and those of Tables I and J.

† RF, RNF, etc., are abbreviations for community types shown in Tables I and J. RNF includes small urban communities, as above.

TABLE L.

Respondent's Vote Intention by Usual Vote of Father, Elmira, 1948

(Two-Party Vote Only)

		Father Usually Votes		
		Republican	*Democrat*	
Respondent's vote intention	R	252	90	342
	D	52	106	158
		304	196	500

Source: Berelson, Lazarsfeld, and McPhee, 1954, p. 89.

Respondent's Vote Intention by Usual Vote of Father, by Present Spouse's Vote Intention,

Elmira, 1948

		Present Spouse Republican				*Present Spouse Democrat*		
		Father is				*Father is*		
		R	*D*			*R*	*D*	
Respondent's vote intention	R	167	47	214	R	8	6	14
	D	9	3	12	D	17	48	65
		176	50	226		25	54	79

Source: Berelson, Lazarsfeld, and McPhee, 1954, p. 135.

TABLE N.

Mobility Inclinations by Satisfaction with Present Housing, Philadelphia, 1950

	Number of Complaints about Housing			
	None	*1–3*	*4 or More*	
Want to move	67	136	220	423
Want to stay	237	170	76	483
	304	306	296	906

Source: Rossi, 1955, p. 88.

TABLE O.

Mobility Inclinations by Tenure Status by Satisfaction with Present Housing

	Satisfied				Dissatisfied		
	Owns	*Rents*			*Owns*	*Rents*	
Move	76	130	206		52	112	164
Stay	230	147	377		177	92	269
	306	277	583		229	204	433

Source: Rossi, 1955, p. 89.

TABLE P.

Effects of Education Campaign on Attitudes to British Loan, for Experimental Group
(*Given Information*) and Control Group (*Not Given Information*), by Trust in
England's Cooperation, 1946

	Experimental Group			*Control Group*		
	Trust England	*Do Not Trust England*		*Trust England*	*Do Not Trust England*	
Approve loan	169	24	193	175	39	214
Do not approve	73	109	182	213	192	405
	242	133	375	388	231	619

Source: Hyman and Sheatsley, 1947, p. 94.

Chapter 6

WORKBOOK EXERCISES

1. Turn to page 143 and examine Table A. (Read the title, so that you know what the table is about.) Now consider the following questions:

a. What proportion of females 14 years old and over are in the labor force? ....

b. Suppose that you read a report that gave only the first column (*In Labor Force*), and percentaged the column down. What conclusions might this procedure

lead to? How would you criticize the report? ....

....

....

....

....

....

....

....

....

....

....

c. Now percentage the table across. In which direction would you make your comparisons? What conclusions do you draw from the table?

Put the percentages in this table.*

100%

100%

100%

100%

* You don't need to put the original frequencies in if the percentages are shown, provided
that you put the base of the percentages in. This is
usually put in parentheses after the 100% in the
margin.

I would compare .... The table

shows ....

....

....

....

....

....

....

d. If you were given the table just as it is, in which direction would you decide to
percentage? What considerations would determine your decision? What rules would you

follow? ....

....

....

....

....

....

....

....

....

....

2. Now look at Table B, page 144.

a. Suppose that you read in one report that about 11% of employed females are in
professional and kindred occupations, compared to 9% of the employed males; in another
report, however, you read that about 63% of the persons employed in professional and kindred occupations are males, compared to 37% who are female. Is one of these statements

incorrect? ....

....

....

(Show your calculations in answering this question.)   If they are both correct, in what way do

they differ? ....

....

....

....

b. In the following table, for the selected occupations listed on the stub, show the percentages calculated *across* in Part II, and *down* in Part I, for Table B.

	Part I		Part II		
Occupational Group	*Male*	*Female*	*Male*	*Female*	
Professional and kindred					100%
Managers, officials, etc.					100%
Clerical and kindred					100%
Operatives					100%
Private household workers					100%
Laborers, nonfarm					100%
	100%	100%			

Which table would you use to draw data for an assertion that "more males are in the *X* group of occupations than any other occupation"? ....

....

Which table would you use to document the assertion that "occupation *X* has the largest proportion of males of all the occupations tabulated"? ....

Suppose that your purpose is to analyze differences in the distribution of the two sexes in the occupational structure; which table would you use? ....

because ....

....

....

Would your conclusions be much different if you had used the alternative form of the table?

What would the chief differences be? ....

....

....

....

....

(*Note:* even if you see no basic differences, one table seems more startlingly conclusive than the other. Why? Which is the more appropriate?)

c. Prepare a systematic analysis of the same problem by computing and discussing the sex ratios of each of the occupations in Table B. Enter in the table below the name of each occupation on the stub, and the ratio of males to females in each occupation, in the right-hand column. What conclusions do you draw from the evidence of this table? ....

Occupation Group	Occupational Sex Ratio

....

....

....

....

....

....

....

....

....

....

....

....

....

....

3. From Table C, page 144, prepare a report on the occupational distributions of the United States from 1870 to 1950 and on the shifts in occupational structure. In preparing this report compute the percentage distribution of employed persons by occupation in each of the 3 years given; the percentage change from 1870 to 1900 and from 1900 to 1950 in persons employed in each occupation; and the over-all farm/nonfarm ratio in each period. Base your analysis on these computations. (You might discuss in class the effect of the "unclassified" persons on the analysis, and whether or not to take them out of the base to which you percentage the occupational distributions.)

a. Percentage distribution of employed persons by major occupational classes, 1870–1950

Occupation	1870	1900	1950

b. Percentage change in persons employed in major occupational classes, 1870–1950

Occupation	1870–1900	1900–1950

c. Farm to nonfarm ratios, U. S., 1870–1950

1870	1900	1950
/ =	/ =	/ =

....

....

....

....

4. From Table E, page 145, compute the divorce rates for each of the decennial points in the table. Enter the results below and summarize briefly what they show.

a.

Year	Rate

....

....

....

....

....

....

....

....

....

....

b. Now compute the percentage change in *number* divorced, in column 1 below, from 1900 to 1950. Compute the percentage change in *rates* also, in column 2 below. Which is the appropriate procedure? Why? ....

....

Percentage Change from	1	2
00–10		
10–20		
20–30		
30–40		
40–50		

....

....

....

....

....

....

....

....

....

....

5. a. In Table F, 59% of the lowest scorers on a scale of tolerance toward nonconformists, from a national cross-section of the population, have had at least some high school, compared to 41% with a grade school education, or less. Is this the comparison that you would make from the table? Does it show that the more education you have the less tolerant you are? ....

....

....

....

b. Percentage the table, entering the results below. Explain why you percentage it in the direction you do; what considerations do you take into account? ....

....

....

....

....

....

....

....

....

....

c. Suppose the investigators had decided to over-represent the lower educated in the sample, in order to have more cases for analysis among this group. What would this do to the marginal proportions in the other direction (i.e., for the low, medium, and high tolerance scorers)? ....

....

d. What would be the effect on these marginals of over-representing the college-educated group? ....

e. What would either of these procedures do to your decision about the direction in which you would percentage the table?   Why?...

....

....

....

....

f. What effect would either of them have on your analysis of the relation of tolerance to education?   ....

....

....

....

....

Chapter 7

The Association of Attributes and Orders

WHEN, following the procedures of the previous chapter, we find that *A* does in fact affect *B*, we say that *A* and *B* are *associated*. We have already introduced the idea of association in Chapter 5; correlation is simply a special case of association. Corresponding to the idea of "zero correlation," we have the more general term *independence* to designate "no relationship" between two characteristics. In this chapter we discuss association and independence in two fundamental cases; between attributes and between ordered classes.

The Percentage Difference as a Measure of Association

Very frequently we want to know the *degree* of association in contingency tables. A very simple way of measuring this follows from the definition of association. You will recall that from Table 6-1 (see page 132), we have already extracted the following information: the proportion of Republicans last talking politics to a Republican is 0.75 (or 75%), whereas the proportion of Democrats last talking politics to a Republican is about 0.34 (34%). This indicates that the respondent's party affiliation has some effect on whom he talks to about politics. A rough measure of the *degree* of effect (association) is the *difference* between the two percentages, which is 41%. We will use the Greek letter ϵ (epsilon) to represent the percentage difference. We always compute it in the direction of the comparisons. If, for example, we percentage down, we compare across and compute ϵ across; if we percentage across, we compare down and compute ϵ down.

More formally,

	B	$\bar{B}$	
A	$100p_{ab}$	$100p_{a\bar{b}}$	$100p_a$
$\bar{A}$	$100p_{\bar{a}b}$	$100p_{\bar{a}\bar{b}}$	$100p_{\bar{a}}$
	100%	100%	100%

A and B are *associated* if $100p_{ab} > 100p_{a\bar{b}}$ or $100p_{ab} < 100p_{a\bar{b}}$. The *degree* of association is indicated by $\epsilon = 100p_{ab} - 100p_{a\bar{b}}$.

In this particular case we can talk about the *direction* of association between A and B as well as degree. (This will not be true in all cases. See below, pp. 165 and 171.) If the association is *positive*, the proportion p_{ab} will be greater than $p_{a\bar{b}}$, and if it is *negative* this is reversed. (This convention follows that for positive and negative correlation of continuous variables.)

The ϵ measure is, in a sense, the bread-and-butter measure of routine analysis. Examination of association in the $r \times s$ table almost always begins with percentaging the table. We then observe carefully the *size*, *direction*, and *consistency* of the percentage differences in the table. For example, take a somewhat more complex case, a 3×6 table.

TABLE 7-1.

Income by Occupation, Urban Occupations Only, for Males Aged 14 Years and Over,

U. S., 1950

Income	Occupation					
	Prof. and Semi-Prof.	Prop., Mgrs. and Officials	Clerical and Sales	Crafts, Operatives, and Kindred Workers	Service	Unskilled Labor
Over $5000	36.0%	34.7%	8.0%	4.6%	1.5%	0.5%
$2500–$5000	39.5	37.0	57.0	56.9	32.4	28.6
0–$2500	24.4	28.4	34.9	38.5	66.1	70.9
	100%	100%	100%	100%	100%	100%
Base in 000's	(2565)	(5345)	(5404)	(15625)	(2550)	(2964)

Source: Adapted from U. S. *Bureau of the Census: Statistical Abstract of the United States*, 1951, Table 320, pp. 272–273.

The procedure for any specific comparison, of course, is simple. For a general treatment of the table, however, there are many possible ϵ's. As a rough general measure for the association in the table as a whole we can take the range in the top row of the table, or in the two top rows combined for some tables in which the row n in the top row is small. (In this particular case, you should be looking at the top left and top right cells—which gives $36.0\% - 0.5\% = 35.5\%$.) In addition to this summary indicator, however, and actually much more important, we have evidence of the over-all *consistency* of the relationship from the signs of the 15 basic ϵ values which represent the differences between adjacent cells. Where we expect some kind of order underlying the table the *pattern* of the differences is fundamental to our understanding of the table. (By "underlying order" we mean that the characteristics cross-classified in the table have intrinsic order in the sense defined in Chapter 1.) Table 7-1, for instance, has this pattern:

$$100p_{11} > 100p_{12} > 100p_{13} > 100p_{14} > 100p_{15} > 100p_{16}$$

$$100p_{21} > 100p_{22} < 100p_{23} > 100p_{24} > 100p_{25} > 100p_{26}$$

$$100p_{31} < 100p_{32} < 100p_{33} < 100p_{34} < 100p_{35} < 100p_{36}$$

If occupation and income are associated, then not only should there be some over-all difference, but the differences should be *consistent* in direction.

But tables without underlying order are more difficult to deal with, or at least they raise more problems in the search for consistency and direction of association. Direction has little meaning when attributes rather than ordered classes are cross-classified—a sign can be obtained but since columns and rows of a classification without order can be changed about (*permuted*) at will the sign has no meaning (see Chapter 1 again). Internal consistency would also have little significance, for the same reason. The solution to this problem is called *replication*. This simply means repetition, and here we mean either of two things (the term has other meanings also):

1. We can test the association of A and B by finding a third item, C, which means substantially the same thing as B and cross-classifying A and C; the pattern of differences should be consistent with the pattern in the table showing the relationship of A and B.

2. We can test the association of A and B by finding some third item, C, which is *not* related to A and B, or related in only a minor degree, and cross-classifying A, B, and C, all three, together; this will give the relation of A and B for $C_1, C_2, C_3, \ldots C_k$, and if in each case the pattern of differences is consistent then we can say that the association holds up well. Three-variable cases, such as this one, will be taken up in the next chapter.*

The chief difficulties with ϵ as a measure of association derive from properties of percentages that we have already observed in the previous chapter. Percentages are sensitive to shifts in marginal distributions; if you shift the proportions of A and B in your sample

---

* The material of these three paragraphs is intended largely for future reference and may be difficult to grasp on first reading, because of its somewhat abstract formulation. An understanding of this paragraph will not be necessary in what follows, although the problem is a crucial one in reading—and writing—reports of sociological investigations.

$$
\begin{array}{ccccc|c}
n_{11} & n_{12} & \cdots & n_{1s} & n_{1.} \\
n_{21} & n_{22} & \cdots & n_{2s} & n_{2.} \\
\vdots & & & & \\
n_{r1} & n_{r2} & \cdots & n_{rs} & n_{r.} \\
\hline
n_{.1} & n_{.2} & \cdots & n_{.s} & N
\end{array}
\longrightarrow
\begin{array}{cccc|c}
100n_{11}/n_{.1} & 100n_{12}/n_{.2} & \cdots & 100n_{1s}/n_{.s} & 100n_{1.}/N \\
100n_{21}/n_{.1} & 100n_{22}/n_{.2} & \cdots & 100n_{1s}/n_{.s} & 100n_{2.}/N \\
\vdots & & & & \\
100n_{r1}/n_{.1} & 100n_{r2}/n_{.2} & \cdots & 100n_{rs}/n_{.s} & 100n_{r.}/N \\
\hline
100\% & 100\% & \cdots & 100\% & 100\% \\
(n_{.1}) & (n_{.2}) & & (n_{.s}) &
\end{array}
$$

1. Compute percentages, following Zeisel's two rules. (*a*) Compute percentages in the direction of the "causal" factor. (*b*) Compute percentages in the direction in which the sample is not representative.

2. As a summary of the table take the over-all magnitude of $100n_{11}/n_{.1} - 100n_{1s}/n_{.s}$ or the difference between the largest and smallest percentages in the row.

3. Examine the over-all consistency and direction of the differences between adjacent columns. If the table has order in both directions and if there is any association between the two characteristics, the differences should be consistent in direction, e.g., $n_{11}/n_{.1} > n_{12}/n_{.2} > n_{13}/n_{.3} > \ldots$.

4. If the table does not have order, consistency may be checked in either of two ways. (*a*) Choose some third characteristic, C, which serves to indicate the same concept as B, and cross-classify A and C. If A and B are associated and C represents the same concept as B, the direction of the differences in the second table should be consistent with the direction in the first. (*b*) Choose some third characteristic, C, which is independent of A and B, and stratify A and B by C (see Chapter 8). If there is association, then the direction of the differences will be consistent in each partial table of C. (Come back to this after reading Chapter 8.)

Wherever possible it is the *pattern* of the ϵ values that should be relied on, rather than the absolute magnitude of the difference in any individual comparison.

the size and interpretation of ϵ are changed. Nor does ϵ give a really *general* picture of association in a table since it is confined to one direction and one row or column; essentially the problem here is the enormous loss of information when ϵ is used as a *summary* indicator. As a result, ϵ is severely limited for this purpose. Yet, either consciously or unconsciously, it is the most commonly employed measure in dealing with a specific table and a specific comparison, and gives by far the best grasp of the *details* of a table when *all*, or the basic set, of ϵ values are used.

Measures of Association Based on the Definition of Independence

Historically speaking, it has been exceedingly difficult to arrive at a perfectly satisfactory measure of association in contingency tables. (The problem of testing the significance of differences—allowing for sampling fluctuation—has, on the other hand, been solved nicely. See Chapter 10.) Most of the measures commonly appearing in contemporary research monographs are based on the definition of independence in contingency tables, which proves to be not entirely satisfactory.

In its simplest terms, independence is obviously the opposite of association; if there is no relationship between two attributes, then the proportion of A's among the B's is the *same* as the proportion of A's among the not-B's. To borrow an illustration from G. U. Yule, we anticipate the same proportion of abnormally wet seasons in leap years as in ordinary years, because we assume that these two attributes—wet/dry, and leap/not-leap— are independent. In other words, when two attributes are independent, the percentage difference is 0, since $p_1 = p_2$. As a matter of fact, in fourfold tables the percentage difference in *every* direction is 0 when two attributes are perfectly independent.

An important result follows from this. If two attributes are independent, then the proportions which are AB, $A\bar{B}$, $\bar{A}B$, etc., depend entirely on the *marginal* distributions of A and B. There is no need to derive this algebraically here, but you should understand that it does follow in the same way from the definition of independence as the fact that between two proportions the difference is 0. And this result is not confined to fourfold tables; it holds for any contingency table. If two attributes are independent, then,

$$n_{ij} = n_i n_j / N$$ This is actually one way to *define* independence.

where n_{ij} is a given second-order frequency in a given cell of the table

n_i is the marginal for the row containing the cell (we avoid the dot notation here since the principle is clear without it)

n_j is the marginal for the column containing the cell

N is the total number of observations

From this definition we can define a measure δ (read "delta"), which represents how *far* a given cell frequency *deviates from independence.*

$$\delta_{ij} = n_{ij} - n_i n_j / N$$

If δ_{ij} is 0, then the attributes are independent; the more they are associated, the more δ_{ij}, or some form of *sum* of the several δ_{ij}'s in a table, departs from 0. Mathematicians have played with this result for half a century, but only for the 2 × 2 have any satisfactory results been achieved. There are two reasons for this. First, the absolute magnitude of δ_{ij} is markedly affected by N, the number of observations in the table. This in itself is not an insuperable obstacle, since if you divide δ_{ij} by N you can solve this part of the problem. But both researchers and mathematicians have always felt that a measure of correlation or association should take values lying between either 0 and 1, or −1 and 1; and they have also felt, quite reasonably, that the measure should be fairly stable regardless of the number of rows and columns in a table. δ_{ij}/N meets neither of these conditions, and a variety of measures developed from δ_{ij}/N or δ_{ij} itself similarly fail to meet these conditions.

The problem is worth bringing up here largely because the most frequently used measures of association in contingency tables are based on delta quantities, e.g., Pearson's *coefficient of contingency*, *C*, and Tschuprov's modification of it, *T*. Both of these are sensitive to the number of rows and columns in a table, in the sense that their range (i.e., the values they take between 0 and complete association) differs depending on the layout of the table. (*T* is affected only if $r \neq s$, that is, if the number of rows is not the same as the number of columns.) Therefore they are unstable, and this means they are hard to interpret. If you get a *C* of 0.50 in one table and a *C* of 0.50 in some other table, you do *not* necessarily have the same degree of association, although it is a little difficult to say just what you do have. In general, for the $r \times s$ case, delta-based measures have been found to be unstable and we say also that they fail to "norm" properly, i.e., they do not range uniformly from −1 to 1 or from 0 to 1 the way we would like them to. And if they do not, they do not admit of a simple and unambiguous interpretation.

The Special Treatment of Fourfold Tables

For the 2 × 2, however, two very common delta-based measures are quite satisfactory. You will see at least one of these often and will be able to use one or both of them often. The restrictions on their use arise only for cases which are not both dichotomous; this might seem excessively restrictive, except that in the first place fourfold tables are very common in sociology and in the second place any table can be reduced to a fourfold if you wish. (*Warning:* Unfortunately, the two measures considered here, and any known measures for contingency tables, are very sensitive to *how* you combine classes to make a fourfold, if you decide to do so.)

1. Yule's Q

Yule invented the following measure, which is accordingly known as Yule's Q.

$$Q = \frac{N\delta_{11}}{(n_{11}n_{22} + n_{12}n_{21})}$$

The reason for using δ_{11} is explained below in a discussion of the sign of Q. In a 2×2 table all four δ values will be the same in absolute magnitude.

Yule very frankly devised this measure on purely pragmatic grounds, not from any consideration of theoretical statistics. It ranges from -1 to 1, as desired. It has the important property of being what we might call "margin-free," i.e., it will not shift with different proportions of A and B in the sample, as the percentage difference measures will.

It is hard to give a precise interpretation of its meaning, as Yule himself pointed out; i.e., in the sense that with the product-moment coefficient you can say, "r^2 of the variance in Y is accounted for by X." But Goodman and Kruskal (1954) have recently offered a nice interpretation which we will show below. Ordinarily, the interpretation of Q is as pragmatic as the measure itself; we merely have some idea of the range of values Q takes in a particular field and judge roughly how a given value of Q fits the usual expectation.

2. The phi coefficient

Before giving a computation design for Q, let's look at another common measure of association in 2×2 tables, the *phi coefficient*. This measure can be derived either from delta quantities or by special restrictions on the product-moment coefficient (showing that there is a relation between these two ideas) in which we talk of "two-valued" variables and give a "one" to the positive frequency and "zero" to the negative frequency of our dichotomy. We show here the delta version of phi, but Edwards (1955, pp. 185–188) gives a derivation and computation design based on r.

The phi coefficient serves much the same purpose as Q, yet it has an important difference in interpretation. It is defined as:

$$\phi = \frac{N\delta_{11}}{\sqrt{n_{.1}n_{.2}n_{1.}n_{2.}}}$$

The easiest way to compare Q and ϕ is to compute them both for the same table. Their essential differences can be seen best in the following kind of case:

	A	$\bar{A}$	
B	0	25	25
$\bar{B}$	25	25	50
	25	50	75

As usual the theoretically most meaningful formula for a measure is not the easiest from which to compute it; for the fourfold table, at least, the computations are most easily made from the following set-up:

a	b	$a + b$
c	d	$c + d$
$a + c$	$b + d$	N

$$Q = \frac{ad - bc}{ad + bc}$$

$$\phi = \frac{ad - bc}{\sqrt{(a + b)(c + d)(a + c)(b + d)}}$$

where the letters represent the frequencies in the cells as labeled in the table at the left.

Substituting in the formula for Q,

$$Q = \frac{(0)(25) - (25)(25)}{(0)(25) + (25)(25)}$$

$$= -1.00$$

And substituting in the formula for the phi coefficient,

$$\phi = \frac{(0)(25) - (25)(25)}{\sqrt{(25)(50)(25)(50)}}$$

$$= -0.50$$

In other words, the two measures do *not* give the same results. This is not to be wondered at, since they are very differently defined; and we cannot complain much about either of them, since we have no criteria in this case by which we can decide which is "better" than the other. The difference actually turns on the ambiguity of the term "complete association"; it may mean either of the following:

	+	−
+	25	0
−	0	25

	+	−
+	25	0
−	25	25

The value of Q will be 1 for either of these, but the value of ϕ will be 1 only for the first. In other words, they imply different definitions of complete positive (or negative) association. With the phi coefficient we get "complete" association only when all the A's are B's and all the B's are A's; with Q we get complete association under less restrictive conditions. The choice between the two depends a good deal on what kind of interpretation one can make of the two measures, and until recently it was difficult to give an interpretation of Q, as we have already remarked. We will try to show how to interpret Q more adequately at the conclusion of the chapter, and then take up again the problem of the choice between ϕ and Q.

One final remark on the interpretation of Q and ϕ. Both coefficients theoretically take the range from -1 to 1. It happens that the sign of a correlation coefficient usually implies some order underlying the characteristics we are correlating. Frequently Q and ϕ are used in instances where no assumption of order is admissible. In such cases we simply throw the sign away. Technically, a measure designed for attributes without order should range only from 0 to 1; this kind of result is obtained from Goodman and Kruskal's lambda, which we will introduce in the next section, but it is also obtained by using Q or ϕ without sign. On the other hand, if the cross-classified characteristics have some meaningful order you should save the sign. The sign will show exactly in *which* cells, and thus in what order, the frequencies are concentrated. The use of the sign *includes* such cases as the cross-classification of two dichotomous attributes both having positively defined frequencies (e.g., "yes" on item 1 of a questionnaire and "yes" on item 2; or two attributes that can both be classified "plus" and "minus," etc.). In this case the sign tells you whether "yes" is associated with "yes," or on the other hand whether it is associated consistently with "no"; i.e.,

	+	−
+	50	0
−	0	50

I

	+	−
+	0	50
−	50	0

II

In I both Q and ϕ will be positive, and the sign will have meaning; in II both Q and ϕ will be negative, and the sign will again have meaning. If the order is not admissible, however, ignore the sign.

As an example of this, look at Table 6-1, on page 132. The sign of a measure of association here will have meaning even though the attributes themselves are not ordered, since *Republican* will be associated with *Republican*, *Democrat* with *Democrat*, and arranged in this way Q or ϕ would be positive.

When it *is* appropriate to use the sign, in order to preserve the conventions we have established defining positive and negative association, we must define Q and ϕ with δ_{11}, the delta value from the upper-left cell. When the numerator used is $ad - bc$ the result will automatically correspond to the convention.

Association in the General r x s Table*

You will recall that for what we called the symmetrical table, we put the table into a form in which all the figures were proportions of N (including N, which becomes 1.00).

* The student interested in the extension of delta-based quantities to the $r \times s$ table should see Yule and Kendall, 1950, pp. 52–57; however, since these measures are relatively unsuccessful we do not discuss them here. The Goodman-Kruskal measures that we do describe are relatively new and are not as yet frequent in the research literature; but they appear to be much better suited to our purpose than the traditional measures. In addition they generalize Q, and also a less-known measure called the "coefficient of predictability," invented by Guttman.

Computation of Q and the phi coefficient from fourfold tables

	A	$\bar{A}$	
B	a	b	$a + b$
$\bar{B}$	c	d	$c + d$
	$a + c$	$b + d$	N

1. For Yule's Q you need

$$ad =$$
$$bc =$$

2. And for ϕ you need in addition

$$(a + b)(c + d)(a + c)(b + d) =$$

1. Computation of Yule's Q:
   a. Compute the cross-products, ad and bc.
   b. Subtract bc from ad.
   c. Add bc and ad.
   d. Divide the result of step (b) by the result of (c), giving

$$Q = \frac{ad - bc}{ad + bc}$$

2. Computation of the phi coefficient:
   a. Compute the cross-products, ad and bc.
   b. Compute the product of the four marginals.
   c. Subtract bc from ad.
   d. Divide the result of step (c) by the square root of the result of step (b), giving

$$\phi = \frac{ad - bc}{\sqrt{(a + b)(c + d)(a + c)(b + d)}}$$

A Note on the Sign of Q *and* ϕ

The sign of both Q and ϕ will have a stable meaning if you always use the letters a, b, c, d, as we have distributed them in the 2 × 2 above. If the frequencies run from upper-left to lower-right, i.e., positively, then $ad - bc$ will be positive and Q and ϕ will be positive; if they run upper right to lower left, i.e., negatively, then $ad - bc$ will be negative and Q and ϕ will be negative. If there is no way to interpret the sign, simply throw it away. But if the attributes A and B can be given some kind of ordered significance (even the association of $++$, $--$, i.e. AB, $\overline{AB}$, has a significance) save the sign.

If you compute Q and ϕ from $N\delta$, as you might if you are computing delta anyway for use in computing chi-square (see Chapter 10), the sign of Q and ϕ will be ambiguous unless you use the delta value for the upper left cell (cell a) only. The delta quantities for all the cells of the fourfold will turn out to be the same, but the signs will be half positive and half negative. To be consistent, and of course only if the sign really has meaning, you should use the sign which will give the same result as the small a, b, c, d, scheme above.

This is a convenient way to look at the general form of a table. One of the interesting ways of looking at the proportions in this table is in terms of the *probability* of an event occurring.

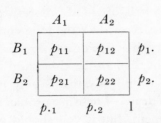

$$\begin{array}{c|c|c|c}
 & A_1 & A_2 & \\
\hline
B_1 & p_{11} & p_{12} & p_{1\cdot} \\
\hline
B_2 & p_{21} & p_{22} & p_{2\cdot} \\
\hline
 & p_{\cdot 1} & p_{\cdot 2} & 1
\end{array}$$

One interpretation of the proportions in this table is in terms of the *probability* of an event occurring. For instance, suppose this to be a population from which we draw a sample; the probability that the first sample member we draw is A_1B_1 is p_{11}, i.e., n_{11}/N. By this definition of probability, the probability of an event is its *relative frequency*.

The definition of the term "probability" is controversial, and it has exercised both philosophers and mathematicians a good deal in this century, but for the time being we will avoid most of the argument. We will say simply that a probability of the occurrence of the event A is its relative frequency of occurrence; and this is given by noting how often it *does* occur out of all occasions on which it conceivably could occur. This in turn reduces to the simple expression A/N, where $N = A + \bar{A}$. And this is also, of course, the definition of a proportion.

Now, the chief use of such a definition of probability is in the *prediction* of events; and it is on a model of the prediction of events that we are going to base our measures of association for the $r \times s$ table. (The prediction itself may be of interest, however, in what follows.)

Suppose that we take the two hypothetical populations of males and females we used in the previous chapter. Suppose further that we know nothing about the individual members and that we have someone write their names on slips of paper and mix up the slips in two bowls, each bowl containing the names of one of the populations. We reach in to draw a name from the bowl containing the names of the first population. Now what are the chances that we will get the name of a male on our first draw from the first population?

Look at our definition of probability again. The question we have just asked is equivalent to asking the probability of the event "I draw a male" under certain conditions. And the probability is defined as the relative frequency of the event. In this case the relative frequency is obviously the relative frequency of males in the first population. The probability of drawing a male in the first population is 0.375 (i.e., the proportion of males); there are 150 chances out of 400 possible first draws we might make that we will get a male.

Suppose you ask yourself *this* question: "If I draw a name and have to guess before I look at it, whether it is the name of a male or a female, what is the best guess that I can make?" In other words, you are now asked to make a *prediction*. We will help you out by giving you a piece of information. We will tell you that you are drawing from the first bowl, and that the probability of drawing a male in the first bowl is 0.375; or, alternatively, we will tell you when you are drawing from the second bowl: the probability of drawing a male this time is 0.750.

If you are shrewd you will guess "female" when you are drawing from the first population *every time you draw*; and you will guess "male" every time when you are drawing from the second bowl. The logic of this rests on the idea that *if* you keep on drawing and keep on guessing, you will be *wrong* a certain part of the time but you will be *right* more often than you will be wrong. If you make predictions very often, it is obviously more practical to choose that method of prediction which gives you the least error over the long run. If you draw every name out of the bowl for population I, and every time you draw you say "female," you will be wrong 38% of the time. But you will be right 62% of the time, and this is the only way that you can *ensure* a minimum error. (Note: technically this is only true of an infinite population or when you *replace* the names after each draw. These are problems of more advanced probability which are not essential at the moment, but if you should get into a game like this look up "conditional probability" in an advanced text before you become involved.) In the second population, if you guess "male" every time you will be wrong 25% of the time, but you will be right 75% of the time.

IMPROVING PREDICTIONS: LAMBDA

We are going to use this game as a model for a measure of association; the measure will consist in the *improvement* in our predictions that we are able to obtain from knowing which bowl we are going to draw from. More generally, we suggest the following model (after Goodman and Kruskal, 1954). We have two attributes, A and B, which we assume for the time being are asymmetrical (i.e., A affects B). We draw one member of a population at random and we are asked to predict his B class, either with *no* other information, or given his A class.

Assume that we have a 5×4 table like Table 7-2 (page 175). We convert this table into its general form by dividing through by N to get

Ethnicity

		Anglo	Sp.-Am.	Ital.	Other	
	NE	.063	.097	.011	.000	.171
	NW	.023	.092	.006	.017	.137
Resi-dence	SE	.274	.017	.051	.046	.389
	SW	.143	.074	.023	.040	.280
	OT	.011	.000	.006	.006	.023
		.514	.280	.097	.109	1.000

We will call Ethnicity the A classification and Residence the B classification. Now, if we know nothing about the individual we draw and we want to guess his B class, we guess that B class in which the largest proportion of the population falls; this follows from our game with the bowls. Just for short let us call this proportion *b-max*. In the present case we are trying to guess in which quadrant of town a randomly drawn resident will live;

b-max is 0.389, so we guess that he will live in the southeast quadrant. We will be right 39% of the time and wrong the remainder, or 61%, of the time.

More generally, we choose the largest marginal proportion of B's, max p_b, and our error is given by $1 - \text{max } p_b$. (We will use max p_b synonymously with b-max.)

Now take a case in which we are again asked to guess the individual's B class, but we are given some additional information. We are, in fact, told what his A class is. In *this* case we shall do best by guessing the B class which has the largest proportion of the kind of A's we are told that the individual is. Suppose, in other words, that we are told that the individual drawn is Spanish-American. In our model the B class that contains the largest

TABLE 7-2.

Ethnicity and Residence, Gallup, New Mexico, 1951

		Anglo	*Sp.-Am.*	*Ital.*	*Other*	
	NE	11	17	2	0	30
	NW	4	16	1	3	24
Resi- dence	SE	48	3	9	8	68
	SW	25	13	4	7	49
	OT	2	0	1	1	4
		90	49	17	19	175

Ethnicity spans the Anglo, Sp.-Am., Ital., Other columns.

Source: original data.

Note: Ethnicity is obtained by classifying names drawn randomly from a telephone directory; thus the Spanish-American population is under-represented, although this has no particular effect on this kind of table (see pp. 138–140 if you do not understand why).

Residence is classified by quadrants of the town, which happen to be formed neatly by two major highways that cross each other in the center of the town; these quadrants happen to be sociologically meaningful, i.e., they are seen by the local population as the chief structural features of the community.

OT means "outside of town."

proportion of Spanish-Americans is the northeast quadrant of town. So we guess NE. This time we call the maximum ab-max for short, and this means (literally) the class in a given column of A for which B is a maximum. Since each time we draw we are told the individual's A class, our error is actually now $1 - \sum \text{max } p_{ab}$, i.e., one minus the sum of the ab-max classes.

More generally, we now choose the largest joint occurrence of the known A class and B. In other words, we guess the B class for which max p_{ab} (i.e., ab-max) occurs. Our error is given by $1 - \sum \max p_{ab}$.

If you have gotten this far, the rest is clear sailing. If there is any association between A and B then we ought to do better guessing an individual's B class if we *know* his A class than if we do not; i.e., the second method of prediction ought to be more successful than the first. So we define a measure of association which shows simply whether we improve or not, and if we do, how much. Such a measure is:

$$\lambda_{b \cdot a} = \frac{\sum \max p_{ab} - \max p_b}{1 - \max p_b}$$ λ is the Greek letter for "l" and is read "lambda."

where max p_{ab} is the largest proportion of B for a given A

max p_b is the largest marginal proportion of B

$\lambda_{b \cdot a}$ means we are predicting B from a knowledge of A

One advantage of this measure is that it is extremely easy to compute unless the number of columns and rows is very large. And for computation purposes it is not necessary to convert the table into its p_{ij} form; we can work directly from the original form, altering slightly the definition above. Using the original form of Table 7-1, we have:

$$\lambda_{b \cdot a} = \frac{\sum \max n_{ab} - \max n_b}{N - \max n_b}$$ A_1-max $= 48$
$$= \frac{(48 + 17 + 9 + 8) - 68}{175 - 68}$$ A_2-max $= 17$
A_3-max $= 9$
A_4-max $= 8$
B-max $= 68$
$$= 0.13$$

This is interpreted rather simply as an improvement of 13% in our predictions. Incidentally, if you wish to predict an individual's ethnicity from a knowledge of where he lives—equally legitimate—you use $\lambda_{a \cdot b}$, which is simply the reverse, i.e.,

$$\lambda_{a \cdot b} = \frac{\sum \max n_{ba} - \max n_a}{N - \max n_a}$$ B_1-max $= 17$
$$= \frac{(17 + 16 + 48 + 25 + 2) - 90}{175 - 90}$$ B_2-max $= 16$
B_3-max $= 48$
B_4-max $= 25$
B_5-max $= 2$
$$= 0.21$$ A-max $= 90$

or a 21% improvement in our predictions.

Now let us look at the assumptions underlying this measure more closely. First, the measure is designed for a special problem, and should be used only when you have the appropriate type of problem. It assumes that there is neither (a) an underlying continuous variable, *nor* (b) an intrinsic order to either of the attributes; and it likewise assumes the asymmetrical case we described earlier. Since there is no order, it is designed to range from 0 to 1. A sign is irrelevant when it makes no difference which class comes first, and if you had one you would just have to throw it away. Consequently you can change around the rows and columns (permute them, as it is called) and you won't change the measure. (This does *not* mean you can *combine* them indiscriminately and not change it.)

If you want to measure association for the same kind of attributes (neither continuous nor ordered), but do not wish to assume asymmetry, then you can use a simple adaptation of the same logic, giving a measure labeled simply "lambda" without a subscript. The formula looks fearsome, but it is not really complex. It is derived by assuming that half the time you predict A and half the time you predict B, and again are, alternatively, given no information and information about the B or A class. Then lambda is defined as:

$$\lambda = \frac{\frac{1}{2}(\sum \max p_{ab} + \sum \max p_{ba} - \max p_a - \max p_b)}{1 - \frac{1}{2}(\max p_a + \max p_b)}$$

To compute λ you need the maximum of the second-order frequencies taken in both directions; i.e., you need the maximum B classes for each A *and* the maximum A classes for each B. Converting the formula into a computation form:

$$\lambda = \frac{\sum \max n_{ab} + \sum \max n_{ba} - \max n_a - \max n_b}{2N - (\max n_a + \max n_b)}$$

$$= \frac{(82 + 108 - 90 - 68)}{(2)(175) - (90 + 68)}$$

$$= 0.17$$

$$\sum \max n_{ab} = 82$$
$$\sum \max n_{ba} = 108$$
$$\max n_a = 90$$
$$\max n_b = 68$$

The necessary quantities at the left are already summed. Can you find the cells contributing to each sum?

ONE PROBLEM IN THE USE OF LAMBDA

There is one severe limitation of the lambda measures, particularly the asymmetrical ones, which derives from their mathematical properties. We can illustrate this by examining Table 7-3 (page 179), showing the relation of region to tolerance of nonconformists (atheists, Communists, etc.) in the United States, from a recent national survey.

Look first at the percentaged table at the right. Most sociologists would agree with Stouffer, who analyzed these data, that the table shows some relation between region and tolerance; and particularly that the West is more tolerant than the South (e.g., look at the bottom row, the percentage difference between West and South in the "more tolerant" class). If you compute $\lambda_{b \cdot a}$, however, predicting tolerance from region, the computation

Computation of lambda measures of association for cross-classified manifold classifications having r and s classes

	A_1	A_2	$\cdots$	A_s	
B_1	n_{11}	n_{12}	$\cdots$	n_{1s}	$n_1.$
B_2	n_{21}	n_{22}	$\cdots$	n_{2s}	$n_2.$
$\vdots$	$\vdots$	$\vdots$		$\vdots$	$\vdots$
B_r	n_{r1}	n_{r2}	$\cdots$	n_{rs}	$n_r.$
	$n._1$	$n._2$	$\cdots$	$n._s$	N

1. For $\lambda_{b \cdot a}$ you need

$$\text{max } A_1 =$$
$$\text{max } A_2 =$$
$$\text{max } A_3 =$$
$$\vdots$$
$$\text{max } A_s =$$
_____
$$\sum \text{max } n_{ab} =$$
$$\text{max } n_b =$$

2. For $\lambda_{a \cdot b}$ you need

$$\text{max } B_1 =$$
$$\text{max } B_2 =$$
$$\text{max } B_3 =$$
$$\vdots$$
$$\text{max } B_r =$$
_____
$$\sum \text{max } n_{ba} =$$
$$\text{max } n_a =$$

1. *For the asymmetrical case, predicting* B *from* A:
   a. Find the class of B for which A_1 is a maximum and enter at the right of the table (max A_1 =) the frequency in this class, n_{ij}. Then find the class of B for which A_2 is a maximum, etc.
   b. Find the largest first-order frequency of the attribute B, and enter at the right of the table (max n_b =).
   c. Add the max n_{ab}, and compute $\lambda_{b \cdot a}$ from the formula,

$$\lambda_{b \cdot a} = \frac{\sum \text{max } n_{ab} - \text{max } n_b}{N - \text{max } n_b}$$

2. *For the asymmetrical case, predicting* A *from* B:
   a. Find the class of A for which B_1 is maximum, etc., as in step (a) above. Find also the largest first-order A, as in (b) above, add the max n_{ba} and compute $\lambda_{a \cdot b}$ from

$$\lambda_{a \cdot b} = \frac{\sum \text{max } n_{ba} - \text{max } n_a}{N - \text{max } n_a}$$

3. *For the symmetrical case:*
   a. Obtain both the B maximums for A and the A maximums for B, following steps 1(a) and 2(a) above.
   b. Obtain both the maximum first-order frequency of A and of B, as in 1 and 2 above.
   c. After adding both the max n_{ab} and max n_{ba} compute λ from the following formula,

$$\lambda = \frac{\sum \text{max } n_{ab} + \sum \text{max } n_{ba} - \text{max } n_b - \text{max } n_a}{2N - (\text{max } n_b + \text{max } n_a)}$$

TABLE 7-3.

Tolerance of Nonconformists, by Region, U. S., 1954

	West	East	Midwest	South			West	East	Midwest	South
Less tolerant	86	189	234	417	926	LT	13%	15%	16%	27%
In between	257	581	776	887	2501	IB	39	46	53	57
More tolerant	316	492	455	247	1510	MT	48	39	31	16
	659	1262	1465	1551	4937		100%	100%	100%	100%

$$\lambda_{b \cdot a} = 0.02$$

Source: Stouffer, 1955, p. 112.

shows an almost negligible association, 0.02. The reason is that the column maxima are almost all in the same row, i.e., "in between." Now this is not at all an exceptional instance in sociological data. We are frequently interested in examining differences in tables having the bulk of the population in some one B class; the differences will be interesting because they may have a spread of as much as 20%, perhaps more, between A_1 and A_s, but if all the column maxima are in the same row these differences will not be discriminated by $\lambda_{b \cdot a}$, and there could very well appear to be a zero association.

The lambda measures, then, are designed to give you 1.00 for a case like this:

p_{11}	0	0
0	p_{22}	0
0	0	p_{33}

λ is 1.00 if all the maxima are in the diagonal cells. (Note that there are other cases in which $\lambda = 1.00$. Can you identify them?)

but 0.00 for a case like this:

0	0	0
p_{21}	p_{22}	p_{23}
0	0	0

λ is 0 if all the maxima are in one row or one column. (The remaining proportions need not be zero, of course, so long as they are less than the maximum in their column or row.)

The second table will give 0 no matter what the percentage difference $p_{23} - p_{21}$ may happen to be, so long as all the column *maxima* are in this row.

To weigh against this disadvantage (which is not shared by delta-based measures) there is the ease of computation and the directness and simplicity of the interpretation of lambda measures. We can say, however, that wherever it is possible to assume that there *is* an intrinsic order underlying the characteristics measured, the gamma measures of the next section are preferred to lambda; gamma will give a more powerful and efficient result.

PREDICTING ORDER

Based on the same kind of logic, Goodman and Kruskal also give a measure that will deal with association between what we have called quasi-variables. You will recall that we said two things about such variables: they have intrinsic order, but at the same time they are not continuous and have neither zero point nor equal intervals. So far we have not talked much about variables like this, but they are as frequent as unordered attributes and we will discuss them more as we go along. Here is the kind of case we mean:

	A_1 Good	A_2 Fair	A_3 Poor
B_1 High			
B_2 Medium			
B_3 Low			

We can't say how *much* greater A_1 is than A_2, but we *can* say that it *is* greater; in general, we can say $A_1 > A_2 > A_3$. The same is true of B, so that we can say $B_1 > B_2 > B_3$.

Here is what we do. This time we draw *two* individuals and compare them. Suppose that the first of our two individuals is Fair on A and Medium on B (we will call him FM for short). What will the second one be? Well, we have basically three possibilities:

	A_1 G	A_2 F	A_3 P
B_1 H	a		c
B_2 M		1	
B_3 L	b		d

Suppose that the second individual is anything else, but not F or M or both. Then he can be:
   a. Higher on A and higher on B
   b. Higher on A and lower on B
   c. Lower on A and higher on B
   d. Lower on A and lower on B
We can reduce these possibilities by calling (a) and (d) *like orders* and (b) and (c) *unlike orders*; we have, of course, always the possibility that he will be a tie on either A or B or both, contingencies which we have not listed.

If there is any association between A and B we ought consistently to get either like orders (representing positive association) or unlike orders (negative association), not counting the ties. And if there is no association we get neither consistently; like will follow unlike order more or less at random. We have in mind, in other words, making a number of draws, each of two individuals, and comparing the order of the A and B classes for the two on each draw. And we might get results something like this:

	1	2	Order
	1	2	Order
Draw I	FM	GH	$A_1 < A_2$ and $B_1 < B_2$
Draw II	GH	PL	$A_1 > A_2$ and $B_1 > B_2$
Draw III	PL	GH	$A_1 < A_2$ and $B_1 < B_2$
etc.	etc.	etc.	etc.

Notice that the order of the A's, whichever way it runs, is consistently reproduced in the order of the B's; this is *like order* or positive association.

Or we could, of course, also get:

	1	2	Order
Draw I	FM	GL	$A_1 < A_2$ and $B_1 > B_2$
Draw II	GL	PH	$A_1 > A_2$ and $B_1 < B_2$
Draw III	PH	GL	$A_1 < A_2$ and $B_1 > B_2$
etc.	etc.	etc.	etc.

Here the order of the A's is consistently reversed by the order of the B's; this is *unlike order* or negative association.

Now we are going to construct a measure that is essentially based on predicting the direction of the order and how consistently this order is reproduced. We have to get three quantities:

the probability of like order, which is indicated by π_s (read pi-s)
the probability of unlike order, π_d (s is for "same," d for "different")
the probability of a tie, π_t (t is for "tie")

The measure constructed from these probabilities is called "gamma," and is defined as

$$\gamma = \frac{\pi_s - \pi_d}{1 - \pi_t}$$

γ is the Greek letter for "g" and is read "gamma."

This measure goes from -1 to 1 and tells you how much more probable a like order is than an unlike order. If you have a value close to 1 you have high positive association and if you have -1 you have high negative association.

Before computing gamma there are two things we want to note about it. In the first place, when used in the 2×2 table it is identical with Yule's Q; for a fourfold table, it is

$$\gamma = \frac{p_{11}p_{22} - p_{12}p_{21}}{p_{11}p_{22} + p_{12}p_{21}}$$

which is exactly Yule's Q. Thus we can give a very simple and meaningful interpretation of Yule's Q now, in terms of the Goodman-Kruskal more general model, and of course Q is generalized so that it applies to any $r \times s$ table. It is, then, based essentially on the idea of predicting the order of B with respect to A on successive draws. It follows, incidentally, that gamma defines "complete association" in the same way as Q, i.e., for the table

$$
\begin{array}{cc}
p_{11} & 0 \\
p_{21} & p_{22}
\end{array}
$$

gamma gives 1, and of course if the bottom left or top right cell contains the zero it gives -1.

COMPUTATION OF GAMMA

Unfortunately, gamma is not so simple to compute as lambda, although the difficulty is entirely one of arithmetic. We will compute gamma for the following table:

TABLE 7-4.

Class Homogamy in the United States

		Husband's Occupational Class			
		Upper	*Middle*	*Lower*	
Wife's Father's Occupational Class	Upper	9	26	13	48
	Middle	19	75	83	177
	Lower	16	56	110	182
		44	157	206	407

Source: Adapted from Centers, 1949.

For ease of computation, we will compute γ in terms of absolute frequencies rather than proportions. Corresponding to π_s we will have an expression n_s, from which the probability of like order is derived, and corresponding to π_d we will have the expression n_d.

We suggest this time that you look first at the general model for the computation on page 184. Note first how n_s is obtained; we start with the upper-left cell frequency 9. We are going to multiply 9 by all the frequencies that are in like order with respect to 9, i.e., 75, 83, 56, and 110. These are the frequencies that in step 1(a) are shaded in the computation design; they are *both* to the right of *and* below n_{11}, and note that both these conditions must be satisfied simultaneously. So for step 1(a) we have $(9)(75 + 83 + 56 + 110) = (9)(324)$. For step 1(b) we move to the cell containing 26 and we must multiply 26 by $83 + 110$; only these two cells are both to the right of and below 26. If you used cells in the same column and row, of course, you would be computing the ties; and if you used the cells above and to the left you would be working on n_d, the probability of unlike order. Continuing in this way, then,

$$n_s = (9)(75 + 83 + 56 + 110) + 26(83 + 110) + 19(56 + 110) + (75)(110)$$
$$= 19,338$$

Can you see why we did not use 13, 83, 110, 56, and 16 as the starting points for one of the steps in finding n_s? (Read 1(c) and 1(e) again if you do not.) Now we are going to find n_d. We start this time with 13, and the frequencies that are both to the *left* of and below 13 are 19, 75, 16, and 56. Then we go to 26, which we must multiply by $19 + 16$, and so on, reversing the procedure for n_s. This gives

$$n_d = 13(19 + 75 + 16 + 56) + 26(19 + 16) + 83(16 + 56) + 75(16)$$
$$= 10,244$$

Fortunately we don't need to find n_t for the computing formula, which is simply

$$\gamma = \frac{n_s - n_d}{n_s + n_d}$$
$$= \frac{19,338 - 10,244}{19,338 + 10,244}$$
$$= \frac{9094}{29,582}$$
$$= 0.307$$

The Interpretation of, and Choice Among, Lambda, Gamma, Q, and Phi

We now have four quantities we can use for various types of contingency tables, all of which measure association. There are, as a matter of fact, even more such measures which we have not yet mentioned, and some which we will not mention at all. Like the choice between the mean, the median, and the mode we must choose here among several measures each of which represents the same general concept (association), but each of which measures

1. To find n_s, representing the probability of *like order*:

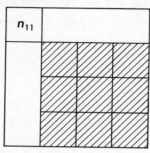

a. Start with n_{11}, the upper left cell. Add all the frequencies in the *shaded* area in the diagram, and then multiply them by n_{11}. The shaded area *excludes* the row and column containing the cell n_{11}.

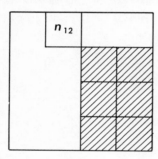

b. Then take n_{12}, the adjacent cell in the same row. Add all the frequencies in the shaded area, and then multiply them by n_{12}. The shaded area excludes the row and column containing the cell n_{12} *and* the column to the left of the column containing n_{12}.

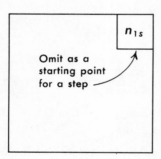

Omit as a starting point for a step —

c. Then take $n_{13}, \ldots$, always adding the frequencies that are simultaneously to the right of *and* below the cell n_{ij} and always excluding cells in the same row and same column, and all cells above and to the left of these rows and columns. *Omit* cells in the last column, since there are no cells to the right of them, from the role of *starting* point for a step.

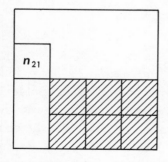

d. Return to the next row and n_{21}. Add all the frequencies in the shaded area and multiply by n_{21}. The shaded area excludes row 2 and column 1, containing n_{21}, and *also* the row above.

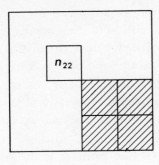

e. Move to n_{22}, and so forth. Note that what you are doing, essentially, is summing up all the chances of drawing a joint frequency of *like order* with respect to n_{ij}.

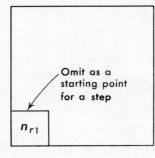

Omit as a starting point for a step

n_{r1}

f. Continue until you have used up all the cells for which you can find cells to the right and below the column and row containing n_{ij}; this means you will omit not only the last column but also the bottom row, since there are no cells below it.

g. Now add up all the products that result from multiplying n_{ij} by the sum of the frequencies below and to the right of n_{ij}.

2. To find n_d, representing the probability of *unlike order*:

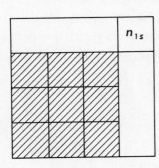

n_{1s}

a. Start this time with n_{1s}, the upper right cell, and add the frequencies to the left of and below, as in the shaded area. Continue according to the procedure of steps 1(a) to 1(f), simply reversing the order of the moves. Stop with the left-hand column and bottom row this time, neither of which have cells both to the left and below.

b. Add up all the products of the sum of frequencies below and to the left times n_{ij}, as in step 1(g).

3. Now compute gamma, according to the formula

$$\gamma = \frac{n_s - n_d}{n_s + n_d}$$

it in a different way and is suited to a somewhat different situation. Gamma and Q, it turns out, are essentially the same; that leaves us with three to choose among.

In choosing among statistical measures, it is wise to pay attention to their assumptions and how the measures were originally constructed. In the first place we have the distinction between the ordered and unordered case, and we know that for gamma the basic assumption is that both cross-classified characteristics have an intrinsic order. And since Q is a special case of gamma for fourfold tables, Q also implies an underlying order. Actually Q is very often used for unordered attributes, simply by ignoring the sign. But this, of course, wastes about the only simple and understandable meaning that can be given to Q, other than the purely pragmatic meaning it has tended to have in the past. Q, like gamma, is the probability that for every pair of individuals drawn at random from a population, excluding ties, the order of A_1 to A_2, and B_1 to B_2, will be the same (where the subscripts designate the individual drawn). If you do not want to assume an intrinsic order, then lambda is the appropriate measure of association. In the use of lambda, in turn, you have to distinguish symmetrical and asymmetrical cases in order to choose among $\lambda_{b \cdot a}$, $\lambda_{a \cdot b}$, or just plain λ.

Like gamma and Q, the phi coefficient assumes order. Also like Q, the sign is frequently ignored when there is no sense to the order. In one of its forms this coefficient is derived from the product-moment coefficient r by using only two variate values (1, 0). Conveniently enough, ϕ can be thought of as *like* the product-moment r, for the 2 × 2 case. For practical purposes the chief difference from Q is in the form of table that gives complete association. Q, implying a less restrictive definition of association than ϕ, tends to give higher values than ϕ for the same table. In particular, because of the way it is defined, ϕ gives ±1.00 *only* in the case that the two marginal distributions of a fourfold table are symmetrical. By symmetrical margins we mean that, if the marginal in one direction is n_a and $n_{\bar{a}}$ and in the other direction is n_b and $n_{\bar{b}}$, $n_a = n_b$ and $n_{\bar{a}} = n_{\bar{b}}$. In any other case ϕ cannot be 1.00, for in no other case can a 0 be obtained in *both* diagonal cells. We can think of ϕ, therefore, as measuring degree of diagonal concentration; it reaches its limiting value only when all the observations are in one diagonal. This may be thought of as an excessively restrictive definition of association, but that depends on your data, your problem, your hypothesis, etc.

A Note on *r*-Based Measures for Attributes

There is a whole general class of measures, based on, or derived from, the product-moment coefficient, that we have not mentioned. They are sometimes of use for special problems and we will discuss them very briefly here. The student who is interested should look through Chapter 10 in Edwards (1955); this gives a clear, lucid, and moderately detailed presentation.

The *point-biserial coefficient* is designed for a dichotomous attribute cross-classified with a continuous variate. The *biserial coefficient* deals with the same case, assuming in addition that the dichotomized "attribute" is really a normally distributed continuous variate cut in two at the median. The *tetrachoric correlation coefficient*, quite frequently seen in sociological reports, is designed for the cross-classification of two dichotomies, assuming again that both dichotomies are really normally distributed, continuous variates that have been cut in two at the median. All of these are considered to be estimates of the product-moment coefficient which writers some years ago sometimes thought of as "real" correlation.

Where We Stand

The subject of this chapter is essentially the same as that of chapter 5—the examination of the relationship of two characteristics, given a set of bivariate observations. Here, however, we have attributes and orders rather than variables (letting *variable* have the meaning given to it in Chapter 1). We are now able both to describe in detail and to summarize essential aspects of the relationship of such characteristics.

In the next chapter, however, we introduce a topic that we did not consider in dealing with measurement data; namely, the treatment of *multi*variate problems, when we must examine the relationship not of two but of three or more attributes.

Chapter 7

WORKBOOK EXERCISES

1. *Detailed table reading.* In the previous chapter you percentaged tables and compared differences in percentages, much as described in the first section of this chapter. This is the heart of table reading. In the exercises below continue this procedure, but introduce the size of the percentage differences, and their direction, where this is relevant. This time, instead of discussing primarily in which direction to percentage, describe in as much detail as you can *everything* that the table tells you. Begin with the marginals, reporting whatever seems relevant about them. Then move to the cells of the table. After giving them detailed attention, conclude with a general summary of what the table has to say. Use pages 191–194 for these problems.

a. Table D, on page 145, on interlocking directorates

b. Table G, on page 146, on the relation of vote intentions to the vote intentions of one's closest friends

c. Table L, on page 149, on vote intention in relation to father's usual vote.

d. Table I, on page 147, on relation of present occupation to community in which respondent grew up

2. *Measures of association*

a. Compute both Q and ϕ for the following tables. In each case discuss what significance, if any, the sign of the measure has. Use page 195 for parts 2a(1) and 2a(2).

(1) Table L, page 149, respondent's vote by father's vote.

(2) In Table G, page 146, respondent's vote by his friends' vote: combine the RRR and RRD cells into one cell, and the RDD and DDD cells into one cell. This will produce a fourfold table (preserving the distinction between respondent's vote R or D, of course). We have combined the two upper left cells for you.

259	

b. Compute both λ and γ for the following tables. Before computing λ decide whether the table is symmetrical or asymmetrical; and if asymmetrical, decide in which direction you wish to predict. After computing both λ and γ discuss briefly which one is most appropriate to each case. Use pages 196–199.

(1) Table F, page 146, on tolerance of nonconformists
(2) Table G, page 146, on vote intention by friends' intention
(3) Table H, page 147, on length of engagement by length of acquaintance
(4) Table N, page 150, on mobility inclinations by complaints about housing

c. Compute $\lambda_{a \cdot b}$ for Table B on occupation by sex. Use page 200.

Problem I

Problem 1

Problem I

Problem 1

Problem 2a

Problem 2b

Problem 2b

Problem 2b

Problem 2b

Problem 2c

Chapter 8

Multivariate Attributes

FOR ANY given person there is an almost infinite number of properties by which he could be characterized. So far we have talked about only one, or at most two, of these properties at a time. The multivariate case arises when we take three, or more, at the same time. We discuss in this chapter the logic of dealing with this case, although we confine ourselves to attributes for illustration. The logic is the same for variables, but the problems of computation are rather complicated for an elementary text.

Situations of the kind we shall deal with arise in the following way: we have cross-classified two attributes and find a relationship between them. We now wish to know more about this relationship. We therefore introduce some third attribute which will clarify the relationship for us in some way or other. This is called the *elaboration* of the original relationship (following Lazarsfeld and Kendall, 1950; see also Hyman, 1955, Chapters 6 and 7). We may do this either to penetrate further into the relationship—to discover more about it—or in order to discover whether an *apparent* association of the two attributes in the original relationship is genuine or not.

General Form of Multivariate Tables

Adding a third attribute adds a third dimension to our table. A 2 × 2 table, for example, becomes a 2 × 2 × 2 table when dichotomized again by a third attribute. This is called *stratifying* the 2 × 2 (or *r* × *s* in general). Table 8-1 (page 202) is an example.

TABLE 8-1.

Socioeconomic Status, Union Membership, and the Two-party Vote, Elmira, 1948

	Socioeconomic Status					*Union Membership*						
	High	*Low*				*Member*				*Nonmember*		
						High	*Low*				*High*	*Low*	
Rep.	242	150	392	stratified by union membership becomes:	Rep.	14	37	51	Rep.	228	113	341
Dem.	78	111	189		Dem.	14	56	70	Dem.	64	55	119
	320	261	581			28	93	121		292	168	460

Source: Berelson, Lazarsfeld, and McPhee, 1954, p. 47.

The stratified table has 2 rows, 2 columns, and 2 "partial" tables (one for members, one for nonmembers); we call it a $2 \times 2 \times 2$ table. The number of partials is mentioned first (representing the number of classes of the third variable, C), and then the rows and columns.

In the set-up of this table we have, on the left, the familiar two-dimensional table, showing the relation of status to party preference in Elmira. (Pause here, and read the 2×2; what does it show?) We now attempt to clarify this relation by introducing a third variable, union membership. Note exactly what we do. The third variable is in this case dichotomous (either you are a member or you are not), and we have shown two separate tables on the right, one for the positive class of C and one for the negative class. (If the attribute we introduced had been a manifold classification, then we would have had 3, 4, 5, etc., tables on the right instead of two.) In each 2×2 on the right, we have the relation of A and B, first under the condition C, and then under the condition $\bar{C}$. These 2×2 tables are called the *partials* of A and B, i.e., they represent the partial association of A and B in each of the classes of C. When we stratify a two-dimensional table this way, we call it *holding constant* the third variable; so the partials represent the relation of A and B with C held constant. In general form,

	C_1					C_2				$\cdots$	C_k
	A_1	A_2				A_1	A_2				
B_1	n_{111}	n_{121}	$n_{1\cdot1}$	B_1		n_{112}	n_{122}	$n_{1\cdot2}$			
B_2	n_{211}	n_{221}	$n_{2\cdot1}$	B_2		n_{212}	n_{222}	$n_{2\cdot2}$			
	$n_{\cdot11}$	$n_{\cdot21}$	$n_{\cdot\cdot1}$			$n_{\cdot12}$	$n_{\cdot22}$	$n_{\cdot\cdot2}$	$N = n_{\cdot\cdot1} + n_{\cdot\cdot2} \cdots$		

A and *B* are stratified by *C*. This shows only a $2 \times 2 \times 2$ but you could just as easily have a $3 \times 3 \times 3$ or a $2 \times 3 \times 2$, or a $5 \times 5 \times 5$, etc. Note that each cell frequency has three subscripts, telling you which *A*, which *B*, and which *C* the cell represents, with the *C* in third position. The dots, as before, stand in place of missing subscripts (missing because they do not define the frequency in question) and merely tell you position; for example, $n_{..1}$ is the first order frequency of C_1, the dots telling you that this subscript is a 1 in the third position. The third-order frequencies are now the ones that we call *ultimate* frequencies.

The Control of Confounding Factors

When two variables appear to be related there is a danger that in fact they are not related; it is this kind of problem that we will discuss in this section. The danger arises because it is possible that both variables may be related to some third variable, independently. But this does not show in a bivariate table, so that the first two *seem* to be related to each other. When this happens we say that the effect of the third (unseen) variable is *confounded* with the *A* and *B* effects, and the relation of *A* and *B* is spurious, i.e., it is illusory, an incidental result of the relation of *A* and *B*, each independently, to a third variable. Goldhamer and Marshall (1953), for instance, have shown that the apparent increase in psychoses in the last century is a spurious result of several confounded factors, particularly of shifts in age-sex distributions during this period. When you control for age and sex there is no increase in rates of first-admission in the central age groups (20–50) from about the middle of the nineteenth century to about the middle of the twentieth.

This is a fundamental problem in the interpretation of any research, and you should try to grasp the idea. Spurious associations result, as a matter of fact, from the simplest sort of arithmetic relation between the cells of the $r \times s$ table and its $n \times r \times s$ partials (we will use $n \times r \times s$ to refer to the general three-attribute case). Look at the following simple example:

$$
\begin{array}{cc}
10 \quad 10 \\
 + \\
10 \quad 10
\end{array}
\quad
\begin{array}{cc}
15 \quad 15 \\
 = \\
15 \quad 15
\end{array}
\quad
\begin{array}{cc}
25 \quad 25 \\
 \\
25 \quad 25
\end{array}
\quad
\begin{array}{l}
\text{The } 2 \times 2 \text{ on the right is found by add-} \\
\text{ing the frequencies in corresponding cells} \\
\text{of the partials.}
\end{array}
$$

The upper left cell of the 2×2 is found by adding the upper left cells in each of the two partial 2×2's on the left. If you will recall, we used the term *second-order* frequency to refer to n_{ij}; now we can extend this easily and call n_{ijk} a frequency of the third order. What we are saying then, is that the second-order frequencies are found by adding up corresponding third-order frequencies. This is, in fact, true at each level of the table. The zero-order frequency, N, is found by adding up first-order frequencies (marginals), the first-order frequencies are found by adding up the appropriate second-order frequencies, etc. For the $2 \times 2 \times 2$, for instance,

$$N = n_1 + n_2 \qquad n_{11} = n_{111} + n_{112}$$
$$n_{12} = n_{121} + n_{122}$$
$$n_1 = n_{11} + n_{12} \qquad n_{21} = n_{211} + n_{212}$$
$$n_2 = n_{21} + n_{22} \qquad n_{22} = n_{221} + n_{222}$$

Note that in order to know which ones to add up you see which ones have subscripts that are the same in the *same* positions and differ only in the *final* position. For instance, to get n_1 you add two second-order frequencies that have the subscript 1 in common in the first position, but differ from each other in the second position. To get n_{11} you add two third-order frequencies that have 11 in the same (first) two positions, but differ in the final (third) position, etc. If you have the tables in front of you, of course, you don't have to go through them putting in all the subscripts; just add up corresponding cells.

Incidentally, it follows that you can get any order of frequency if you have only the ultimate frequencies, by adding up the appropriate third-order frequencies. Now look at the following situation:

C

	A	$\bar{A}$	
B	1	5	6
$\bar{B}$	8	40	48
	9	45	54

$\delta = 0$
$Q = 0$

$+$

$\bar{C}$

	A	$\bar{A}$	
B	40	8	48
$\bar{B}$	5	1	6
	45	9	54

$\delta = 0$
$Q = 0$

$=$

	A	$\bar{A}$	
B	41	13	54
$\bar{B}$	13	41	54
	54	54	108

$\delta = 14$
$Q = 0.82$

There is no relation between A and B in the partials of this table. Both δ and Q are 0. (Compare also the ratios across and down and the percentage differences across and down.) But in the 2×2 on the right, A and B appear to be related quite strongly. Q is 0.82, and delta (taken from the upper left cell, as suggested in Chapter 7) is 14. The reason for this appearance of association, of course, is the markedly different distributions of the marginals in the two partial tables. This is a result, in turn, of the association of both A and B, quite independently, with C. That is:

Relation of A with C

	C	$\bar{C}$	
A	9	45	54
$\bar{A}$	45	9	54
	54	54	108

$\delta = -18$
$Q = -0.92$

Relation of B with C

	C	$\bar{C}$	
B	6	48	54
$\bar{B}$	48	6	54
	54	54	108

$\delta = -21$
$Q = -0.97$

Although A and B are not associated with each other, each is markedly associated with a third variable, C.

Yule offers a simple and typical example (Yule and Kendall, 1950, pp. 39–40). The mean annual death rates in England and Wales, 1930–1932, show that the death rate of the Anglican clergy was considerably higher than the death rate for coal miners. Can we conclude that it is less healthy to be an Anglican clergyman than to be a coal miner? You can guess the answer, of course. Death rates are correlated with age, and the Anglican clergy were, on the average, older than coal miners—i.e., occupation is correlated also with age. We have, then, an age-effect confounded with our occupation-effect. When the age-effect is taken out the relation is, as a matter of fact, reversed; it is less healthy to be a coal miner.

Problems like this have led all competent researchers to use what are called *specific* rates, and to *control* automatically for factors known to be related to the two attributes whose relation we seek to examine. As a parenthetical note, rates and ratios can be dealt with like percentage distributions in that they can be controlled. There is, however, a somewhat special terminology, particularly in population research, for this kind of procedure. Rates controlled for age, for instance, are called *age-specific*; rates controlled for sex are called *sex-specific*. We use age-specific and sex-specific mortality rates, for instance, or age- and sex-specific morbidity rates, crime rates, fertility rates, hospital first-admission rates, etc. Such specific rates mean that the identifying factor, whatever it is, is taken into account as a confounding factor and allowed for. The terminology is equivalent to our use of the terms *controls, partials,* etc.

FORMULA FOR MULTIVARIATE ASSOCIATION

An important formula summarizes our results so far, and if you grasp what it means you will be able to visualize multivariate problems. We give it here in terms of delta-quantities:

$$\delta_{ab} = \delta_{ab \cdot c_1} + \delta_{ab \cdot c_2} + \frac{N}{c_1 c_2} \delta_{ac} \delta_{bc}$$

where δ_{ab} is the relation of A and B in the 2×2

$\delta_{ab \cdot c_1}$ is the relation of A and B in the C_1 partial

$\delta_{ab \cdot c_2}$ is the relation of A and B in the C_2 partial

δ_{ac} is the relation of A to C

δ_{bc} is the relation of B to C

$N/c_1 c_2$ is the total N divided by the product of the number that are c_1 and the number that are c_2

This may be generalized for the $r \times s$ and the $n \times r \times s$.*

This formula is not primarily for computation; it is given here to help you think about and understand multivariate problems. It tells you that, as a result of the arithmetical relations that we have shown above, the relation of A and B is a result of adding up the relations of A and B in the partials *plus* the relation of A to C and B to C. We can state concisely, now, what we have been discussing in the last few pages. Assume that A and B are unrelated, i.e., independent. If this is so, $\delta_{ab \cdot c_1}$ and $\delta_{ab \cdot c_2}$ will each be zero and will vanish from the equation. But if A and B are both related to some third factor C, then δ_{ab} will *not* be zero, since the last term on the right will not be zero. Then,

1. If A and C are associated, and
2. If B and C are associated, then
3. A and B may *appear* to be associated, whether or not they are actually related, when A and B are cross-classified without holding C constant.

Only if A and B are unrelated to *any* common third factor will their relation to each other come out nil, even when they are themselves unrelated. Therefore, in any investigation of A and B it is always necessary to consider all the factors which they might have in common and which might be related independently to them. We stratify our $r \times s$ table into values of C, in order to control for C. *If the relation between A and B is not a spurious result of their relation to C, the partials will still show a relationship between A and B; if, on the other hand, the association is spurious it will disappear in the partials of C.*

AN EXTENDED EXAMPLE

Now let us consider a more extended example. This example also comes from the Elmira study and investigates the relationship between A, belonging to voluntary organiza-

---

* By this we mean that the *logic* underlying the formula is general to any multivariate problem, not only to the $2 \times 2 \times 2$. The *exact* elaboration formula for other cases, however, will differ in the *weights* of the terms of the formula, and no example of the exact formula for any specific case except the $2 \times 2 \times 2$ has been published. In addition, although again the logic is the same, the exact elaboration formula for other measures of association would be different.

tions, and B, exposure to the 1948 campaign through the mass media of communication (newspapers, radios, etc.). We find, first, a relationship between membership in organizations and exposure: the more organizations you belong to, the more you hear and see of the campaign through the mass media.

Step 1. The cross-classification of A and B, showing their relationship: belonging to organizations is positively associated with exposure to the campaign.

	Number of Organizations to Which Respondents Belong:				
		2+	1	0	
Exposure	High	169 (67%)	116 (54%)	145 (43%)	430 (53%)
	Low	85 (33%)	97 (46%)	193 (57%)	375 (47%)
		254 (100%)	213 (100%)	338 (100%)	805 (100%)

$$\gamma = 0.33$$

Source: Adapted from Berelson, Lazarsfeld, and McPhee, 1954, p. 243.

At the same time, we know (from other data) that C, interest in the campaign, is also correlated with B, i.e., exposure. Those with a great deal of interest are more exposed: 72% of those with a great deal of interest are high on exposure, while, of the moderately interested, 56% are high and, of the not much interested, only 31% are high on exposure to the campaign. We may also know, or guess, that interest in the campaign is itself correlated with organizational membership. (Can you explain why?) In order to find out whether the relation of A, membership, to B, exposure, is spurious, caused entirely by the relation of each to interest in the campaign, we control on interest.

Step 2. Stratify A and B by C. If belonging to organizations is genuinely related to exposure to the campaign, then the partials may be smaller than in the original relationship, but they *will not vanish*; that is, the relation of A and B will hold up at each interest level. If the relation is spurious, due to the confounding of the interest effect, then the relationship will disappear in the partials.

Level of Interest

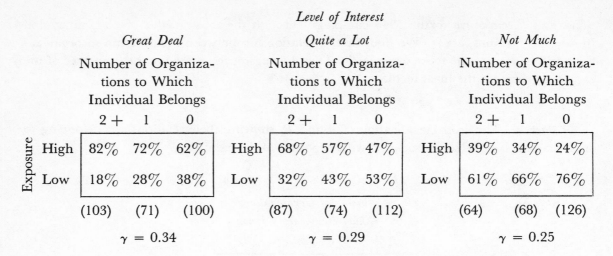

		Great Deal			*Quite a Lot*			*Not Much*		
		Number of Organizations to Which Individual Belongs			Number of Organizations to Which Individual Belongs			Number of Organizations to Which Individual Belongs		
		2+	1	0	2+	1	0	2+	1	0
Exposure	High	82%	72%	62%	68%	57%	47%	39%	34%	24%
	Low	18%	28%	38%	32%	43%	53%	61%	66%	76%
		(103)	(71)	(100)	(87)	(74)	(112)	(64)	(68)	(126)
		$\gamma = 0.34$			$\gamma = 0.29$			$\gamma = 0.25$		

In this case, clearly, the association of *A* and *B* is not spurious. With interest controlled, organizational membership and exposure to the campaign still appear to be related.

Interpreting a Relationship

Ironically enough, two very different research procedures have equivalent delta forms. We can use the same example to illustrate this. So far we have controlled for *C*, interest, in order to discover whether the relation of *A*, organizational membership, and *B*, exposure to campaign can be *explained away*. When we have shown that the relationship is, in this sense, genuine, we go on and try to *interpret* it. Here we are not explaining it *away*, we are simply explaining it.

We might suggest, for instance, that belonging to organizations brings one in contact with persons who prize "the well-informed man," and who expect a certain (high) level of political awareness. This would explain the relationship in terms of an *intervening variable*, as it is frequently called. This is to be offered as an interpretation of the relationship between *A*, organizational membership, and *B*, exposure to mass media during the campaign. Now the problem arises, how shall we test such a hypothesis? The answer is obvious: we must try to find organizations in which awareness is not expected and we must try to find non-belongers who are nevertheless involved in a social atmosphere prizing awareness. If expectation of political awareness is called *D*, we *again* stratify *A* and *B*, this time by *D*, compare the partials, *and again expect that if our hypothesis is correct the association of A and B disappears in the partials*. In other words, we have explained or interpreted the relationship successfully when, whether or not he *A*, belongs to an organization, a person is *B*, highly exposed to the campaign, if *D*, political awareness is expected of him.

So far as the form of our procedure is concerned, interpretation of a relationship and the control for spurious association are equivalent; in both cases we stratify by a third variable and expect the relationship to disappear in the partials. If it does not disappear, then we have failed in the first case to confirm a hypothesis and in the second we have failed to "explain away" an association.

There is, nevertheless, an essential difference between the two. This is illustrated in the following scheme, from Lazarsfeld and Kendall (1950, p. 157):

1. In an interpretation, the "test factor" (in general we will label any third factor C) is assumed to intervene between A and B.

$$A \longrightarrow C \longrightarrow B$$

Example: More men work than women. Interpretation: Sex-roles are defined differently and female sex-role inhibits labor force participation.

Comment: It is also often felt that in the case of spurious association the test factor is extraneous, inessential, outside the relationship, whereas in the case of interpretation the test factor is the essential link in the argument.

2. In controlling for spurious association, the "test factor" is antecedent to *both A and B*.

Example: It is generally assumed that having children inhibits divorce because there are striking differences in the divorce rates of couples with and without children. Several efforts have been made in the last five years to show that this is the result largely of the association of both childlessness and divorce with duration of marriage. (Divorces are heavily concentrated in the earlier years of marriage.) Note that duration of marriage can hardly intervene between these two variables. The association of childlessness and divorce, incidentally, is materially reduced but not wiped out by a duration control.

Specification of a Relationship

Now let us look at another number scheme:

10	50	60	+	50	10	60	=	60	60	120
50	10	60		10	50	60		60	60	120
60	60	120		60	60	120		120	120	240

$\delta = -20$ $\delta = 20$ $\delta = 0$

$Q = -0.92$ $Q = 0.92$ $Q = 0$

Here the partials show an association of *A* and *B*, but the 2 × 2 on the right does not. The relationship to *C* itself is not responsible here. But *A* and *B* are *differently* related in the two partials. In the first, C_1, *A* and *B* are negatively associated. In the second, C_2, *A* and *B* are positively associated. Added up, it all comes to 0.

This type of situation also may be represented by the delta formula. Since *A* and *B* are not related to *C*, the final term on the right drops out. Then the relation of *A* and *B* is simply the sum of their partial deltas. But these average out to 0, and the association is wiped out.

The solution is again to stratify by *C*, but our purpose is different and our expectation about the effect on the partial associations is different. In studying the relation of *A* and *B*, we now have to think of conditions under which the relation might differ from that apparent in the 2 × 2 (or *r* × *s*), and we stratify by these conditions. The difference need not be so marked as in the example above; it may be only that *A* and *B* are much more strongly related in C_1 than C_2, so that their average reduces the strength of the association apparent in the 2 × 2. In any case, instead of looking for a *decrease* in the partial associations, we now look for an *increase* as compared with the total association. It may be that only one of the partials increases, or it may be that both will, if the partials are not associated in the same direction.

Halbwachs, for example, found that suicide rates for Catholics in France were significantly lower than suicide rates for Protestants, just as Durkheim had. (Catholic rate: approximately 198 per million annually. Protestant rate: approximately 396.) When, however, rural *vs.* urban residence is introduced as a third variable, the following results are obtained.

TABLE 8-2.

Annual Suicide Rates (per Million), by Religion and Community, France

	Rural			*Urban*	
Catholic	*Protestant*		*Catholic*	*Protestant*
88	414		309	378

Source: Originally adapted from Halbwachs, *Les Causes de Suicide*, Paris, 1930. Quoted from Zeisel, 1957, pp. 184–186.

Note that the partial association on the right is actually reduced; but the association on the left is considerably increased. The original rates concealed the fact that there is an overwhelmingly marked difference between Catholic and Protestant rates in rural areas.

At the same time it also concealed the fact that the difference is rather slight in urban areas, far less marked than in rural areas.

An extended example

We can now consider a second example a little more thoroughly. We take the relationship between social activity and opinion leadership in public affairs in a sample of women from Decatur, Illinois. Here "social activity" means both belonging to organizations and having friends; and "opinion leadership" means the give and take of relatively casual advice in everyday, routine contacts rather than formal leadership.

It is found that A, the more socially active women are B, more likely to be sought as advisers and sources of information. An interpretation of this would be, of course, that they have a larger available "market," i.e., more buyers of their advice because of their greater social activity.

Step 1. A and B are cross-classified, and a relationship is shown between them: the more socially active women are more likely to be public-affairs opinion leaders.

		Social Activity	
	High	Med.	Low
Opinion Leadership +	20%	11%	4%
Opinion Leadership −	80%	89%	96%

ϵ, high − low = 16%

Source: Katz and Lazarsfeld, 1955, p. 288.

We suspect, perhaps, that this association ought to be even stronger, or else we suspect that it is not the same on every status level. (We usually suspect this from past experience or the examination of other data.) We find, in fact, that the relation is even stronger on the highest status level than in our initial cross-classification, but it is reduced in the middle and lower statuses.

Step 2. We stratify by C, social status, and examine the behavior of the partials. In this case we can measure simply the high − low (H − L) percentage difference to indicate association. Note that in the partial for high status this difference is now 22, whereas in the other two it has dropped to 11 and 10; the 16% difference in Step 1 is a somewhat complex average of these differences.

	High Status		
	H	M	L
+	25%	17%	3%
−	75%	83%	97%

$\epsilon = 22\%$

	Middle Status		
	H	M	L
+	17%	12%	6%
−	83%	88%	94%

$\epsilon = 11\%$

	Low Status		
	H	M	L
+	13%	5%	3%
−	87%	95%	97%

$\epsilon = 10\%$

We see now that the difference in the high-status group is greater than in our original table, and greater than in the middle- and low-status groups; and we also see, incidentally, that even high-status women are unlikely to be asked advice about political affairs if they are not socially active, but on the other hand even socially active low-status women are less likely to be asked their advice on these matters than only moderately active high-status women.

Where We Stand

This completes the discussion of the description of attributes and their relationship. Our primary concern in this chapter has been the logic of the three-attribute problem, rather than any specific mathematical details. As a matter of fact, the delta formula we have used as a point of departure cannot be extended to apply to other measures of relationship, without altering the weighting factors incorporated in the formula. *Only* the logic is essentially the same in all cases. This logic, incidentally, is equally applicable to the problems of multivariate measurement data.

What we may do now, is: (1) test whether the relationship between two factors, A and B, is genuine or merely the inadvertent consequence of their both being related to some third variable, C, the effect of which is confounded with the A and B effects; (2) test whether an interpretation offered to explain the relation of A and B, in the form of a factor C (which is presumed to intervene in time between A and B), will actually interpret the relationship; and (3) specify a relationship between A and B, by showing the special conditions affecting the degree and direction of the relationship. The procedure of stratifying A and B by a third variable, C, called *holding C constant*, may be extended to four-, five-, ... k-variable problems without difficulty (except in reading the resulting tables, which become very complex) by making further stratification after C is introduced.

We have now completed our discussion of techniques of description. In the remaining chapters we encounter quite different problems. In Chapters 2 to 8 little attention has been given to the difference between sample and population, although in most cases we have implied that we are treating a sample of observations rather than an entire population. In the remaining chapters the relation of sample to population becomes our central problem.

Steps in multivariate analysis, for attributes having 2 classes

Item 1	Item 2
n_1	n_1
n_2	n_2
N	N

You are given the marginals (first-order frequencies) of two items.

Step 1. The beginning of analysis: cross-classify the two distributions.

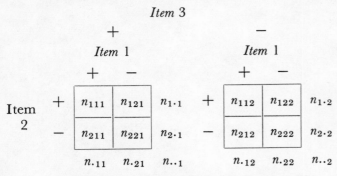

Detailed analysis: ratios, proportions, or percentages, and their differences, cell by cell. Summary description: measures of association (choose the most suitable among Q, ϕ, λ; and for the general case, γ also).

Step 2. Control for spurious factors: introduce a third variable preceding *both* items in time, which might account for the apparent relationship of Items 1 and 2, when in fact *it does not exist*.

Detailed analysis: as above.

Summary description: measures of partial association.

Expectation and decision: If associations of Items 1 and 2 approach 0 in the partial tables, the relation is spurious; if they remain substantial, then Item 3 does not account for the relationship.

The format is similar for steps 3 and 4

Step 3. Interpretation of the relationship: introduce a variable which might explain the relationship of Items 1 and 2, in the sense that Item 3 *intervenes* between 1 and 2. Detailed analysis, summary, and expectation are the same as in Step 2.

Step 4. Specification of the relationship: introduce a variable which elaborates the *conditions* surrounding the relation of Items 1 and 2. Detailed analysis and summary are the same as in Step 2. Our expectation is that one or both partial associations will increase in size over the relationship in the two dimensional table.

The extension to attributes having more than two classes is straightforward.

Chapter 8

WORKBOOK EXERCISES

1. *Table reading.* In each of the following tables explain what the investigator has done. Follow the course of his logic, telling briefly for each case what each table in the series shows and explaining what has happened with the introduction of the third variable. Explain, of course, just why the third variable was introduced and what type of elaboration is involved. You will need to percentage the tables and you may also wish to compute one or more of the measures of association of Chapter 7. Use the space provided on pages 219–226.

a. Tables I to K, on pages 147–148, on present occupation by community of orientation.

b. Tables L to M, page 149, on respondent's vote intention by family's vote intention.

c. Tables N to O, page 150, on mobility inclinations (desire to move) by satisfaction with present housing (number of complaints).

d. Table P, page 151, on the effects of an education campaign on attitude to a British loan.

2. a. For Tables L to M, page 149, you should be able to reconstruct, from the marginals of Table M, a third table which explains why the "hereditary vote" persists despite the effect of present family on the vote. The reason, of course, is that there is a strong tendency for people to marry others of the same political affiliation as their fathers. Use page 227 for your table.

b. When you finish constructing the table, compute *Q* for your new table, and compare it with *Q* for Table L which you computed in Chapter 7.

3. a. Stouffer (1955) shows that there is a relation between region and tolerance of nonconformists in the United States. (See Table 7-3 on page 179.) He also shows that there is a relation between type of community (metropolitan community, other city, small town, farm) and tolerance—the farms are least tolerant, the metropolitan areas are most tolerant.

It is generally known, of course, that the West and East are more urbanized than the Midwest and South, and this is true of Stouffer's sample. Set up, below, the *form* of the table Stouffer most probably uses to control for community type in the relation of region and tolerance. (Use four community types, four regions, and three degrees of tolerance—less tolerant, in-between, more tolerant.)

b. Stouffer concludes that the effect of region is independent of the effect of community type, or in other words that community type alone does not account for the effect of region on tolerance. This means that in the partial tables, the relation of tolerance to region has

....

4. Schroeder and Beegle (1953) report a correlation between rate of suicide and rural-urban residence in Michigan for 1945–1949. When suicide rates for the period are classified by sex and residence, the rural male population is almost twice as likely to commit suicide as the urban male population, although residence makes little difference among women. Classified by occupation rather than by residence, the farmers and farm managers have a rate almost three times as great as the highest-rate urban occupation; but farm laborers do not differ much from urban occupations.

a. Schroeder and Beegle control for age and for native *vs.* foreign birth. Can you think of other controls? (Look again, for instance, at the table of suicides in France, Table 8-2 on page 210.) Show below how you would set up a table to control for the relation between residence (rural, urban) and suicide (yes, no), and some third variable. What will happen if the relation is spurious?

b. Assume that the relation is genuine.   How might you interpret it?   Show below the form of the table you would use to verify your interpretation.   What will happen if your interpretation is correct?

....

....

....

....

....

....

....

Problem 1

Problem 1

Problem 1

Problem 1

Problem I

Problem I

Problem 1

Problem 1

Problem 2

Chapter 9

Introduction to Statistical Inference

I N CHAPTER 1 we have defined a *population*, or *universe*, as any collection of persons, objects, or events in which we may, for some purpose, be interested; and a *sample* as a selection of a portion of the objects in the population. We have also claimed that it is not necessary to enumerate an entire population in order to obtain information about the population; quite often we obtain sufficient information by sampling from the population. It is true that our inferences about the population may be to some extent uncertain—a sample mean may not exactly equal the population mean, and successive samples may yield different estimates of the population mean—but if we have followed certain procedures in sampling we are able to make certain kinds of assertions with a known degree of confidence. It is our purpose in this chapter to consider how to draw samples in such a way that valid assertions about the population may be made, and to discuss the *kinds* of assertions that may be made about populations with knowledge obtained only from samples.

Drawing Random Samples

As a device for defining terms and procedures we will exercise our imagination a little. We are going to let a population with only six members be our model for a population that could well have a million members. We are going to put some simple round discs in a bowl, each disc having a number from 1 to 6, and we will call the first disc a_1, the second a_2, and so on. We will review some old definitions and make some new ones before we start. A *population*, or *universe*, is the aggregate of all six discs in the bowl. A *sample* is some set of discs less than the whole set; we might have a sample of only one disc, of two discs, three discs, etc., up to five discs. The number of discs in the sample, of course, is the sample size. (We can use N for the size of the population and N for the sample size.) A sample can be drawn from the bowl in a number of different ways, and we want to consider a few of them.

Let us deal with samples of two discs, simply for convenience. Few people ever actually sample in the way we are about to sample, but our procedure is the way everyone *imagines* it to be done. We make a list of every possible sample of size two from this population; there are 36 such samples. We replace each disc after each draw, so that it is possible to draw the same one twice (for this reason our procedure can be thought of as equivalent to drawing an infinite number of samples).

	a_1	a_2	a_3	a_4	a_5	a_6
a_1	11	12	13	14	15	16
a_2	21	22	23	24	25	26
a_3	31	32	33	34	35	36
a_4	41	42	43	44	45	46
a_5	51	52	53	54	55	56
a_6	61	62	63	64	65	66

These are your possible samples. The numbers in the cells are the subscripts of the possible combinations of sample members. In the first row, for example, 11 designates a sample in which we first drew a_1, replaced it, and drew a_1 a second time; 12 is a sample in which we first drew a_1, replaced it, and drew a_2 the second time. In the same way, 21 is a sample in which we first drew a_2, replaced it, and then drew a_1, and so on.

Now we need to know the probability that any one of these 36 samples will be drawn, on any given draw. This takes us back to a problem we avoided the last time we had to define probability. There are two ways of defining probability, and the way we have already defined it (as a relative frequency of an observed outcome) is not the definition usually applied to our present problem. What we need is the so-called *classical*, or *a priori*, definition of probability.

THE CLASSICAL DEFINITION OF PROBABILITY

The classical definition is based on something like the following logic. First, each of the samples we have listed is about *equally likely* to be drawn on any given draw. There is no reason, is there, why one should be more likely than another? This is usually illustrated, in fact, with the concept of the "true coin" or the "true die." If I toss a penny is there any reason why I should be more likely to get a head than a tail? If I toss a die is there any reason why I should be more likely to get a one than a two, three, four, etc.? This is what we intuitively mean by "chance." Now according to the classical definition of probability, if out of N possible outcomes, all of which are equally likely, we want to know the probability that outcomes of type A occur, this probability is given by n_a/N. This is the number we *expect* on the assumption that the A outcomes are just as likely, and no more likely, than the not-A outcomes.

Two other ideas are essential to the classical notion of probability, however, and they are crucial to us, since they determine some of the rules for drawing samples. The definition can apply only to *mutually exclusive* outcomes. We say that if a coin falls heads on the first toss it cannot also fall tails on the first toss, so that the two possible outcomes of a single toss, heads and tails, are mutually exclusive. Also, the definition applies only to *independent* events. We say that our second toss is independent of the first because the outcome of the second does not depend on the outcome of the first, or any other toss.

Now back to our bowl. There are 36 possible outcomes of any one draw; that is, on any one draw we might get any one of the 36 samples: 11, 12, 13, 14, etc. (Read across the top of the table if you are confused; and read "one-one," "one-two," etc., not "eleven," "twelve," since these are subscripts representing a_1a_1, a_1a_2, etc., not cardinal numbers.) Assume that every one of them is equally likely. It is clear that they are mutually exclusive. And so long as we always replace our sample after every draw, each draw is independent of every other draw. It is then possible to assign a known probability to each possible sample, following the classical definition: the probability is $1/36$.

TYPES OF RANDOM SAMPLES

We can now define *simple random sampling*. If every possible sample of a fixed size from our population has an equal probability of being drawn, we say that the result of drawing one such sample gives a simple random sample. Of the two words defining the sample here, by far the more important is the word "random." The word "simple" merely distinguishes this from the several other ways of choosing a random sample.

A variation of the simple random sample, for instance, is the *stratified random sample*. (The "simple random sample" can be shortened to SRS; technically it is more accurate to call the stratified sample a "stratified SRS.") With this kind of sampling procedure divide your population first into k *strata* (e.g., regions, income groups, ecological subareas, etc.) and *then* take an SRS *within* each stratum. This is equivalent to sampling from several bowls. If the stratification is appropriate to your problem and executed properly, this is not only perfectly legitimate but actually more efficient than the SRS.

What is known as *systematic random sampling* involves making a list of some sort of each person in the population (called the *sampling frame*), which is then sampled at some constant interval after making a random start. For instance, suppose you are to sample an army company. A first sergeant provides you with a roster; this is your sampling frame. You blindfold yourself and pull some number from one to ten out of the bowl; say, for example, you draw 4. You then take the fourth name on the roster as your start. From this point on you take every tenth, or every fifth, or every third name, the interval depending on the sample size desired. This, too, is legitimate so long as the *order* of the names has nothing to do with the problem you are investigating.

Nonrandom samples

It may be instructive to compare some cases in which sampling is *not* random, and to see just why they are not. The most famous example is the *Literary Digest* poll predicting the 1936 election.

The *Literary Digest* took a sample of about 2 million and predicted that Landon would win the election by a considerable margin. This is an interesting example for two reasons: first, because the sample size was so extraordinarily large, and very accurate results have been obtained with much smaller samples chosen correctly; and second, because the error was made in the very first step. The *Digest* took its sampling frame from lists of its subscribers and telephone directories. The result might conceivably have been an accurate prediction of how the subscribers and those who had telephones in 1936 were going to vote. This was not, however, a random sample of all eligible voters, since those who did not have telephones or subscribe to the *Literary Digest* did not have an equal chance of being chosen for the sample.

Other simple examples of departures from randomness are the following: a sample from a barrel of apples taken by scooping a handful from the top; interviews with a group of persons who volunteer for the purpose; a mail questionnaire to a group of persons, only part of whom return responses. (Can you see why the last is not random?) All of these are what Deming (1950) calls "chunks"—samples taken primarily by using the most *convenient* observations.

It is worth stopping for a moment and considering just what the effect of such departures from randomness is on the inferences you make about populations. Look carefully, for instance, at some of the examples we gave in defining probability and in defining random sampling. We talked about a coin or a die, actually a "true coin" or a "true die"; we talked about a bowl filled with discs—Deming has it filled with poker chips, but more Puritan writers fill it with identification tags. Many classical theorists are partial to urns filled with marbles or billiard balls. Biometric statisticians occasionally fill the bowl with beans. The draws are made preferably by a person who is blindfolded.

Shewhart calls the example we have used the *ideal bowl* experiment, which is a good name for it (Shewhart, 1939). What we are doing here is giving an idealized physical representation of an activity for which we can build a mathematical model. The model is—in a more advanced text, at least—powerful and sophisticated, and from the assumptions of the model are derived many results that are of practical value in making inferences about populations. We will be able, for instance, to predict the behavior of *sampling distributions*, i.e., the results of successive samples from the same population. And it is from these sampling distributions that all predictions about populations come. The model, however, assumes conditions like those of our ideal bowl before it can be legitimately applied. The practical problem of sample design, therefore, is how to meet these ideal conditions as closely as possible. Samples which meet these conditions are called *probability samples.*

Departures from randomness have the effect of destroying our effort to approximate the ideal bowl experiment; consequently the whole theory of statistical inference, built on this model, is inapplicable. Furthermore, there is *no theory which can be used instead*, and it seems unlikely that there ever will be such a theory. Statisticians have been able to invent mathematical models that sacrifice almost every other assumption in their kit; but no model has yet been invented that does not first assume that the observations with which you deal were drawn randomly from the population which they "represent."

Quota sampling, in use by many leading poll organizations, is an example of a popular sampling procedure that is not random. (Deming, 1950, calls samples of this type *judgment* samples; judgment samples include also the "chunks" we referred to above.) The distinguishing characteristic of these samples is that the interviewer is given a certain "quota" of persons to question, and it is up to him how he obtains them. He must have so many who are "professionals," so many who are "housewives," etc., but the *final* choice is left to the human biases of availability and selectivity. (The famous, if perhaps apocryphal instance, is the interviewer who filled his quota in the local railroad station.) The quota sample's chief defect is *not*, however, the possibility that it might be in greater error than the probability sample. In the first place, such samples are often quite accurate, or no more inaccurate than a probability sample drawn from the same population, and they are considerably cheaper. *Their real defect is that we can never really calculate just how great our error is.* In order to calculate our error we must use a mathematical formula that is based on the assumption of random sampling, and it is on the basis of this calculated error that we make inferences about populations. There is no known alternative model for nonrandom sampling—no mathematical model, that is, that can reproduce the results of successive samples in which the final choice of sample members depends on a human act of choice instead of some more or less random procedure.

Confidence Intervals: Large Sample Theory

We will now try to show what kind of statements it is possible to make about populations with data provided only by samples. We have an estimate, say $\bar{X}$, from a sample, and we want to know what statement we can safely make about μ (read *mu*), the mean of the population from which the sample was drawn. We do not actually know what μ is, and we are unhappily aware that if we draw additional samples from the same population we will get a new, and probably different, estimate from each sample. The problem is the same if we are sampling from attribute populations; we will have an estimate, $\hat{p}_a$, and want to know what we can safely say about P_a, the proportion of A's in the population. (The sample estimate is technically called a *statistic*, while the population value is called a *parameter*.

Usually a *Greek* letter is used for a parameter and its corresponding *Roman* form for the statistic, although this is not quite a universal notation, and is not usual for proportions.)

The solution to our problem is to set an interval around $\bar{X}$, or $\hat{p}_a$, which we can assume with some confidence will probably contain μ, or P_a. The problem is to attain this confidence. Each of our sample estimates is fallible, but if our sample is correctly chosen we will be able to set exact limits to that fallibility. We can then make, *with a calculable degree of error*, inferences about the population.

We begin with a procedure for setting *confidence intervals* around proportions. The logic of our procedure depends on the notion that we will draw samples a great number of times, all according to the ideal-bowl model. From each sample we draw we will get an estimate $\hat{p}_a$ of the parameter P_a (i.e., the proportion in the population that is A). We must find some way to set an interval about $\hat{p}_a$ so that *most of the time* we will be right if we guess that P_a lies in that interval. From each sample we want an inequality like the following:

$$l_1 \leq P_a \leq l_2$$

This says that the population parameter P_a is not less than l_1 and not more than l_2; this is one of the basic inferences you can make from the sample estimate $\hat{p}_a$, provided certain conditions are met.

where P_a is the proportion of the population that are A
          l_1 and l_2 are estimated from sample data

We want some way of being confident that if we write 100 such inequalities we will be right, say, 95 or 99 times out of 100.

As we have remarked before, the problem is to attain this confidence. The heart of the solution to our problem lies in being able to predict the behavior of the successive samples we are going to draw. We can usually do this if we can make certain assumptions about the population. From each of our samples we get an estimate $\hat{p}$ of P, and we have as a result of many such samplings a distribution of $\hat{p}$ which is called a *sampling distribution*. More precisely, a sampling distribution is defined as the distribution of the estimates of a statistic from *all possible*, or an *infinite number* of, samples of the same size from the same population. It can be shown that the mean of the sampling distribution of $\hat{p}$ is an "unbiased" estimate of P, in the sense that, with due precautions in the sampling, the mean of the sampling distribution will give the same value as P. Furthermore, the standard deviation of the sampling distribution can also be shown. It is:

$$\sigma_{\hat{p}} = \sqrt{\frac{PQ}{N}}$$

Note that P is a parameter, not an estimate from the sample. We do not know what P is, in practice, and have to estimate it from $\hat{p}$. A new estimate of $\sigma_{\hat{p}}$, designated $s_{\hat{p}}$, is obtained from each sample.

where $\sigma_{\hat{p}}$ is called the *standard error of a proportion*, and is the standard deviation of the sampling distribution of a proportion

P is the proportion of the population that are A

Q is the proportion of the population that are not-A, and is given most simply by $1 - P$

N is the sample size

We will use the symbol $s_{\hat{p}}$ to designate an estimate of $\sigma_{\hat{p}}$ from any given sample.

The standard error of the proportion is the statistic that we need to make our inferences, but we do not know P itself; so we must estimate it from our sample. This is safe when certain conditions are met—we will specify these conditions after we consider the logic of the procedure.

There are several things we can say about this sampling distribution of $\hat{p}$ and its standard deviation. We have already said that its mean will be exactly equal to P. It can also be shown that the distribution will have a smaller and smaller variance, and consequently a smaller standard error, as the sample size becomes larger. You can see this easily enough if you grasp the formula: N, the sample size, is in the denominator, so that as N increases the value of PQ/N becomes smaller, meaning that the dispersion about the mean is reduced. Thus, the larger our sample is, the closer our estimate is likely to be to P.

COMPUTATION OF CONFIDENCE INTERVALS FOR $\hat{p}$

If N is quite large and P is not too small (disregard the vagueness; we will be more precise in a minute), we have an important result that simplifies our problem considerably. Granted both these conditions, the sampling distribution of $\hat{p}$ will be approximately normal. (Refer to Chapter 2 if you do not know what "normal" means.) If this is so, then we proceed as follows:

1. We use $\hat{p}$ as an estimate of P in the formula for the standard error of a proportion. Q, of course, is estimated by $1 - \hat{p}$.

2. We assume that the sampling distribution of $\hat{p}$ is approximately normal, so that we may use our knowledge of the normal curve in predicting the behavior of $\hat{p}$. We use our knowledge in this way:

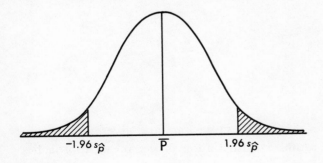

The sampling distribution of $\hat{p}$ for samples that are large, and from populations in which P is not too small, tends to be normal with $s_{\hat{p}} = \sqrt{\hat{p}\hat{q}/N}$; *then 95% of the sample estimates, $\hat{p}$, of P will lie in the unshaded portion of the curve,* in the long run.

a. In the normal curve 95% of the area under the curve lies inside 1.96 standard deviations on both sides of the mean; therefore, if our sampling distribution is normal, 95% of the estimates we make of P will be within $1.96 s_{\hat{p}}$ of $\bar{P}$, where $\bar{P}$ is the mean of the sampling distribution and is equal to P.

b. If we sample often enough our odds are therefore 19 to 1 that we will enclose P within about 2 standard errors (more exactly, within 1.96 standard errors).

c. We decide that 19 to 1 odds are sufficient to give us confidence in our results; but if we want better odds we can take 2.58 standard errors which will give 99 to 1 odds.

3. Now we solve the inequality $l_1 \leq P \leq l_2$ for l_1 and l_2, by setting the lower bound of the interval equal to $\hat{p} - 1.96 s_{\hat{p}}$ and the upper bound of the interval equal to $\hat{p} + 1.96 s_{\hat{p}}$. This gives us:

$$\hat{p} - 1.96\sqrt{\hat{p}\hat{q}/N} \leq P \leq \hat{p} + 1.96\sqrt{\hat{p}\hat{q}/N}$$

It is essential that you note carefully how to interpret this interval. If you sample continually, then 95% of the time you will be right when you say that this interval encloses P. Note that you compute a *new* interval from every sample, even though you might be sampling from the same population. Your interval, therefore, like $\hat{p}$ itself, varies on each draw. And part of the time (5% of the time if you use $1.96 s_{\hat{p}}$ intervals) you will get an interval that does *not* contain P. This is neatly conveyed in the following diagram (adapted from Edwards, 1955):

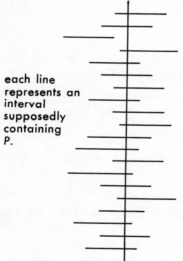

each line represents an interval supposedly containing P.

The vertical line represents P. This, of course, does not change and is in no way affected by sampling. Confidence intervals are calculated for each sample. Each time you calculate such intervals you say "I am confident that the proportion P lies somewhere in this interval." The measure of your confidence is that 95% of the time this assertion should prove to be right (or 99% of the time if you use $2.58 s_{\hat{p}}$ intervals). Sometimes, however, you will be wrong.

Figure 9-1. Diagram showing confidence intervals calculated for successive samples from the same population

COMPUTATION OF CONFIDENCE INTERVALS FOR $\bar{X}$

We place intervals around the mean in exactly the same way, and give them exactly the same interpretation. If N is large, the sampling distribution of the mean approaches normality with a mean equal to μ and a standard deviation equal to

$$\sigma_{\bar{x}} = \frac{\sigma}{\sqrt{N}}$$

This formula for $\sigma_{\bar{x}}$ holds for all N. In practice we do not know σ, however, and must estimate it from s.

where $\sigma_{\bar{x}}$ is the *standard error of the mean*

σ is the Greek letter *sigma* (lower case) and represents the standard deviation of the population

N is the sample size

We will use $s_{\bar{x}}$ to designate an estimate of $\sigma_{\bar{x}}$ from any given sample.

We can set up an interval 1.96, or 2.58, $s_{\bar{x}}$ on either side of $\bar{X}$, our sample estimate of μ, which should, about 95% or 99% of the time (depending on which interval you choose) contain μ. Since we do not know the parameter σ, we again estimate it by using s, the sample standard deviation. We say then, that

$$\bar{X} - 1.96s/\sqrt{N} \leq \mu \leq \bar{X} + 1.96s/\sqrt{N}$$

and we are confident enough to give 19 : 1 odds on this assertion.

Small-Sample Statistics

LARGE SAMPLE AND SMALL SAMPLE THEORY

The methods discussed in the two previous sections depend on the condition that N is large. (For proportions they depend on the additional condition that P is not too small, a problem that we will take up in the next chapter.) If N is small—say 30 or less—we cannot assume that the sampling distribution of the mean or proportion will be normal, or even approximately so; at the same time, the sample estimates of the standard error, which we used instead of $\sigma_{\bar{x}}$ itself, will be so unreliable as to be useless. Under certain conditions however, we may still compute confidence intervals. For the case in which the population sampled is itself normally distributed, a new distribution, called the t distribution, may be used in place of the normal. It is used in the same way, but the value of t (unlike the value of z) which corresponds to 95% and 99% probabilities varies as the sample size varies. In the curve of the t distribution, for example, for a sample of size 20 an interval containing μ with a 95% probability would be found by taking $\bar{X} \pm ts_{\bar{x}} = \bar{X} \pm 2.09s_{\bar{x}}$; for a sample of size 25, however, an interval containing μ with a 95% probability would

Confidence intervals for means and proportions for large samples

$$\hat{p}_a = n_a/N = \qquad\qquad\qquad \bar{X} = \sum X/N =$$

$$\hat{q}_a = 1 - \hat{p}_a = \qquad\qquad\qquad s = \sqrt{\sum x^2/(N-1)} =$$

1. $s_{\hat{p}} = \sqrt{\hat{p}_a \hat{q}_a/N} =$ 1. $s_{\bar{x}} = s/\sqrt{N} =$

2. $l_1 = \hat{p}_a - z s_{\hat{p}} =$ 2. $l_1 = \bar{X} - z s_{\bar{x}} =$

3. $l_2 = \hat{p}_a + z s_{\hat{p}} =$ 3. $l_2 = \bar{X} + z s_{\bar{x}} =$

1. Assume that the sample estimates of P or μ are given ($\hat{p}$ or $\bar{X}$), and $\hat{q}$ and s are also given, or computed according to instructions in preceding chapters.

2. Choose the probability measuring the confidence with which you wish to make inferences about P or μ. It is customary to choose either 95% or 99%. This probability sets z.
   a. If the probability chosen is 95%, z is 1.96.
   b. If the probability chosen is 99%, z is 2.58.

3. Compute the *standard error* ($s_{\hat{p}}$ or $s_{\bar{x}}$) of the statistic for which you are setting confidence intervals. Enter the result on line 1 above.

4. Compute the lower limit of the interval. If, for instance, you are computing a 95% interval for the proportion P_a, take $\hat{p}_a - 1.96 s_{\hat{p}}$. Enter on line 2 above.

5. Compute the upper limit of the interval. If, for instance, you are computing a 99% interval for the mean $\bar{X}$, take $\bar{X} + 2.58 s_{\bar{x}}$. Enter on line 3 above.

6. You now make statements of the following kind:
   a. $P(l_1 \leq P_a \leq l_2) = 95\%$, or $P(l_1 \leq \mu \leq l_2) = 95\%$.
   b. $P(l_1 \leq P_a \leq l_2) = 99\%$, or $P(l_1 \leq \mu \leq l_2) = 99\%$.

These statements are interpreted as follows: the probability that P_a is contained in the interval between l_1 and l_2 is 95% (or 99%); similarly for μ.

Warning: These expressions do *not* say that 95% (or 99%) of the *population values*, X_i, fall in the limits from l_1 to l_2. If, for instance, our sample is one of the 5% (or 1%) that are far off in estimating the parameter, relatively few of the population values will lie in these limits. The appropriate interval for such an assertion is $\mu \pm 2\sigma$, *not* $\bar{X} \pm 2s/\sqrt{N}$. The confusion of the two assertions is common among beginners.

be found by taking $\bar{X} \pm 2.06s_{\bar{x}}$. If the sample were large, say 50, you would take $\bar{X} \pm zs_{\bar{x}} = \bar{X} \pm 1.96s_{\bar{x}}$, and would use the same value of z if the sample size were 100, 200, 500, etc. We will illustrate the use of the t distribution in more detail in the process of introducing a somewhat different kind of inference than we have encountered in setting confidence intervals.

TESTS OF SIGNIFICANCE

Suppose we design the following experiment: We randomly assign 80 subjects to 40 groups.* Half of these groups are given instructions, during the experiment, designed to induce high cohesion (or involvement in the group) and half are given instructions designed to induce low cohesion. We wish to test the hypothesis that in the high cohesive groups, the members will exert more pressure on each other toward uniformity of opinion, trying to reach agreement, than in low cohesive groups. We find that, in fact, the "high cohesive" treatment produces a higher mean number of pressures toward uniformity than the "low cohesive" treatment. The question we now ask is: Are the means of the two experimental treatments *significantly different*, or could the difference have occurred by chance? We answer this question with what is known as a *test of significance*.

There are a number of such tests, differing in the kinds of hypotheses they test or the assumptions they make, and we are going to illustrate the logic of these tests rather

TABLE 9-1.

Distribution of Pressures to Uniformity in High and Low Cohesive Groups,

Sweden, 1951

Number of Pressures Recorded	X	0	1	2	3	4	5	6	7	8	9	10	11	12	13	14	15
High cohesive treatment	f_1					1			1	2	3	6	2	3	1		1
Low cohesive treatment	f_2				1		1	3	2	5	3	3		1	1		

$$\sum X_1 = 200 \qquad\qquad \sum X_2 = 162$$
$$\sum X_1{}^2 = 2104 \qquad\qquad \sum X_2{}^2 = 1416$$
$$\bar{X}_1 = 10.00 \qquad\qquad \bar{X}_2 = 8.10$$
$$s_1{}^2 = 104/19 \qquad\qquad s_2{}^2 = 103.8/19$$
$$= 5.47 \qquad\qquad\qquad = 5.46$$

Source: Adapted from Zetterberg, 1952. The actual distributions shown here are *not* from the original source; they are fictitious. The means, and the results, however, closely approximate the original.

* This example is adapted from a Swedish replication, by Zetterberg (1952), of a famous group dynamics experiment.

than give a systematic survey of them. The first one we use finds very limited application in sociology but is perhaps the best known significance test, the *t test*. It is used very frequently to test, for instance, whether the means obtained in two different samples could have been obtained by sampling both times from the same population. If they could not both reasonably have come from the same population, we say that they are *significantly different*. We are asking, in other words, if there is really a difference between the two means; our alternative hypothesis is that the difference is accounted for entirely by random sampling fluctuation and in fact there is no difference between the two means.

The hypothesis we actually test is called a *null hypothesis*, and takes the form: $H_0: \mu_1 \leq \mu_2$. There are other forms of null hypotheses that we can set up, but they always take the form of stating that what we do *not* think is so is in fact so; we construct an investigation precisely for the purpose of *disproving* the null hypothesis. Here we set up an hypothesis which says that the mean pressures toward uniformity in the high cohesive group are the same as or less than the mean pressures in the low cohesive group; the purpose of designing the experiment is really to *reject* this hypothesis.

We may define t as

$$t = \frac{\bar{X} - \mu}{s_{\bar{x}}}$$

where $\bar{X}$ is a sample mean

μ is a population mean

$s_{\bar{x}}$ is an estimate of the standard error of the mean, i.e., of the standard deviation of its sampling distribution

Before we adapt this to our present purpose, note the most important property of the definition. Except for μ itself, there are no population values in it. This rids us of the problem of using unreliable estimates of the population variance.

Now for the difference between two means we substitute $\bar{X}_1 - \bar{X}_2$ in place of $\bar{X} - \mu$;* and for the standard error of the mean we substitute a quantity called the *standard error of the difference between means*, which is, for two independent samples,

$$s_{\bar{x}_1 - \bar{x}_2} = \sqrt{s_{\bar{x}_1}^2 + s_{\bar{x}_2}^2}$$

You should think of a population of *differences* between observations in the two treatments, which are distributed about a *mean difference*. This is the standard error of the mean difference for independent samples.

where $s_{\bar{x}_1 - \bar{x}_2}$ designates an estimate of the standard error of the difference between two means

$s_{\bar{x}_1}$ is an estimate of the standard error of the mean of the first sample

$s_{\bar{x}_2}$ is an estimate of the standard error of the mean of the second sample

* More precisely, we substitute the quantity $(\bar{X}_1 - \bar{X}_2) - (\mu_1 - \mu_2)$ for $\bar{X} - \mu$, but we ignore the quantity $\mu_1 - \mu_2$, assuming it to be 0.

Do not forget the radical just because the two numbers inside are squares; the square root of the sum of two squares is not the same as the sum of the square roots of two squares.

Assuming again that both samples are from the same population, both s_1 and s_2 are estimates of the same parameter, σ. The best estimate of σ, therefore, is obtained by *pooling* s_1 and s_2. By extension, we pool the two estimates in obtaining $s_{x_1 - x_2}$. This produces a rather fearsome looking computation formula, but the quantities involved are, as usual, essentially simple and familiar. The computation formula is

$$s_{\bar{x}_1 - \bar{x}_2} = \sqrt{\left(\frac{\sum x_1^2 + \sum x_2^2}{N_1 + N_2 - 2}\right)\left(\frac{1}{N_1} + \frac{1}{N_1}\right)}$$

Note that these are your sums of squares again and the only other quantities are sample sizes.

where $\sum x_1^2$ is the sum of squared deviations from the mean of the first sample
$\sum x_2^2$ is the sum of squared deviations from the mean of the second sample
N_1 is the number of observations in the first sample
N_2 is the number of observations in the second sample

For the problem above, we now have the following set-up:

$$\sum x_1^2 = \sum X_1^2 - (\sum X_1)^2 / N_1 \qquad \sum x_2^2 = \sum X_2^2 - (\sum X_2)^2 / N_2$$
$$= 2104 - (200)^2 / 20 \qquad\qquad = 1416 - (162)^2 / 20$$
$$= 104.0 \qquad\qquad\qquad\qquad = 103.8$$

$$s_{\bar{x}_1 - \bar{x}_2} = \sqrt{\left(\frac{104.0 + 103.8}{20 + 20 - 2}\right)\left(\frac{1}{20} + \frac{1}{20}\right)} = \sqrt{\left(\frac{207.8}{38}\right)\left(\frac{1}{10}\right)} = \sqrt{0.547} = 0.74$$

$$t = \frac{\bar{X}_1 - \bar{X}_2}{s_{\bar{x}_1 - \bar{x}_2}} = \frac{10.00 - 8.10}{0.74} = 2.57$$

THE t DISTRIBUTION AND THE CONCEPT OF DEGREES OF FREEDOM

Now with the value of t we have obtained, we must enter a table of the t distribution. (Table 3 in the Appendix.) But we must know a little about this distribution in order to use the table. There is a different t distribution for each value of N, and the table shows, usually, the amount of area in *both* tails of the distribution, to the right of t and to the left of $-t$. We have to spell out both of these points a little. The t distribution actually depends on what we call the number of *degrees of freedom* in the data. In calculating t we use certain information from the observations we have made, and once part of this information is used for a given set of observations, certain restrictions are placed on the manner in which the observations can vary. For example, notice that in the computation of $s_{\bar{x}_1 - \bar{x}_2}$ we make use of $\sum x_1^2$ and

$\sum x_2{}^2$. Each of these is defined in terms of deviations from $\bar{X}_i$. Now since $\sum x_i = 0$, which is true because of the way x_i is defined (see Chapter 4), the deviations are not all independent. By this we mean that if $N - 1$ deviations are given, the Nth is determined automatically. If, for instance, the first nine out of ten deviations are

$$1,\ -2,\ 3,\ 4,\ 5,\ 6,\ -7,\ 8,\ -9;\quad \text{this gives}\quad \sum x = 27 - 18 = 9$$

$$x_{10} = -9$$

The sum of the nine deviations is 9. We know that $\sum x_i = 0$, therefore x_{10} must equal -9 since $9 + (-9) = 0$. After $N - 1$ deviations are known, therefore, the Nth is also known. The $N - 1$ that are free to vary are called *degrees of freedom*. We say that one d.f. has been used up in calculating the mean from which x_i was measured. The t distribution, finally, is tabled in terms of the number of observations free to vary, or degrees of freedom (abbreviated *d.f.*), in the data. When you compute the difference between two means, you introduce two constraints or restrictions on the data and reduce the number of degrees of freedom by two. You can tell, as a matter of fact, rather simply in this case, since the number of degrees of freedom appears in the denominator of the formula for $s_{\bar{x}_1 - \bar{x}_2}$.

$$s_{\bar{x}_1 - \bar{x}_2} = \sqrt{\left(\frac{\sum x_1{}^2 + \sum x_2{}^2}{N_1 + N_2 - 2}\right)\left(\frac{1}{N_1} + \frac{1}{N_2}\right)}$$

This part of the denominator tells you how many degrees of freedom you have.

You will always enter the table of t with $N_1 + N_2 - 2$ degrees of freedom.

Now as to how the table is set up. We show here a small part of a t table.

TABLE 9-2.

Portion of a Table of t, Showing Area under Curve in Both

Tails of Distribution

d.f.	0.50	0.10	0.05	0.01	
					P is the sum of
1	1.000	6.314	12.706	63.657	
5	.727	2.015	2.571	4.032	
10	.700	1.812	2.228	3.169	
20	.687	1.725	2.086	2.845	
30	.683	1.697	2.042	2.750	
38			2.025	2.711	
40			2.021	2.704	

P

The column headings, labeled P, are the probabilities of getting a t as *large as or larger than* the tabled value, for the given number of degrees of freedom (*d.f.*, along the stub). The tabled value is the sum of the area under *both* the right-hand and left-hand tails of the curve of the t distribution, *outside* the limits $\pm t$. Look at the figure at the right of the table. This shows the t distribution for, say, 20 d.f. You read in the table that for 20 d.f. the probability is 0.05 that you get a t of 2.086 or larger (if the null hypothesis is correct, that is); in other words 95% of the area under the curve is inside the limits ± 2.086. The area under a curve can be interpreted as a probability, with the area as a whole having a probability of 1.000. To the left and right of $t = 2.086$ lies 5/100 of the entire area, so there is a probability of a t as large as, or larger than, ± 2.086, about 5 times out of 100. If you are willing to say these are safe probabilities, you can say that a t of ± 2.086 is *significant at the 5% level of significance*. If you want an even smaller probability, say 1 in 100, then you use the 1% level of significance ($P = 0.01$) and need a t of 2.845 or better.

TWO-TAILED AND ONE-TAILED HYPOTHESES

The table, as it is constructed, is not quite suited to test the hypothesis we have set up. The table is set up for what we call a *two-tailed test*; the hypothesis we are testing, on the other hand, is called a *one-tailed test*. In a two-tailed test we are interested in finding out whether one population mean, say, is *either* larger *or* smaller than the other. In a one-tailed test we are interested only in whether *one* is larger than the other. If it is significantly smaller we do not count the hypothesis as true; if it is equal we do not count it as true. For instance, if the high cohesive groups really have about the same mean pressures to uniformity as the low cohesive groups the null hypothesis is accepted, and the hypothesis underlying the experiment is rejected. But it is also true that if the high cohesive groups are significantly *less* likely to exert such pressures than low cohesive groups we also want to reject our hypothesis about pressures in high *vs.* low groups, and accordingly want to *accept* the null hypothesis. We are interested, consequently, in only one tail of the t distribution, the tail showing the probability of getting a $+t$ as large or larger than we have. The difference in the two tests is expressed in the null hypothesis you formulate; for instance:

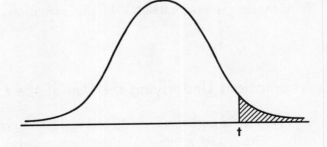

$H_0: \mu_1 \leq \mu_2$, the hypothesis we are testing, is a *one-tailed* hypothesis. We want only the right-hand tail, the probability of getting a *positive* difference as large or larger than we got. If t falls anywhere in the *unshaded* area, we *accept* the null hypothesis.

H_0: $\mu_1 \geq \mu_2$ is also a one-tailed hypothesis. This time we want only the left-hand tail, the probability of $\bar{X}_1$ being as much smaller than $\bar{X}_2$ as the difference we have found. The actual area is exactly the same as the area to the right of the same (positive) value of t.

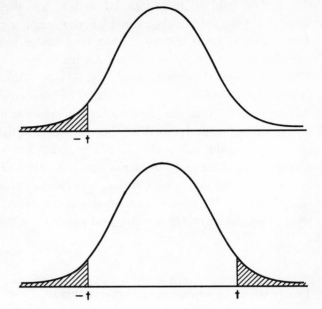

H_0: $\mu_1 = \mu_2$ is a *two-tailed* hypothesis; we are interested in whether the means differ significantly in *either* direction and to find this probability we add up the two tails.

Where it is appropriate, the one-tailed test is more sensitive than the two-tailed test, obviously, since we can detect a significant difference with a smaller value of t. All we need to do to find the one-tailed probability is to take *one-half* the tabled probability, since the area outside a given t is the same in either tail. For example, we have found that t for our experiment on cohesion and pressures toward uniformity is 2.57. Our hypothesis is a one-tailed hypothesis. We look in the table of t for the probability of getting t as large as or larger than 2.57, with 38 degrees of freedom. The table does not give every probability for 38 d.f., but it does tell us that a t of 2.025 gives a probability of 0.05, for a *two*-tailed test. Half of this is 0.025, which is the probability of getting a t of 2.025 or larger in *one* direction. (In Table 3, in the Appendix, we show both one-tailed and two-tailed probabilities, for convenience.) Obviously 2.57 gives us better than the 5% level. We decide, therefore, to reject the null hypothesis and conclude, alternatively, that the difference between the high and low cohesive treatments could *not* have occurred simply as a result of chance unless a rather unusual event has occurred. The high cohesive groups do exert more pressures toward uniformity than the low cohesive groups. (*Warning*: we accept this alternative only after an evaluation of the entire experimental design, not simply as a result of the test of significance. See page 248 on the interpretation of tests of significance.)

Assumptions Underlying the Use of the *t* Test

There is a general rule in the application of statistical methods that it is well to learn early. The cruder a method is, the more general, usually, is its application; conversely, the

Computation design for *t* test of the difference between two means, for two independent samples

from S_1: $\bar{X}_1 = \sum X_{1i}/N_1$

$\qquad \sum x_1{}^2 = \sum X_{1i}{}^2 - (\sum X_{1i})^2/N_1$

from S_2: $\bar{X}_2 = \sum X_{2i}/N_2$

$\qquad \sum x_2{}^2 = \sum X_{2i}{}^2 - (\sum X_{2i})^2/N_2$

1. $H_0:$

2. $s_{\bar{x}_1 - \bar{x}_2} = \sqrt{\left(\dfrac{\sum x_1{}^2 + \sum x_2{}^2}{N_1 + N_2 - 2}\right)\left(\dfrac{1}{N_1} + \dfrac{1}{N_2}\right)}$

$\qquad =$

3. $t = \dfrac{\bar{X}_1 - \bar{X}_2}{s_{\bar{x}_1 - \bar{x}_2}} =$

4. d.f. $= N_1 + N_2 - 2 =$

5. $P =$

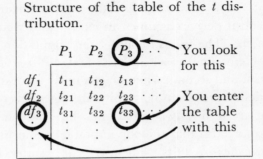

Structure of the table of the *t* distribution.

1. Formulate the null hypothesis you wish to test. This will determine whether you are to make a two-sided or one-sided test. The chief null hypotheses are $\mu_1 = \mu_2$ (two-sided), $\mu_1 \leq \mu_2$, or $\mu_1 \geq \mu_2$ (both one-sided). Write the hypothesis on line 1.

2. Compute the standard error of the difference by pooling estimates of the sums of squares. Enter on line 2.

3. Assume that both samples are normally and independently distributed; assume also that they have equal variances; then the distribution of t, which is the difference between the means divided by the estimated standard error of the difference, follows the t distribution with $N_1 + N_2 - 2$ degrees of freedom. Enter t on line 3 and d.f. on line 4.

4. With the value of t and d.f. you enter the table of t. You are looking for P, the probability that a value of t this large or larger would have been obtained by chance if the null hypothesis were true. P will be shown along the head of the table, d.f. down the side, and the values of t will be shown in the body of the table. The probability shown will be two-tailed (i.e. the *sum* of the probability to the right of t and to the left of $-t$); if the hypothesis is one-sided, use one-half the tabled probability.

5. If P is equal to, or less than, 0.05 reject the null hypothesis. (Set the level of significance at 0.01 if you prefer greater certainty.) If P is greater than 0.05, accept the null hypothesis.

more exact the method, the more restricted its applications are likely to be. The t test is a good example of a powerful, exact test whose applications in sociological research are limited by several rather restrictive assumptions. We will discuss two assumptions peculiarly important to the t test, and a third that has more general implications.

1. When we use the t test we assume that the population from which the observations are drawn is normally distributed.

The power and exactness of the t distribution result from the fact that the model from which it derives assumes an exact, known form of the population from which the sample is drawn. The test is invalid if the population is not normal in form. This raises two separate problems for the sociologist: first, he frequently does not know what form his population takes; and second, when he can make a guess he usually suspects it is not normal. The effects of departures from normality are more severe if you are testing one-tailed hypotheses than if you are testing two-tailed ones, but in general if you suspect (perhaps from the form of the sample data) that the population is not normal it is safest to use what we call *nonparametric*, or *distribution-free* tests. These tests are cruder, but more general in application, than the t test, and we will discuss various examples in the following chapters.

2. When we use the t test we assume that the two samples, or treatments, compared have homogeneous (equal) variances.

For a really precise interpretation of the t test it is also necessary to have the variances about equal in the two samples compared. There is a good deal of controversy over this assumption, or rather over the degree to which this is an insuperable obstacle to using the t test. There are some (not so elegant) ways of getting around it. But in general, if the variances are significantly different and a t test is used, the result is *not* a test of the significance of the difference between the means—you will not, in fact, be able to say how the means, as against the variances, contribute to t from the t test alone. You *will* be able to test the cruder hypothesis that the two samples come from the same population (i.e., that their means, *or* variances, or *both* are significantly different), but this considerably reduces the exactness of the test—and its exactness is one of its strongest recommendations. There are simpler (nonparametric) tests of this latter hypothesis.

You can test the variances, incidentally, by another very well known significance test, called the *F test*. This test is actually easier than the t test to apply, but it has one new element. This is how you go about it: first, divide the larger of the two variances by the smaller, which gives F (also called the *variance ratio*). Now, with F in hand you go to a table of the F distribution. (We have not included a table of F in this text.) This distribution differs from the t distribution in that it is mutually determined by *two* sets of degrees of freedom rather than one. You use the d.f. from group 1 and the d.f. from group 2 in entering the table; each d.f. is simply $N - 1$. Using the Zetterberg experiment, $s_1^2 = 5.47$ and $s_2^2 = 5.46$; d.f. for each group is 19. Then $F = 5.47/5.46 = 1.002$, with d.f. equal to 19 and 19. Now we go to the F table.

Along the top of the *F* table you have the d.f. for the sample which has the larger variance, and along the stub of the table you have the d.f. for the sample with the smaller variance.

TABLE 9-3.

Portion of Table of the 5% Points for the *F* Distribution

		$d.f._1$ (*For the Larger Variance*)				
		14	16	20	24	. . .
d.f.$_2$ (for	17	2.33	2.29	2.23	2.19	
the	18	2.29	2.25	2.19	2.15	
smaller	19	2.26	2.21	2.15	2.11	
variance)	20	2.23	2.18	2.12	2.08	

Source: Snedecor, 1946.

The cells of the table give the values of *F* that are significant at the 5% level. (The original table also gives the values of *F* significant at the 1% level.) If your *F* is larger than the tabled value, the variances differ significantly, i.e., they would not have been drawn from the same population more than 5 times out of 100. The table does not happen to show values for d.f. = 19 in one of the directions, but our *F* is obviously less than 2.15 (d.f. 20, 19) and we therefore accept the null hypothesis that $\sigma_1{}^2 = \sigma_2{}^2$. It is legitimate in this case to use the *t* test, and to interpret it *exactly* to mean that if *t* is significant then the *means* differ significantly.

3. We assume that our samples are each drawn according to the ideal-bowl model; assignment to treatments is random and observations are independent.

The third assumption is more complex to discuss. In the first place, as we have already said, the assumption that the samples are randomly drawn underlies the use of *any* statistical test, since theoretical statistics rests on the analysis of random variables. The assumption, usually made at the same time, that the observations made on the sample are independent is also a very general one and must be considered in every kind of statistical test. It is important that the sociologist particularly understands this assumption of independence, because it is an assumption his data frequently fail to fit.

One way the assumption of independence can fail is in the research design itself. In psychological research, for instance, two frequently used designs employ repeated observations on the same individual, or paired observations on individuals who are alike in some respect. The resulting observations are correlated (not independent) and some adaptation must be made in the use of the *t* test, or any other test of significance for that matter. Solutions are available to this kind of problem, and they involve nothing more complex than subtracting out the correlation in the formula for the standard error of the difference, or working with the distribution of differences itself. (See Edwards, 1950, pp. 86–91; and Edwards, 1955, Chapter 14, for excellent discussions.) These designs are very common and their theory is well worked out.

Much less attention, however, has been devoted to a sociologically more interesting problem. We can use the Zetterberg experiment to illustrate this. If you recall the design, subjects were randomly assigned to groups and groups randomly assigned to experimental treatments. This gave us independent samples. But suppose we had analyzed the observations made on *each individual* instead of those made on each group. We would have doubled N, and certainly this is tempting. But we could not have used the *t* test if we had used individual observations. Why? Because the observations on individuals from the same groups would be correlated. This is a fundamental sociological fact. In a social system, what one individual does is not random with respect to the actions of other individuals in the system. Consequently, in order to get independent observations, we have to lose the larger N—in other words, our solution in this case is to chose *units* in such a way that independence is ensured.

In general, then, the sociologist has to consider this kind of problem every time he begins the analysis of his data; he has to evaluate carefully the independence of his observations and consider how to adapt his statistical methods to this problem. It is certain that in the next few years this problem will receive more attention in the literature of theoretical statistics and the issue of an adequate solution is by no means closed yet.

Interpretation of Significance Tests

Note very carefully the form in which statistical hypotheses are cast. We design an experiment to show that $\mu_1 > \mu_2$; but the hypothesis we actually subject to test is $\mu_1 \leq \mu_2$. Tests of significance can *only* test hypotheses in this negative form and you should remember when you use them that they are only negative insurance against the effects of random errors, *not* positive evidence of proof for any alternative to the null hypothesis. Accepting the alternative hypothesis is contingent not only on the significance test, but on all other elements in the design of the proof as well. If you detect an uncontrolled variable which might have been confounded in the results of an experiment, the proof is invalid regardless of the level of significance shown. The null hypothesis may be rejected, but the alternative you are offered in favor of the null hypothesis is not acceptable without further proof.

Where We Stand

In the first eight chapters of this book we have been concerned primarily with the techniques of description; although once or twice the distinction between sample and population has been of some importance, in general the problem of inferring the population value of a characteristic from its sample value has not been central. In this chapter we have introduced the problem of inference; and in particular we have discussed (1) sampling, (2) confidence intervals, and (3) tests of significance. The logic of statistical inference is based on the assumption that we will sample many times and that we will know something about the distribution of a given sample statistic over the long run. We will make statements on the basis of this knowledge that will be incorrect some of the time, but we will be able to state with what probability we will be incorrect *over the long run*.

Before continuing with the problems of statistical inference, the student should be warned against assuming too hastily that as a result of reading this chapter he is now an expert on sampling. Primarily we have discussed simple random sampling. Although this procedure is the basic point of departure for the elaboration of modern sampling techniques, it is seldom practical on a large scale and seldom used in large-scale surveys. We have talked, for example, about probabilities of selection that are equal for every element in a population, whereas these probabilities need not be equal so long as they are known and are not zero. And as the sample design is changed, so is the behavior of the sampling distribution of statistics computed from the sample. It follows that the standard error which we have used in setting confidence intervals, $s/\sqrt{N}$, is not an accurate estimate for every kind of sample design. This formula is associated primarily with simple random sampling, and for many kinds of sampling plans this formula must be modified before it can be used in estimating confidence intervals, etc. It is also true that different kinds of experimental designs lead to different formulas for the standard error. It should be clear, therefore, that we have been concerned essentially with the *logic* of inference, and that there are many techniques to be mastered before we can handle advanced technical problems. (See Kish, 1953, for a concise treatment of sampling designs, and Deming, 1950, for a very detailed treatment; see also Edwards, 1950, for a discussion of experimental designs.)

Chapter 9

WORKBOOK EXERCISES

In order to help the student to get the feel of sampling and inferences based on sampling the following experiments are recommended. Since some of them demand a good deal of computation that is more or less tedious and not particularly illuminating, it may be advisable to divide the work among teams in some manner that will reduce the work but convey the same idea. Four "populations" are the basis of all the experiments.

Population I: A variable population, rectangular in form (consisting of the digits 0, 1, 2, 3, 4, 5, 6, 7, 8, 9); the following numbers are drawn at random (with replacement) from this population.

59391	58030	52098	82718
99567	76364	77204	04615
10363	97518	51400	25670
86859	19558	64432	16706
11258	24591	36863	55368
95068	88628	35911	14530
54463	47237	73800	91017
16874	62677	57412	13215
92494	63157	76593	91316
15669	56689	35682	40844

These numbers are in random order no matter in which direction you read, across or down. They are taken from a table of 10,000 random numbers (Snedecor, 1946, p. 10) that is very useful in practical sampling, and the table is actually equivalent to drawing numbers, one by one, from the ideal bowl. This merely saves the work of the drawing itself. The only significance in the block arrangement is that it makes reading easier. But you may treat this as 40 samples of $n = 5$ by using each block, reading across, giving samples of 5, 9, 3, 9, 1;

5, 8, 0, 3, 0; 5, 2, 0, 9, 8; etc.; or another 40 samples of the same size by reading down, in the same blocks, 5, 9, 1, 8, 1; 9, 9, 0, 6, 1; 3, 5, 3, 8, 2; etc.; or samples of size 10 or 20 by combining blocks in either direction; or of 25 by using each block as a sample, etc.

Population II: An attribute population, dichotomous in form (consisting of the digits 0, 1, 0, 1, 0, 1, 0, 1, 0, 1), yielding the following samples.

11111	10010	10010	00110
11101	10100	11000	00011
10101	11110	11000	01010
00011	11110	00010	10100
11010	00111	10001	11100
11000	00000	11111	10110
10001	01011	11000	11011
10010	00011	11010	11011
10010	01111	10111	11110
11001	10001	11000	00000

This table is actually the first table with 0 for even numbers and 1 for odd numbers; however, it should represent just as well the actual sampling of a population of dichotomous attributes in which the probability of drawing either 1 or 0 is 1/2.

Population III: Random samples of two-digit numbers from an almost normal population with $\mu = 30$ and $\sigma = 10$.

26	29	26	38	42	39	42	34	17	31
20	25	42	23	30	32	30	31	32	17
34	30	41	30	18	30	42	23	30	30
30	26	43	44	34	26	21	20	26	27
22	27	21	36	24	28	33	11	49	25
32	47	31	42	30	27	40	19	28	15
57	30	37	30	38	36	13	43	31	30
18	20	49	33	30	31	24	19	27	42
41	44	21	33	33	37	20	43	41	30
18	19	23	31	27	27	31	28	24	34

These numbers were drawn from a typical example of a normal distribution, a table of pig-gains, i.e., gains in weight of pigs (Snedecor, 1946, p. 55). They were drawn by giving each pig-gain a number, entering a random number table, and reading down. Since there were 99 pig-gains in the original table, two columns were read at a time from the random number table. For example, using the random numbers in Population I, the first pig-gain chosen, had we started with the first random number, top left, would have been item 59, the second would have been item 99 (reading down), and so on.

Population IV: Random samples from a single-digit skewed population, 1, 2, 2, 2, 3, 3, 4, 5, 6, 7.

22125	15472	22466	21736
62732	32324	42213	62532
62663	52373	35551	42325
41225	33321	54267	66357
32346	57572	72233	37625
23564	37221	21214	43662
65223	53671	22274	52237
62532	13263	54416	32523
11334	35413	62262	36522
32553	27772	23312	12622

These numbers were drawn in the same way, using single columns of the random number table, from the 10 digits above.

On the following pages you will do approximately the same things for each of the four populations. (The instructor may wish to sample from I and II only, for the time being. See (f) below.)

a. Draw a histogram of the form of each population.

b. Compute the parameters of the populations and the true values of their standard errors. For Population I, for example, this will mean adding 0, 1, 2, 3, . . . 9, and dividing by 10 to obtain μ; adding the squares of these numbers, subtracting $(\sum X)^2/N$, and dividing the result again by N, to obtain σ^2 (*note:* you do not divide by $N - 1$ because this is a population, not a sample); taking the square root of this to find σ; and dividing σ by $\sqrt{N}$, the square root of the sample size, to obtain the "true" value of the standard error for samples of size 5 and 10. For Population II, $P_{(1)}$ is $1/2$ and the standard error is $\sqrt{PQ/N} = \sqrt{(1/2)(1/2)/5}$, and so on. Actually, since sampling is by replacement (i.e., we conceive of replacing each number, so that it is not used up and may be drawn again), it would be more strictly accurate to think of the population as an infinite (uncountable) number of repetitions of the sampling procedure, rather than as the 10 digits we are calling populations, and to think of our so-called parameters as *estimates* of the true value of the parameters. In the exercises that follow, however, we shall speak of the values computed as we have just shown as parameters, and of the basic digits from which we sample as populations.

c. Draw 40 samples of size 5 from each population. You do this simply by reading across the random number tables. (For III you read across *and* down to get 40 samples.) For instance, the first sample from I may be 5, 9, 3, 9, 1; the second may be 5, 8, 0, 3, 0, etc. If teams are used, additional samples can be obtained by reading down, or diagonally, etc.; the tables are random in no matter which direction they are used.

d. For each sample compute the mean (or proportion of 1's for II), and tabulate the means (proportions) to obtain a sampling distribution of the statistic. Then:

(1) Verify that the mean of the sampling distribution approximates the population parameter.

(2) Verify that the standard deviation of the sampling distribution approximates $\sigma/\sqrt{N}$.

(3) Calculate the proportion of sample estimates within 2 and 3 standard errors of the mean of the sampling distribution.

(4) Examine the form of the sampling distribution compared to the population. As a visual aid construct a histogram or polygon of the sampling distribution on the same axes as the histogram of the population.

e. Now draw samples of size 10 by reading across but taking two blocks at a time. Repeat the same operations. In addition you should observe that:

(1) The mean of the sampling distribution should approximate the parameter more closely than in (d).

(2) The standard deviation of the sampling distribution should be smaller than in (d).

(3) The form of the sampling distributions should more closely approach a normal, or at least symmetrical, form.

f. Comparisons of the form of sampling distributions from different populations will be of particular use for Chapter 11. (In fact, the instructor may wish to reserve sampling from Populations II and IV for later.) For later use, however, the student should compare the form of the sampling distributions from Populations I, III, and IV. In comparing these distributions he should verify that:

(1) The sampling distribution of $\bar{X}_i$ from III closely approximates a normal distribution.

(2) The sampling distribution of $\bar{X}_i$ from I is symmetrical and as the sample size increases, it more closely approximates a normal distribution. (The student is not equipped to test rigorously for normality, but may answer by inspection.)

(3) The sampling distribution of $\bar{X}_i$ from IV is more symmetrical and nearly normal than the population and more so as the sample size, increases.

It is necessary to distinguish the three sets of symbols required in the exercises of Chapter 9. We collect these here in order to point out and emphasize the differences among the three sets.

I. *Population Parameters.* Acting as if the digits from which the random numbers in the exercises are generated constitute a population, from each set of digits a set of parameters may be computed. These are designated

μ, the population mean

P, the population proportion

σ, the standard deviation of the population

σ_p, the standard deviation of the population proportion

$\sigma_{\bar{x}}$, the standard error of the sampling distribution of the mean

$\sigma_{\hat{p}}$, the standard error of the sampling distribution of a proportion

II. *Sample Statistics.* From each sample an estimate of these parameters is computed. These are designated

$\bar{X}$, sample estimate of the mean

$\hat{p}$, sample estimate of the population proportion

s, sample estimate of the standard deviation

s_p, sample estimate of the standard deviation of the population proportion

$s_{\bar{x}}$, sample estimate of the standard error of the mean

$s_{\hat{p}}$, sample estimate of the standard error of a proportion.

III. *Statistics of Experimentally Obtained Approximations to Sampling Distributions.* A sampling distribution is the distribution of all possible, or an infinite number of, samples of the same size from the same population. In Chapter 9 we approximate such a sampling distribution by recording the results of sampling experiments. For these distributions a third set of symbols is required, since certain estimates are computed from them. These are designated,

$\bar{X}_{\bar{x}}$, the mean of the distribution of sample estimates of the mean

$\bar{X}_{\hat{p}}$, the mean of the distribution of sample estimates of a proportion

$s_{\bar{x}\bar{x}}$, the standard deviation of the distribution of the sample estimates of the mean

$s_{\hat{p}\hat{p}}$, the standard deviation of the distribution of sample estimates of a proportion

1. Sampling Experiments with Population I. (Boldface letters refer to instructions on pages 253–254.)

a.

b.

$$\mu =$$

$$\sigma^2 =$$

$$\sigma =$$

$$\sigma_{\bar{x}} = \sigma/\sqrt{N}$$

$$= \sigma/\sqrt{5} =$$

$$= \sigma/\sqrt{10} =$$

d. Sampling Distribution of the Mean; Samples of Size 5.

$$\bar{X}_i$$

$$\bar{X}_{\bar{x}} =$$

$$s_{\bar{x}_{\bar{x}}}{}^2 =$$

$$s_{\bar{x}_{\bar{x}}} =$$

About .... % of the means are within $\bar{X}_{\bar{x}} \pm 2s_{\bar{x}}$.

About .... % of the means are within $\bar{X}_{\bar{x}} \pm 3s_{\bar{x}}$.

e. Sampling Distribution of the Mean; Samples of Size 10.

$\bar{X}_i$

$$\bar{X}_{\bar{x}} =$$
$$s_{\bar{x}_{\bar{x}}}{}^2 =$$
$$s_{\bar{x}_{\bar{x}}} =$$

About ....% of the means are within $\bar{X}_{\bar{x}} \pm 2s_{\bar{x}_{\bar{x}}}$.

About ....% of the means are within $\bar{X}_{\bar{x}} \pm 3s_{\bar{x}_{\bar{x}}}$.

2. Sampling Experiments with Population II. (Boldface letters refer to instructions on pages 253–254.)

a.   **b.**

$$P_{(1)} =$$
$$Q = 1 - P_{(1)} =$$
$$\sigma_{\hat{p}} = \sqrt{PQ/N}$$
$$= \sqrt{PQ/5} =$$
$$= \sqrt{PQ/10} =$$

d. Sampling Distribution of a Proportion; Samples of Size 5.

$\hat{p}_i$

$$\bar{X}_{\hat{p}} =$$

$$s_{\hat{p}_{\hat{p}}}{}^2 =$$

$$s_{\hat{p}_{\hat{p}}} =$$

About ＿＿＿＿＿＿ % of the proportions are within $\bar{X}_{\hat{p}} \pm 2s_{\hat{p}_{\hat{p}}}$.

About ＿＿＿＿＿＿ % of the proportions are within $\bar{X}_{\hat{p}} \pm 3s_{\hat{p}_{\hat{p}}}$.

e. Sampling Distribution of a Proportion; Samples of Size 10.

$\hat{p}_i$

$$\bar{X}_{\hat{p}} =$$

$$s_{\hat{p}_{\hat{p}}}{}^2 =$$

$$s_{\hat{p}_{\hat{p}}} =$$

About ＿＿＿＿＿＿ % of the proportions are within $\bar{X}_{\hat{p}} \pm 2s_{\hat{p}_{\hat{p}}}$.

About ＿＿＿＿＿＿ % of the proportions are within $\bar{X}_{\hat{p}} \pm 3s_{\hat{p}_{\hat{p}}}$.

3. Sampling Experiments with Population III. (Boldface letters refer to instructions on pages 253–254.)

a. Draw a smooth normal curve (see Figure 4-1) with $\mu = 30$ and $\sigma = 10$. The curve will begin turning down (will *inflect*) one σ on either side of the mean.

b.

$$\mu =$$

$$\sigma^2 =$$

$$\sigma =$$

$$\sigma_{\bar{x}} = \sigma/\sqrt{N} =$$

$$= \sigma/\sqrt{5} =$$

$$= \sigma/\sqrt{10} =$$

d. Sampling Distribution of the Mean; Samples of Size 5.

$\bar{X}_i$

$$\bar{X}_{\bar{x}} =$$

$$s_{\bar{x}_{\bar{x}}}^2 =$$

$$s_{\bar{x}_{\bar{x}}} =$$

About ....% of the means are within $\bar{X}_{\bar{x}} \pm 2s_{\bar{x}_{\bar{x}}}$.

About ....% of the means are within $\bar{X}_{\bar{x}} \pm 3s_{\bar{x}_{\bar{x}}}$.

e. Sampling Distribution of the Mean; Samples of Size 10.

$\bar{X}_i$

$$\bar{X}_{\bar{x}} =$$

$$s_{\bar{x}_{\bar{x}}}{}^2 =$$

$$s_{\bar{x}_{\bar{x}}} =$$

About _____ % of the means are within $\bar{X}_{\bar{x}} \pm 2s_{\bar{x}_{\bar{x}}}$.

About _____ % of the means are within $\bar{X}_{\bar{x}} \pm 3s_{\bar{x}_{\bar{x}}}$.

4. Sampling Experiments with Population IV. (Boldface letters refer to instructions on pages 253–254.)

a.   **b.**

$$\mu =$$

$$\sigma^2 =$$

$$\sigma =$$

$$\sigma_{\bar{x}} = \sigma/\sqrt{N}$$

$$= \sigma/\sqrt{5} =$$

$$= \sigma/\sqrt{10} =$$

d. Sampling Distribution of the Mean; Samples of Size 5.

$\bar{X}_i$

$$\bar{\bar{X}}_{\bar{x}} =$$
$$s_{\bar{x}_{\bar{x}}}{}^2 =$$
$$s_{\bar{x}_{\bar{x}}} =$$

About ....% of the means are within $\bar{\bar{X}}_{\bar{x}} \pm 2s_{\bar{x}_{\bar{x}}}$.

About ....% of the means are within $\bar{\bar{X}}_{\bar{x}} \pm 3s_{\bar{x}_{\bar{x}}}$.

e. Sampling Distribution of the Mean; Samples of Size 10.

$\bar{X}_i$

$$\bar{\bar{X}}_{\bar{x}} =$$
$$s_{\bar{x}_{\bar{x}}}{}^2 =$$
$$s_{\bar{x}_{\bar{x}}} =$$

About ....% of the means are within $\bar{\bar{X}}_{\bar{x}} \pm 2s_{\bar{x}_{\bar{x}}}$.

About ....% of the means are within $\bar{\bar{X}}_{\bar{x}} \pm 3s_{\bar{x}_{\bar{x}}}$.

5. Take five samples of size 40 from Population II by using the two top lines as the first sample (labeled S_1 below); the next two lines as the second sample, etc. Set 95% confidence intervals for each sample (i.e., use $1.96s_{\hat{p}}$ to compute the limits). How many intervals contain P?

$$S_1: \quad P(\qquad \leq P \leq \qquad) = 0.95*$$

$$S_2: \quad P(\qquad \leq P \leq \qquad) = 0.95$$

$$S_3: \quad P(\qquad \leq P \leq \qquad) = 0.95$$

$$S_4: \quad P(\qquad \leq P \leq \qquad) = 0.95$$

$$S_5: \quad P(\qquad \leq P \leq \qquad) = 0.95$$

.... of these intervals contain P. (This is .... %.)

Use the space below to show the mean and standard deviation of each sample.

* Read, "the probability that P is greater than ......, but less than ...... is 0.95."

6. Take five samples of size 40 from Population I in the same manner and set 99% confidence intervals for each sample (i.e., use $2.58s_{\bar{x}}$ to compute the limits). How many intervals contain μ?

S_1: $P($ $\leq \mu \leq$ $) = 0.99$

S_2: $P($ $\leq \mu \leq$ $) = 0.99$

S_3: $P($ $\leq \mu \leq$ $) = 0.99$

S_4: $P($ $\leq \mu \leq$ $) = 0.99$

S_5: $P($ $\leq \mu \leq$ $) = 0.99$

.... of these intervals contain μ. (This is ....%.)

Use the space below for your work.

7. The following two samples are drawn from Population III. Using the t test, test the H_0: $\mu_1 = \mu_2$.

S_1: X_i	S_2: X_i
26	39
25	30
41	23
44	26
24	25

8. Thibaut (1950) designed the following experiment to examine two factors related to the cohesiveness of groups. Twenty-two groups of boys were recruited from settlement houses and camps. They were given, before the experiment itself began, a sociometric questionnaire asking them to choose those members of the group they would most like to have on their side during some games they were going to play. Then each of the 22 groups was split into two teams in such a way that each boy would find an equal number of those he named on his own team and on the team he was to play against.

Thibaut was interested in the relation of group status to cohesion, where by "status" he meant the relative evaluation of the group's activities; and he was interested both in the status of one group relative to another and in the effect of success in *improving* status relative to another. In order to experiment with these variables he had each of the 22 groups play three games. In each game one group served more or less as an "underprivileged" group. In one game, for example, the underprivileged (low-status) group was the target and retriever for the other (high-status) group in a game of throwing bean bags. He used three variations, or experimental treatments:

(1) Unsuccessful group action: An observer encourages the low-status group, during an intermission in the game, to agitate for a better deal, but the experimenter refuses to let them improve status. This gives two kinds of groups: (a) a consistently high-status group, and (b) a consistently low-status group.

(2) Successful group action: The low-status group agitates for improvement in status, but in this variation it succeeds. ·This gives two kinds of groups again: (c) a high-status group which is displaced to low status, and (d) a low-status group which is able to improve status.

(3) Control groups: An equal rotation of opportunities among teams with no differential favoritism serves as a control on the effect of the experimental variables. (These groups will be labeled "e" below.)

Immediately after the games a questionnaire was given out, including a repetition of the pre-session sociometric question which made up the basic data of the experiment.

a. Using a *t* test for the difference between means, compare the following sociometric scores, obtained *before* the experiment to see if in fact the experimenter matched the groups sociometrically. (Compare groups (a) and (b), and (c) and (d) with each other, and compare (a) and (c) with (e).)*

TABLE 1.

Pre-session Sociometric Scores, by Experimental Condition

(Thibaut Experiment)

Experimental Condition	Number of Groups	Mean Indices of Attractiveness of Own Team
(a)	9	1.29
(b)	9	1.28
(c)	9	1.27
(d)	9	1.26
(e)	4†	1.37

Source: Thibaut, 1950, p. 106.

* A more appropriate test would be the *analysis of variance*, a test which is based on the *F* test we made use of on page 246 but do not discuss further in this text. The analysis of variance would be more appropriate because it compares three or more means at the same time, whereas the *t* test compares them only two at a time. The effect of comparing two at a time where there are three or more means is to increase the probability that a difference would be accepted as significant when in fact the null hypothesis is true. In this particular example *t* will not mislead us, but it would not, in general, be as appropriate for this problem as analysis of variance. In part b, on the other hand, *t* is the appropriate test because two means at a time (before and after in each group) are legitimately being compared.

† In the first four conditions 18 of the 22 groups are split into halves for the experimental treatment. In condition (e) the remaining 4 groups are also split, but are rotated with no favoritism, so that the split halves are combined again into four groups for analysis.

Use $\sum x^2 = 2.56$ in each experimental condition.

The substantive hypothesis you are testing is that the groups are exactly matched.

Stated as a statistical hypothesis (called a .... hypothesis), this is: ....

....

or, in symbols H_0: .... Is this a one-tailed hypothesis or a two-tailed hypothesis?

....

Why is this kind of hypothesis used? ....

....

Make your computations for t on page 269. (Label the comparisons you are making.) Then, for each comparison, summarize your results by writing (in symbols) the hypothesis tested; the result of the test (P either greater or less than 0.05 or 0.01, shown by writing $P > 0.05$ or $P < 0.05$); whether the statistical hypothesis is accepted or rejected; and what this implies about the substantive hypothesis.

b. You can use the definition $t = (\bar{X} - \mu)/s_{\bar{x}}$ to test the significance of the results of the experiment. The table below shows, for each condition, the mean *shift* in the index of attractiveness (cohesion) of own team, the standard deviation, and N. (The *shift* is the score *after* the experiment minus the score *before*.) From this you may compute $s_{\bar{x}}$, and test the hypothesis that $\mu = 0$ for each condition, where μ is the mean of the distribution of the *shifts* in attractiveness. (In other words, in the formula put 0 for μ. You use $N - 1$ d.f.)

TABLE 2.

Differences in Attractiveness of Group after Experimental Variables
Are Introduced (Thibaut Experiment)

Experimental Condition	Number of Groups	Mean Shifts in Attractiveness of Own Team (After − Before)	s (of Shifts)
(a)	9	0.266	0.469
(b)	9	0.402	0.390
(c)	9	0.048	0.439
(d)	9	0.077	0.395
(e)	4	0.108	0.250

Source: Adapted from Thibaut, 1950, Table 9.2, p. 110.

This time the substantive hypotheses are two: (1), that consistent high status will make the group more attractive to its members and lead to increased cohesion (i.e., more choices *within* the group as opposed to *outside* the group); (2) that successful improvement in status will have the same result. Stated in a form useful for a statistical test, this would mean ....

....

.... and ....

....

....

Symbolically, ... and ....

....

Are these one-tailed or two-tailed?...

....

Why is this the kind of hypothesis that is appropriate?...

....

....

(You can label the means by the letter designating the conditions of the experiment, in order to make symbolic statement of the hypotheses manageable.)

Show the computations for *t* in the space provided on page 270. Again summarize your results and the implications of these results, as instructed in section (a) above.

c. Now write a very brief summary of the experiment, reporting its chief substantive result. (Additional results, comparing high- and low-status members within each kind of group, are reported in the original.)

....

....

....

....

....

....

....

d. What part did the statistical tests play in coming to this conclusion? What *else*, besides the tests of significance, would be required to interpret the conclusions?

Problem 8a

Problem 8b

Chapter 10

Binomial and Chi-square Tests

WE HAVE shown, so far, how to make statements about μ and P with some (known) degree of confidence, and also how to test one kind of hypothesis about the means of two samples. In this chapter we continue the discussion of statistical inference, concentrating primarily on problems connected with testing hypotheses about attribute data. We frequently ask, for instance, if there is a "real" difference between two sample proportions; or in other words, we wish to test the null hypothesis $H_0 : P_1 = P_2$. We will discuss three ways of doing this, and also ways of extending the same procedures to test the *significance* of *association* in $r \times s$ tables.

Tests of Significance for Proportions

There are several ways to test for significance with attribute data. One way is to use a special distribution called the binomial to evaluate the level of significance. We may also approximate the exact binomial probabilities by using the normal distribution, when N is sufficiently large. A third method, finally, uses the *chi-square* distribution (chi-square is written χ^2 and is read ki-square), which simply approximates the binomial probabilities in another way.* We will discuss each of these methods in some detail.

* More precisely, χ^2 approximates binomial probabilities when d.f. $= 1$; for higher degrees of freedom it approximates *multi*nomial probabilities, i.e. the distribution resulting from expansion of $(p + q + r + \ldots)^N$. This more precise rendering would be relevant, for example, in the final section of this chapter (on application of χ^2 to the general $r \times s$ table) although we make no further point of it.

The *binomial distribution* is the distribution associated with the sampling of proportions and can be used for the computation of the *exact* probability of getting a $\hat{p}$ as large as, or larger than, a given P, as small as or smaller than a given P, or both. The reason that the normal distribution may be used for large samples (as we did in the last chapter) is that as N increases the binomial distribution (which is discrete) more and more closely approximates a continuous normal curve. Conversely, as N becomes smaller this approximation is no longer very close and the normal should not be used.

As we indicated before, the shape of the binomial depends not only on N but also on P. This is a problem that we did not face with the t distribution, which in no way depends on μ. As P gets very small, the binomial tends to approximate another special distribution which is called the *Poisson distribution*. This curve is rather like a J-shaped curve, and has the peculiar property that its mean and variance are equal. In any case, even in large samples the binomial in this case is not approximated by the normal curve.

A simple rule of thumb which will tell you just when either N or P is too small for normal approximations is that $N\hat{p}$ should be greater than 5. A slightly more sensitive rule of thumb is:

$$N\hat{p} + 9\hat{p} > 9, \qquad \hat{p} < \hat{q}$$

where N is the sample size

   $\hat{p}$ is the sample estimate of the proportion P, and means *either* $\hat{p}$ *or* $\hat{q}$, whichever is *smaller*

Taking an example from Hagood and Price (1952, pp. 234–36), we will illustrate the use of the binomial in computing exact probabilities when we cannot use the normal approximation. This will be for the case when N is too small. If it is P that is too small, then we must use the Poisson, which we will not take up here. (The Poisson is a somewhat more advanced topic.)

Suppose we draw a sample of 6 and find that there are 4 males and 2 females in the sample. We want to know if this disproportion is due to random sampling error, or if in fact there are more males than females in the population from which the sample is drawn; i.e., we wish to test the null hypothesis that the difference is really zero.

Our tool here is the binomial expansion $(p + q)^N$, which you may recognize from high school algebra. This expansion gives us a distribution, the function of which is exactly the same as the t distribution. But unlike the t, it will give a different distribution for each N *and* for each P. Again, we do not actually know P and cannot safely estimate it from $\hat{p}$. What we do instead of estimating P, this time, is to let our null hypothesis determine P. We are testing the hypothesis that $P = Q = 0.50$, i.e., that there are really the same number of males as females in the population. We are asking, therefore, for the probability of getting $\hat{p}$ as large, or larger, than 0.67 from samples of size 6 drawn from a population in which P is really 0.50. This probability is given from the sampling distribution of $\hat{p}$; we must learn to handle the binomial in order to get this sampling distribution.

The general term of the binomial is

$$P_{(r)} = \binom{N}{r} p^r q^{N-r}$$

$\binom{N}{r}$ means the same thing as $_N C_r$, which may be familiar to you from algebra texts.

where $\binom{N}{r}$ is the binomial coefficient, frequently read "the number of combinations of N things taken r at a time"; this is useful in probability problems of many kinds, most of which we do not take up in this text.

In turn, the symbol for the binomial coefficient is shorthand for

$$\binom{N}{r} \equiv \frac{N!}{r!(N-r)!}$$

We will explain the meaning and function of r later.

where the sign ! is called the factorial sign and means the product of N, $N - 1$, $N - 2$, etc.; for example $6! = (6)(5)(4)(3)(2)(1)$. By convention, $0!$ always means 1. The sign $\equiv$ means "is identical with."

We can find any exact probability, or the exact probability of getting any proportion $\hat{p}$, by using successive terms of the binomial expansion for a given P and N; we will get these successive terms out of the general term of the expansion. We have assumed that P is 0.5, and we know N is 6, so that we need the expansion of $(p + q)^N = (0.5 + 0.5)^6$. Building it up gradually, we ask, first, what are the chances of getting no males at all in a sample of 6 when we assume that there are in fact as many males as females in the population? We will use A for "male" and not-A for "female." We are interested, then, in the probability that, in a sample of 6, we could have obtained

$$\hat{p}_A = \frac{n_A}{N} = \frac{0}{6} = 0 \quad \text{if} \quad P_A = 0.5.$$

Note first that p and q in the expansion are known, since they are the assumed population values; and N, the sample size, is known. The only things we need are the exponents and coefficients of the expansion. P, q, and N remain unchanged as long as we deal with this particular distribution; they change only when we turn to a different sample or a different hypothesis about P. The only thing that changes in the general term, which we are going to use to generate the successive terms of the expansion, is the value of r. We are going to let r be the number of A's we expect, with a given probability, in this distribution. For instance, the term we want first is the one that gives the probability of getting no A's at all ($\hat{p} = 0$). What we want, then, is the term,

$P_{(0)}$ means the probability of drawing a sample with *no* A's from this population. In the formula on page 273 we substitute 6 for N, 0.5 for p, $1 - 0.5 = 0.5$ for q, and 0 for r. Only r, representing the number of A's, changes for the rest of the problem. We will want $P_{(1)}$, the probability of drawing a sample with one A from this population; we let $r = 1$; we will want $P_{(2)}$; let $r = 2$, etc.

$$P_{(0)} = \binom{6}{0} (0.5)^0 (0.5)^{6-0}$$

If you recall how to deal with exponents, you recall that a zero exponent gives 1, whatever p is, so p^0 will drop out of the expression. (More precisely, it becomes 1 but the 1 is not usually written out.) So, spelling out the binomial coefficient, we have the term:

$$P_{(0)} = \frac{6!}{0!(6 - 0)!} (0.5)^6$$

Now 0!, as we have indicated above, is also always equal to 1, so it also drops out and we have left $(6!/6!)(0.5)^6$. The whole coefficient, $(6!/6!)$, drops out in turn, since it also is equal to 1, and we have left $(0.5)^6$. We now say that the probability of getting $\hat{p}_A = 0$ in a sample of 6, if the population is really half A and half not-A, is $(0.5)^6 = 0.0156$. It will always turn out, incidentally, that the first term of the binomial, corresponding to $r = 0$ (i.e., there are no A's), is q^N. We could have stated this simply enough, but you should become familiar with the use of the general term—you can always deduce *any* term from the general term.

Now we ask: What is the probability of getting two A's in samples of size 6, when P is 0.5? The logic is the same, with $r = 2$ and the term we want is

$$P_{(2)} = \binom{6}{2} (0.5)^2 (0.5)^4$$

This will give us

$$P_{(2)} = \frac{\overset{3}{\cancel{(6)}}(5)\,\cancel{(4)}\,\cancel{(3)}\,\cancel{(2)}\,\cancel{(1)}}{\cancel{(4)}\,\cancel{(3)}\,\cancel{(2)}\,\cancel{(1)}\,\cancel{(2)}\,(1)} (0.5)^2 (0.5)^4$$

$$= (3)(5)(0.5)^2(0.5)^4$$

$$= 0.2344$$

Following through, we can find the chances of getting any number of A's—0, 1, 2, 3, 4, 5, 6—in the sample of 6, by using the general term. In the general term, for any given problem P and Q are constant, N is constant, and r is the number of A's we are interested in.

Still going slowly here, we break up the distribution as a whole into its coefficients and its pq parts. The sampling distribution of $\hat{p}$ (which is, of course, n_a/N) will be given by the following series of coefficients:

$$\binom{6}{0}, \binom{6}{1}, \binom{6}{2}, \binom{6}{3}, \binom{6}{4}, \binom{6}{5}, \binom{6}{6} \qquad \begin{array}{l} N \text{ is constant for a particular problem;} \\ r \text{ is the variable.} \end{array}$$

multiplied by the corresponding terms in the following series of pq terms:

$$(0.5)^6, \quad (0.5)(0.5)^5, \quad (0.5)^2(0.5)^4, \quad (0.5)^3(0.5)^3, \quad (0.5)^4(0.5)^4, \quad (0.5)^5(0.5), \quad (0.5)^6$$

Watch the exponents; p and q are fixed for any given problem, and it is the exponent, dependent on r, that changes.

The successive terms give the probability of getting A_i in successive draws from the population specified, where the samples are always of the same size. The fact that the distribution is symmetrical, incidentally, is an accident, due to the fact that P is 0.5. If P is something else the distribution will not be symmetrical. (Try using $P = 0.6$ with the same N.)

Now let us look at the sampling distribution we have derived.

TABLE 10-1.

Sampling Distribution of $\hat{p}$ for Samples of Size 6, from a Population in Which P Is 0.5

n_A	$\hat{p}$	Binomial Term, $P_{(r)}$	Probability of $\hat{p}$
0	0.0000	$\binom{6}{0}(0.5)^0(0.5)^6$	0.0156
1	0.1667	$\binom{6}{1}(0.5)^1(0.5)^5$	0.0938
2	0.3333	$\binom{6}{2}(0.5)^2(0.5)^4$	0.2344
3	0.5000	$\binom{6}{3}(0.5)^3(0.5)^3$	0.3125
4	0.6667	$\binom{6}{4}(0.5)^4(0.5)^2$	0.2344
5	0.8333	$\binom{6}{5}(0.5)^5(0.5)^1$	0.0938
6	1.000	$\binom{6}{6}(0.5)^6(0.5)^0$	0.0156

Source: Adapted from Hagood and Price, 1952, p. 243.

We use this distribution in the same way we used t above. Our hypothesis is that $P = Q = 0.5$, so we use a two-tailed test. We want to know the probability of obtaining, by chance, a value *as far, or farther*, in *either* direction from the mean of the sampling distribution as 0.6667.

In Figure 10-1 we have shaded in the tails of the distribution again, only this time we shade in the *whole* area outside the limits in which we are interested, rather than just the 5% area. We now want to add up the terms which tell us how much of the area is in the shaded part. The terms we add up are the terms for 0, 1, 2 and 4, 5, 6. (We have to take the sum to get the probability of falling *anywhere* in the shaded area.) This gives a probability of 0.6876, so we say that we could easily have fallen as far off as 4/6 if the true value of P were 3/6 in samples of size 6. If we had wanted a one-tailed test we would have added up the terms for 4, 5, 6. Our result would have been 0.3438, indicating that it would still be reasonable to expect a sample of 4 males if N were 6. However, it is hard to justify a one-tailed test for this example. In any case, we do not reject the null hypothesis.

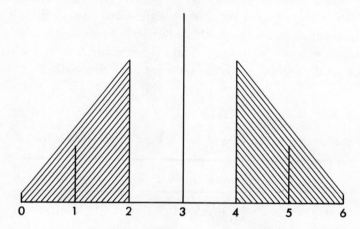

Figure 10-1. Probability that a value as large as or larger than $\hat{p}$ could have been obtained from a population in which $P = 0.5$ when $N = 6$

It should be clear that the computation of exact probabilities can become tedious if the samples are large. It is fortunate that approximations are possible.

THE DIFFERENCE BETWEEN TWO PROPORTIONS WHEN N IS LARGE: THE NORMAL APPROXIMATION TO BINOMIAL PROBABILITIES

When $N\hat{p}$ is greater than 5 we are able to approximate binomial probabilities with the normal distribution. We will illustrate this for the case in which we wish to test hypotheses about proportions from two independent samples; e.g., the hypothesis that the two are actually drawn from a common population. We use a procedure that is very much like the t test, but we make use of the normal distribution to evaluate the probability of obtaining the difference $\hat{p}_1 - \hat{p}_2$ by chance. This is, of course, simply an approximation of the exact treatment.

Computation of exact binomial probabilities of obtaining r A's in samples of size N

Probability of Obtaining $\hat{p}_a$

n_a	$\hat{p}_a$	$P_{(r)}$
0	0	$P_{(0)} = Q^N$
1	$1/N$	$P_{(1)} = \binom{N}{1} PQ^{N-1}$
$\vdots$	$\vdots$	$\vdots$
r	r/N	$P_{(r)} = \binom{N}{r} P^r Q^{N-r}$
$\vdots$	$\vdots$	$\vdots$
N	N/N	$P_{(N)} = P^N$

A	$\bar{A}$	
n_a	$n_{\bar{a}}$	N

$\hat{p}_a = n_a/N$

$\hat{p}_{\bar{a}} = \hat{q}_a = 1 - \hat{p}_a$

$r = n_a \qquad \binom{N}{r} = \dfrac{N!}{r!(N-r)!}$

1. H_0 :

2. a. $P_a =$
   b. $Q_a = 1 - P_a =$
   c. $N =$

3. $P_{(r)} = \binom{N}{r} P_a{}^r Q_a{}^{N-r} =$

4. a. $P_{(i \leq r)} = \sum\limits_{0}^{r} P_{(i)} = P_{(0)} + P_{(1)} + P_{(2)} + \cdots P_{(r)} =$

   b. $P_{(i \geq N-r)} = \sum\limits_{N-r}^{N} P_{(i)} = P_{(N-r)} + P_{(N-r+1)} + P_{(N-r+2)} + \cdots P_{(N)} =$

5. $\sum\limits_{0}^{r} P_{(i)} + \sum\limits_{N-r}^{N} P_{(i)} =$

1. Formulate the null hypothesis. This will determine the parameters of the binomial expansion required to generate the sampling distribution of $\hat{p}_a$. The chief null hypothesis is $P_a = P_{\bar{a}} = \frac{1}{2}$, but any other hypothesis is possible. A one-tailed null hypothesis would be possible if it is predicted *in advance* that, if H_1 (the alternative to the null hypothesis) is accepted, $P_a > P_{\bar{a}}$ or $P_a < P_{\bar{a}}$; i.e., you are predicting the *direction* in which the observations depart from H_0. Enter H_0 on line 1 and the constants of the sampling distribution on line 2.

2. The exact probability of obtaining r A's in a sample of size N is given by the binomial term corresponding to $P_{(r)}$. If the information is of any use, enter on line 3. Ordinarily, however, we are more interested in the next step.

3. The exact probability of obtaining a sample value as extreme, or *more* extreme, if H_0 is true, is given by a *sum* of the binomial terms more extreme than the rth term.

   a. If the null hypothesis is one-tailed, take the sum $\sum_0^r P_{(i)}$ for the left tail or $\sum_{N-r}^N P_{(i)}$* for the right tail, and enter on line 4(a) or (b).

   b. If the null hypothesis is two-tailed, take the sum $\sum_0^r P_{(i)} + \sum_{N-r}^N P_{(i)}$, or, if $P_a = \frac{1}{2}$, simply take $2\sum_0^r P_{(i)}$.

4. If $P < 0.05$, reject H_0.

---

* We assume here that r is some number in the left half (smaller values) of the distribution. Note that in the example in the text we have a case in which r is a number in the *right* half of the distribution (larger values). In this case our procedure is the same, but in the computation design we replace each occurrence of r with $N - r$ and $N - r$ with r. In the text example, for instance, $r = 4$ and we add $P_{(4)} + P_{(5)} + P_{(6)}$ on the right; $N - r = 6 - 4 = 2$ and we add $P_{(0)} + P_{(1)} + P_{(2)}$ on the left.

We assume, again, that the null hypothesis is true. On this assumption we proceed to pool $\hat{p}_1$ and $\hat{p}_2$ to make a common estimate of P and Q; then we use this estimate to give the standard error of the difference, which (in its computation form) is

$$s_{\hat{p}_1-\hat{p}_2} = \sqrt{\hat{p}_0\hat{q}_0(1/N_1 + 1/N_2)}$$

where $s_{\hat{p}_1-\hat{p}_2}$ is the standard error of the difference between proportions
$\hat{p}_0$ is the pooled estimate of P; this is given by $(N_1\hat{p}_1 + N_2\hat{p}_2)/(N_1 + N_2)$ (i.e., add up the original frequencies and divide by the sum of the two sample sizes) and $\hat{q}_0$ is $1 - \hat{p}_0$
N_i is the size of the ith sample

For example, we can use the following data (from McCormick, 1934). A sample is drawn of the adult offspring of Arkansas farm families. It is found that of those still living on farms, 28% (65 out of 236 children) have over 10 years of schooling; of those living in towns at the time of the study (1934), however, 39% (119 out of 306 children) have over 10 years of schooling. Is this a significant difference? If we pool the proportions to estimate P on the assumption that they are really from the same population, we get the following:

$$N_1 = 236 \text{ (children on farms)}, \quad \hat{p}_1 = 0.28$$
$$N_2 = 306 \text{ (children in towns)}, \quad \hat{p}_2 = 0.39$$

then the estimate of P is

$$\frac{65 + 119}{236 + 306} = 0.34$$

and

$$s_{\hat{p}_1-\hat{p}_2} = \sqrt{(0.34)(0.66)\left(\frac{1}{236} + \frac{1}{306}\right)}$$
$$= \sqrt{(0.34)(0.66)(0.0075)}$$
$$= \sqrt{0.00168}$$
$$= 0.041$$

Now we follow a procedure analogous to the t test, but using the normal instead of the t distribution. We compute z, which in this case is

$$z = \frac{\hat{p}_2 - \hat{p}_1}{s_{\hat{p}_1-\hat{p}_2}}$$
$$= \frac{0.39 - 0.28}{0.041}$$
$$= 0.11/0.041$$
$$= 2.68$$

This is significant at the 1% level; in other words, we would expect to obtain z as large or larger than 2.68 less than 1% of the time, if $\hat{p}_1$ and $\hat{p}_2$ were really drawn from the same population. As usual, with the normal distribution the two critical values are $z = 1.96$, which would be significant at the 5% level, and $z = 2.58$, significant at the 1% level. 2.68 exceeds 2.58, so that $P < .01$ in this case.

THE DIFFERENCE BETWEEN TWO PROPORTIONS WHEN N IS LARGE: THE CHI-SQUARE APPROXIMATION TO BINOMIAL PROBABILITIES

There is another way of going about the same task, and because it can be generalized to apply to more complex and difficult questions it is the more important method; this is the *chi-square* test. Chi-square has a number of important uses, but underlying all of them is a common principle: chi-square evaluates the probability of obtaining a set of *observed* frequencies from a population having certain assumed or *theoretical* frequencies. These theoretical frequencies, or expected values, are obtained in a number of ways, depending on the particular case at hand. The cases to which chi-square is applied, however, fall into two general classes: tests of independence (for contingency tables) and goodness-of-fit tests. (In both cases we are dealing with *enumeration* data only.) The problem we happen to be dealing with at the moment is a goodness-of-fit problem; later in this chapter we will take up tests of independence.

In *the goodness-of-fit case:*

1. We have a set of observed frequencies, which we may lay out in the form of a $1 \times s$ table.

2. We have a set of expected frequencies; we will show how they may be obtained in a moment.

3. We wish to test whether the observed frequencies depart significantly from the expected, or, alternatively, whether they depart only by chance.

As usual we test such a hypothesis by comparing some test statistic, in this case χ^2, to a sampling distribution of this statistic, and accept or reject our hypothesis in terms of the proportion of the time we could have obtained a χ^2 as large or larger than we did, simply by chance.

In the goodness-of-fit case we may derive our expected values in a number of ways:

1. We may be comparing our observed frequencies to some theoretical distribution, such as the normal, Poisson, binomial, etc. In this case the theoretical distribution gives the expected values.

2. We may be comparing our observations to a distribution from some known published source such as the Census, previous research, etc. In this case the source determines

the expected values. If p is the proportion falling in class i in the *source*, and N is the size of the sample from which our *observed* values come, then the expected value in class i is Np.

3. We may set the expected values according to some null hypothesis, e.g., that $P_1 = P_2$, or that $P_1 = P_2 = P_3 = P_4$, etc. This is equivalent to saying that the true proportions are 0.50 and 0.50, or 0.25, 0.25, 0.25, and 0.25. We again take Np as our expected values, with p now established by the null hypothesis.

So far as the logic of the procedure is concerned, it makes no difference how the expected values are obtained; they can even be derived by pure guesswork. The test will still measure the degree to which the departure of the observed from the expected values could have occurred by chance.

We will illustrate the calculation of χ^2 from the simple problem of the previous section. Our expected values are obtained in the third of the above ways; we will test the null hypothesis that the two proportions are actually equal, the difference being due entirely to sampling error. The theoretical distribution, therefore, is 0.50 in each cell. To calculate χ^2 you have to use frequencies, incidentally, and cannot use either percentages or proportions without converting them. (This sometimes raises problems if you are calculating χ^2 from published sources which do not report the original frequencies, or N; you must, somehow, recapture the frequencies.) We have the frequencies of the observed cells, of course; and to get the frequencies of the expected cells we use Np which is 0.50×184 in this case. Thus, we have:

	On Farms	In Towns	
Observed	65	119	184
Expected	92	92	184

From each cell we must get a measure of the departure from expectation; we take simply the observed minus the expected, calling it $O - E$. For the first cell this would give $65 - 92 = -27$, and for the second it would give $119 - 92 = 27$. Now we run into a problem that only bothers us when we deal with tables having only two columns like this. The chi-square distribution is a continuous distribution, but the number we reproduce with our calculations is discrete. When a large number of cells enter into the calculation the discrepancy has little effect on the test; when we have only one degree of freedom, however, the effect is more marked. In this case we must correct for continuity. The correction is a very simple one, fortunately, and only requires subtracting 0.5 from the absolute value of the difference between expected and observed. In other words, instead of $O - E$, we have $|O - E| - 0.5$. The final steps in the calculation are (1) to square this, and then (2) divide again by the expected value; finally (3) add up the results for each cell.

So we have:

$$\chi^2 = \sum \frac{(|O - E| - 0.5)^2}{E}$$

$$= \frac{(|65 - 92| - 0.5)^2}{92} + \frac{(|119 - 92| - 0.5)^2}{92}$$

$$= \frac{(-26.5)^2}{92} + \frac{(26.5)^2}{92}$$

$$= 7.63 + 7.63$$

$$= 15.26$$

Now χ^2, like the t distribution, depends on the number of degrees of freedom; and the number of degrees of freedom depends on how many cell entries are free to vary, where now the fixed constant is the *marginal*. In the present case you can see readily that with the marginal (184) fixed, only one cell is free to vary, since the frequency of the other will be found by subtracting the free cell from N. For the goodness-of-fit case in general, d.f. will be simply the number of columns minus one.

Now we go to the table of χ^2. Like the t table it is constructed with d.f. down the side and the probability of obtaining a given χ^2 along the top. Inside the table you find the minimum values of χ^2 which are significant at the level of probability found at the top. If your value is as large, or larger, you have a χ^2 that is significant at the "P level." It is customary to use either a 5% or 1% level in making decisions about hypotheses, and we are showing the 5% and 1% points for the chi-square distribution. The usual table shows more values of P and goes up to 30 d.f. or more. (See Table 4 in the Appendix.)

TABLE 10-2.

Portion of the Table of Chi-square

d.f.	P = 0.05	P = 0.01
1	3.841	6.635
2	5.991	9.210
3	7.815	11.341
4	9.488	13.277
5	11.070	15.086
10	18.307	23.209
15	24.996	30.578
20	31.410	37.566

This entry tells us that if we get a χ^2 as large as, or larger than, 6.635 with only 1 d.f., then we would have drawn a sample departing this much from the expected values only 1% of the time or less.

With a χ^2 of 15.26 and 1 d.f. we have obviously either brought off a tremendously unlikely chance event or else we have to reject the null hypothesis. We ordinarily choose the latter course, which means we accept the alternative to the null hypothesis—*if*, as we have already warned with respect to the *t* test, the hypothesis is also acceptable on other grounds. As in every case in which significance tests are used, if we achieve an acceptable level of significance this means only that we are reasonably confident that our result did not occur by chance. The test makes no positive assertions of and by itself, and particularly will not choose among any number of reasons *why* the difference was obtained. This can be evaluated only from the design of the research itself.

Independence in 2 x 2 Tables

Suppose that now we have a contingency table like this:

TABLE 10-3.

Visiting Relations Across Strata Boundaries, in a Costa Rican Village

		Families Visited		
		Upper Classes	Labor Class	
Families Visiting	Upper Classes	32	16	48
	Labor Class	33	84	117
		65	100	165

Source: Loomis et al., 1953, p. 190.

We are interested in whether there is any association between the status of visitors and those they visit. We might measure this association with Yule's Q, for instance. We are then interested in asking if we could have obtained a Q this large simply by chance—if in fact the true value of Q for the population were 0. Q itself measures the degree of association and its direction; but we need some sort of significance test to give us the probability that Q does not depart from 0 simply by chance. The problem is the same for any other measure of association or correlation; but tests of significance for the product-moment coefficient, for instance, differ from the tests we are going to describe—the following tests are suitable for any data that can be distributed in a contingency table.

The three chief methods of testing the significance of association in contingency tables are:

1. We may compute the exact probability of drawing this sample (this set of cell frequencies) or one having more extreme association; to do this we start with the marginals we are given from the sample and regard them as fixed.

2. We may test the significance of the difference between any two of the proportions in the table which seem of special relevance to a given problem; to do this we follow the procedure already described, using the standard error of the difference between proportions to evaluate the significance of the difference.

3. We may approximate the exact probability of drawing this sample (this set of cell frequencies); again we assume the marginals are fixed, and with the use of χ^2 we test the hypothesis that the cell frequencies do not significantly depart from independence; the expected values, if independence is assumed, are found from the marginals, as we saw when we were discussing delta quantities in Chapter 7. The χ^2 test for independence is based on these delta quantities. (When d.f. = 1, the second and third methods yield identical results.)

If we actually have a specific comparison to make, the second approach can be used. But usually we want a more general test, one that uses the entire set of frequencies. Only in this way, for instance, do we get a test appropriate to Q, λ, etc. Of the remaining two approaches, the involved computation necessary for the calculation of exact probabilities results in its being seldom used, unless the third method is not acceptable. As usual, the acceptability of the third approach turns on the size of N, or more precisely on the size of the smallest expected value. *Where one of the expected values in a table is less than 5 we use an exact test*; otherwise we use χ^2. (For the general $r \times s$, discussed below, we try to collapse columns or cells to get entries above 5.) We will discuss the exact test first.

FISHER'S EXACT TEST

Suppose we are given the following general table:

a	b	$a + b$
c	d	$c + d$

$a + c \quad b + d \quad N$

The test we are going to use is called *Fisher's exact test*. This test requires that you compute the probability of obtaining this set of frequencies *and* every set that represents more *extreme* association, assuming that the marginals are fixed. In other words, we are assuming a population with the marginal distribution given to us and asking the probability of drawing *this* sample, or a sample with more extreme association, simply by chance. The probability of drawing any one set of frequencies is

$$P_{(r)} = \frac{(a+b)!(c+d)!(a+c)!(b+d)!}{N!a!b!c!d!}$$

where the letters come from the schematic table above and ! is the factorial sign.

This in itself looks bad enough,* but you must also add to this the probability of obtaining *each* of the more *extreme* sets of frequencies. To find the more extreme sets we progressively reduce the cell that has the lowest frequency to begin with. Taking away one observation in each step, we continue until we have a zero in this cell. The observation that we take from this cell is given to its adjacent cell in the same row. At the same time, we also reduce its diagonal partner, giving this observation to the diagonal's adjacent cell. For example:

a. Starting with

2	3	5
3	2	5
5	5	10

The *a* and *d* cells are the smallest; there is a slight tendency to negative association. We will take observations from *a* and *d*, give them to *b* and *c*, and increase this tendency to negative association.

b. On move 1 we get

1	4	5
4	1	5
5	5	10

We take 1 away from *a* and give it to *b*; we take 1 from *d* and give it to *c*. If the association were tending in a positive direction we would take from *b* and *c*, giving to *a* and *d*.

c. On move 2 we get

0	5	5
5	0	5
5	5	10

This is our final move, since now *a* and *d* are at 0. If the marginals are not symmetrical we may have 0 in the *a* cell without having 0 in the *d* cell.

On move 2 you have all the observations concentrated in one of the diagonals, which is the most extreme form of negative association possible with this set of marginals fixed. With larger cell frequencies, of course, it would take more moves to get the most extreme form.

* You can see why approximations are preferred if possible; but tables of logarithms of factorials reduce the problem a great deal if you ever have to make practical use of the exact test. In addition, several tables of these probabilities have been published; see Finney, 1948, Latscha, 1953 (an extension of Finney's tables), and Federighi, 1950.

We can identify the probabilities we need, now, from the value of the upper left cell, since this is the one we are reducing.   Then this is what we have:

$$P_{(2)} = \frac{5!5!5!5!}{10!2!2!3!3!} = \frac{25}{63} = 0.3968$$

$$P_{(1)} = \frac{5!5!5!5!}{10!1!1!4!4!} = \frac{25}{252} = 0.0992$$

$$P_{(0)} = \frac{5!5!5!5!}{10!0!0!5!5!} = \frac{1}{252} = 0.0040$$

The probability of getting this sample or a more extreme sample is the sum of these probabilities.

$$P_{(a \leq 2)} = 0.3968 + 0.0992 + 0.0040$$
$$= 0.5000$$

In other words, we would expect association as good or better than we got about half the time simply by chance.   Considering the odds we are now accustomed to using (5 in 100 or 1 in 100), this is not "extreme" enough to reject the hypothesis that the true correlation in the population is 0; and this is in spite of the fact that Yule's Q would give -0.38 for our sample.

The χ^2 approximation to the exact test

Probably the most versatile and useful test of significance a sociologist can learn is the χ^2 test for independence.   The logic of this test is essentially the same as in the exact test, but the computations are much simpler and it can be applied in any case in which the expected values are not too small.   As usual, "too small" means expected values less than 5.   This test, furthermore, is about the only reasonable solution for the general $r \times s$ table for enumeration data.

The test for independence is like the goodness-of-fit test in the sense that again we are evaluating the significance of a departure from a set of theoretical frequencies.   This time our expected values are obtained on the assumption that in fact there is no association in the table.   If you recall the work of Chapter 7, you know that the expected proportion in a cell, if there is no association in a contingency table, is the product of the marginal proportions, $p_i p_j$. In terms of frequencies rather than proportions, the expected value is $n_i n_j / N$.   From this point the calculation of χ^2 is exactly as before.   Reduced to the simplest possible symbolism,

$$\chi^2 = \sum \frac{(O - E)^2}{E} \qquad (O - E) \text{ is the } \delta \text{ quantity of Chapter 7.}$$

where O is the observed cell frequency n_{ij}
E is the expected cell frequency, given by $n_i n_j / N$

We will illustrate the computation first on a 2×2 table, using the data on visiting in a Costa Rican village. The expected values for Table 10-3 are

19	29	48
46	71	117
65	100	165

If status of visitor and status of visited are independent, the visiting patterns are random, which mathematically means they are determined simply by the marginals. The expected value is the product of the marginals divided by N.

$E_{11} = (65)(48)/165 = 19$

$E_{12} = (100)(48)/165 = 29$, etc.

Now we find the delta quantities, which you should remember from Chapter 7. We subtract the expected values from the observed. This gives the following table in delta form:

13	−13
−13	13

As we pointed out in Chapter 7, in a 2×2 (but only in a 2×2) the deltas in the four cells differ only in sign; this makes possible a simple computation formula for the 2×2, which you will find at the bottom of the computation design on page 290.

Now, to find x^2 we square the deltas to get rid of the signs, and then divide by the expected values. Before we do this, however, for the 2×2 we have to make a correction for continuity (because in a 2×2 table we have only 1 d.f.; go back to the goodness-of-fit test if you are uncertain about the correction). x^2 then is:

$$x^2 = \sum \frac{(|O - E| - 0.5)^2}{E}$$

$$= \frac{(12.5)^2}{19} + \frac{(-12.5)^2}{29} + \frac{(-12.5)^2}{46} + \frac{(12.5)^2}{71}$$

$$= 8.22 + 5.39 + 3.40 + 2.20$$

$$= 19.21$$

To determine the probability of obtaining a x^2 this large or larger we must enter the table of x^2; and to do this we need the number of degrees of freedom in the data. Here it is necessary to recall the logic of our procedure. We have assumed the marginals are fixed. If the marginals are fixed, only one cell is free to vary in a 2×2 table, since filling one automatically determines all the others. For example, suppose we put 20 in the "a" cell of the table we are working with.

20	48–20	48
65–20	117–(65–20)	117
65	100	

In a 2×2 table there is only 1 d.f.; if you fill any one cell, and the marginals are fixed, the remaining three are automatically determined. Filling the "a" cell, you can then find the "b" cell by subtracting "a" from the upper right marginal, and so on around the cells.

The idea underlying χ^2 is that the free cells will vary somewhat as the shift toward more extreme tables in Fisher's exact test. We are able to approximate the exact probability because, if the expected value in the cell is over five, the distribution of the freely variable entry will be approximately normal. But obviously this depends only on the cells which *are* free to vary. In a table of any size whatever you can determine the number of degrees of freedom after the fashion of the small table above; after a certain number of entries are given, the remainder are automatically determined. A convenient device exists, however, saving you even the mild mental effort involved in this; in any contingency table having r rows and s columns, the number of degrees of freedom is equal to $(r-1)(s-1)$. For a 2×2 table, then, d.f. is always 1.

Entering the table of χ^2 with a χ^2 of 19.21 and 1 d.f. (see page 282), we obviously have a value of χ^2 that is significant at better than the 1% level. In other words, we are most unlikely to have obtained a set of frequencies as extreme as this, or more extreme, by chance alone.

Application of χ^2 to the General $r \times s$ Table

One reason for the popularity of χ^2, besides the ease with which it is interpreted, is its simple extension to tables of any size. We will illustrate this extension with the following data.

In a sample of divorced mothers, Goode found a significant proportion of the cases were marriages that crossed status lines. He then wanted to test the hypothesis that there were fewer homogamous unions (marriages between males and females of the same status) in the divorced sample than in a comparable sample of married couples; if there were in fact fewer, of course, this would suggest one of the possible sources of strains on marriages that end in divorce. He chose as a comparison group a sample by Centers, from which it was possible to find the proportion homogamous, and also the proportions hypergamous (wife marries up, husband marries down) and hypogamous (wife marries down, husband marries up) in the sample. The frequencies from the two samples are as follows:

TABLE 10-4.

Comparison of Homogamous Unions in Divorced and Married Samples

	Divorced	*Married*	
Homogamous	193	245	438
Hypergamous	92	108	200
Hypogamous	122	96	218
	407	449	856

Source: Adapted from Goode, 1956, p. 101.

We proceed exactly as we did in the 2×2 case; but the following format may be of some use in keeping track of the computations.

1	2	3	4	5
O	E	$O - E$	$(O - E)^2$	$(O - E)^2/E$
193	208.3	-15.3	234.1	1.12
92	95.1	$-\ 3.1$	9.6	.10
122	103.7	18.3	334.9	3.23
245	229.7	15.3	234.1	1.02
108	104.9	3.1	9.6	.09
96	114.3	-18.3	334.9	2.93

The sum of the fifth column is χ^2. You can follow the steps from the computation design on the following page.

$$\chi^2 = 8.49$$
$$\text{d.f.} = (1)(2) = 2$$
$$p < .05$$

This is significant at better than the 5% level; to indicate this we usually write $P < 0.05$ under the value of χ^2. You will frequently see $P < 0.01$, of course, and occasionally the exact probability is cited. Note, finally, that no correction term is required, since there are more than 1 d.f.

As we have warned before, evaluation of this comparison between divorced and married samples does *not* depend only on the test of significance, nor even *primarily* on this test. For instance, the test has no power to distinguish between differences in the two samples produced by confounding errors not controlled in the comparison (by the methods, for example, of Chapter 8), and differences we *intend* to subject to test. In any case the informa-

Computation design for χ^2 for testing significance of association between two attributes; for the general $r \times s$ case and for the special 2×2

n_{11}	n_{12}	n_{13}	$\ldots$	n_{1s}	$n_1.$
n_{21}	n_{22}	n_{23}	$\ldots$	n_{2s}	$n_2.$
n_{31}	n_{32}	n_{33}	$\ldots$	n_{3s}	$n_3.$
$\vdots$	$\vdots$	$\vdots$		$\vdots$	$\vdots$
n_{r1}	n_{r2}	n_{r3}	$\ldots$	n_{rs}	$n_r.$
$n.1$	$n.2$	$n.3$	$\ldots$	$n.s$	N

1	2	3	4	5
O	E	$O - E$	$(O - E)^2$	$(O - E)^2/E$
n_{11}	$n_1.n._1/N$			
n_{12}	$n_1.n._2/N$			
n_{13}	$n_1.n._3/N$			
$\vdots$	$\vdots$			
n_{rs}	$n_r.n._s/N$			

$$\chi^2 = \sum[(O - E)^2/E]$$
$$\text{d.f.} = (r - 1)(s - 1)$$

1. Enter the observed frequencies in column 1 at the right.
2. Calculate the expected values, E, as follows: find the marginal in the row containing the cell ij and the marginal in the column containing the cell, and multiply them together, giving $n_i.n._j$; then divide by N, the total number of observations in the table, giving $n_i.n._j/N$, and enter in column 2.
3. Subtract the expected values from the observed, column 2 from column 1, and enter the result in column 3. (Note that these are the delta quantities discussed in Chapter 7.)
4. Square the differences obtained and enter in column 4.
5. Divide each entry in column 4 by the expected values in column 2 and enter in column 5.
6. Add up column 5. This gives you χ^2.
7. To find the number of degrees of freedom with which you enter the table, take one less than the number of rows times one less than the number of columns, $(r - 1)(s - 1)$.

Special treatment of the 2×2 table

1. For the 2×2 table, or whenever you have only 1 degree of freedom, you must use a correction for continuity; this involves taking 0.5, from the absolute value of the difference between observed and expected, i.e.
$$|n_{ij} - n_i n_j/N| - 0.5.$$
2. You do not need to use the format for the general $r \times s$ above; you can calculate χ^2 directly from the formula at the right, using the letters in the 2×2 at the right for reference to cells. The correction is built into the formula.

a	b	$a + b$
c	d	$c + d$

$a + c \quad b + d \quad N$

$$\chi^2_{1\text{ d.f.}} = \frac{N(|ad - bc| - N/2)^2}{(a + c)(b + d)(a + b)(c + d)}$$

tion provided by the test is principally negative—it shows only that, other things being equal, this difference probably did not occur by chance. It does not follow that our substantive hypothesis is confirmed; we know only that there is *some* reason, either this or some other, to suppose that the two samples are different. This negative function of the test of significance is frequently confused with a positive confirmation of the alternative to the null hypothesis (designated usually H_1); but such positive confirmation in no way follows from the logical structure of the significance test alone. Choice among H_1 and any number of alternatives $H_2, H_3, \ldots H_k$ (other than H_0) depends on the design of the study under consideration, the control of confounding factors (or their randomization) being critical.*

Where We Stand

In Chapter 9 we discussed inference in a general way, our purpose being to illustrate the logic of the procedure. In this chapter, which is essentially a continuation of Chapter 9, we have developed further the techniques appropriate to certain special problems in inference. These problems involve the testing of hypotheses with respect to enumeration data (attributes).

We are now in a position to compute either exact probabilities or approximations to exact probabilities for either of two cases: (1) given frequencies enumerated with respect to a single characteristic, A (either dichotomous or polytomous), from a single sample, we desire to compare the frequencies with some expected or hypothetical distribution; we call this the goodness-of-fit case; or (2) given frequencies enumerated with respect to two characteristics, A and B (either one dichotomous or polytomous), we desire to test the significance of the degree of association between them. A and B may be two characteristics observed in individuals in the same sample, or may arise as frequencies of A in two different samples. Both cases should be considered as independent samples.

We must warn the student, however, that the same techniques cannot be applied without modification to one kind of problem that is usually confused with case (2) above. Although we will not discuss its treatment, we will describe this third case briefly: You are given observations with respect to one characteristic, A, made on the same individuals at two different times, the problem being to assess the change over time in frequencies that are A and not-A; i.e., you have a before-and-after problem, with repeated measurements made on the same individuals. The two sets of measurements are correlated by their very nature and the problem is essentially the one we have referred to on page 248. Procedures appropriate to this problem are described clearly and thoroughly in Siegel, 1956.

* For a general discussion and a penetrating critique of the use of significance tests in sociology, see Selvin, 1957.

Chapter 10

WORKBOOK EXERCISES

1. In the previous chapter you performed a sampling experiment on a binomial (dichotomous attribute) population. This gave you an empirically obtained sampling distribution. In practice, sampling distributions are usually obtained by derivation from a theoretical model. For a dichotomous population the model is the binomial distribution. From this theoretical distribution you may now generate the sampling distribution of a proportion, for samples of size 5, assuming P to be $1/2$.

When you have done this, choose a sample of size 5 at random from your experiments with Population II. Using the sampling distribution derived from the binomial, test the hypothesis that the estimate $\hat{p}$, of the proportion of 1's, differs from P only by chance. Show your null hypothesis; the binomial distribution you generate; and your work in testing the hypothesis.

$n_{(1)}$ $\hat{p}_{(1)}$

2. Clark and Clark (1941) report the following study on racial awareness and racial preferences among Negro children. They asked a sample of 253 Negro children (134 from Arkansas, 119 from Massachusetts) eight questions as part of a "doll" test, including such questions as (1) "Give me the doll that you like to play with"; (2) "Give me the doll that is a nice color"; (3) "Give me the doll that looks like a Negro child"; (4) "Give me the doll that looks like you." (The question numbers are the key to the tables below.) The subjects were to choose from two white and two colored dolls. The marginals for these four questions were as follows:

TABLE 1a.

Racial Awareness and Racial Preferences of 253 Negro Children (1941)

	Question 1	Question 2	Question 3	Question 4
Colored doll chosen	83	96	182	166
White doll chosen	169	151	50	85
No choice	1	6	21	2
	253	253	253	253

Source: Clark and Clark, 1941, p. 553 and 557. Question numbers are altered.

a. For each question test the hypothesis that there is a difference in the choices. How would you formulate a one-tailed test for each question? A two-tailed test? Under what conditions would you choose a one-tailed test? A two-tailed test?

....

....

....

....

....

Using z, test the hypothesis you choose for each question.

Now use the χ^2 goodness of fit test; note that this is automatically a two-tailed test. Exclude the "no-choice" category and work with the reduced N.

Summarize briefly the results of the study so far.

....

....

....

b. Clark and Clark proceed to analyze these responses (and the responses to the other four questions) by introducing the variables, age, region of residence, and skin color of subject.

TABLE 1b.

Awareness and Identification by Age*

	Question 3						Question 4				
	Age						Age				
	3	4	5	6	7		3	4	5	6	7
Colored doll chosen	17	17	28	56	64		11	19	22	49	65
White doll chosen	9	10	14	12	5		19	9	24	23	10

Source: Clark and Clark, 1941, p. 554.

* Excludes those who made no choice.

TABLE 1c.

Racial Preferences by Age*

	Question 1						Question 2				
	Age						Age				
	3	4	5	6	7		3	4	5	6	7
Colored doll chosen	13	7	12	21	30		12	8	9	31	36
White doll chosen	17	22	34	51	45		18	21	36	40	36

Source: Clark and Clark, 1941, p. 558.

* Excludes those who made no choice.

Prepare a brief discussion of the relation of awareness, identification, and preferences to age.   (Read the tables, of course.)   Include as part of your discussion, in the appropriate places, statistical tests of independence (use χ^2 for these tables).   Use the accompanying work sheets for computations.

O	E	$O - E$	$(O - E)^2$	$(O - E)^2/E$

O	E	$O - E$	$(O - E)^2$	$(O - E)^2/E$

O	E	$O - E$	$(O - E)^2$	$(O - E)^2/E$

O	E	$O - E$	$(O - E)^2$	$(O - E)^2/E$

c. We include the following additional tables from the study. The computations are extensive and the instructor may wish to assign parts of the study to separate teams, or divide it in some other way. The same procedure should be followed here as in (b) above. The class as a whole may wish to prepare an over-all summary of the results. (In such a summary discuss particularly the part statistical tests of significance play relative to the study as a whole.)

TABLE 1d.

Awareness and Identification by Region*

	Question 3			Question 4	
	Region			Region	
	North	South		North	South
Colored doll chosen	88	94		73	93
White doll chosen	24	26		46	39

Source: Clark and Clark, 1941, p. 556.

* Excludes those who made no choice.

TABLE 1e.

Racial Preferences by Region*

	Question 1			Question 2	
	Region			Region	
	North	South		North	South
Colored doll chosen	33	50		43	53
White doll chosen	86	83		74	77

Source: Clark and Clark, 1941, p. 559.

* Excludes those who made no choice:

TABLE 1f.

Awareness and Identification by Skin Color*

	Question 3		
	Skin Color		
	Light	*Medium*	*Dark*
Colored doll chosen	32	91	59
White doll chosen	9	27	14

	Question 4		
	Skin Color		
	Light	*Medium*	*Dark*
Colored doll chosen	9	93	64
White doll chosen	37	33	15

Source: Clark and Clark, 1941, p. 555.

* Excludes those who made no choice.

TABLE 1g.

Racial Preferences by Skin Color*

	Question 1		
	Skin Color		
	Light	*Medium*	*Dark*
Colored doll chosen	11	41	31
White doll chosen	35	86	48

	Question 2		
	Skin Color		
	Light	*Medium*	*Dark*
Colored doll chosen	13	56	27
White doll chosen	32	68	51

Source: Clark and Clark, 1941, p. 558.

* Excludes those who made no choice.

O	E	$O - E$	$(O - E)^2$	$(O - E)^2/E$

O	E	$O - E$	$(O - E)^2$	$(O - E)^2/E$

O	E	$O - E$	$(O - E)^2$	$(O - E)^2/E$

O	E	$O - E$	$(O - E)^2$	$(O - E)^2/E$

O	E	$O - E$	$(O - E)^2$	$(O - E)^2/E$

O	E	$O - E$	$(O - E)^2$	$(O - E)^2/E$

O	E	$O - E$	$(O - E)^2$	$(O - E)^2/E$

O	E	$O - E$	$(O - E)^2$	$(O - E)^2/E$

Chapter 11

The Logic of Nonparametric Methods

LET us review the first problem of statistical inference which we considered in Chapter 9. We want to make an inference, say, about the mean, $\bar{X}$. We want, in fact, to make some assertion about how close it is to μ, the mean of the population. Our inference is based on knowledge of the sampling distribution of $\bar{X}$. This knowledge consists in three important theorems: (1) The mean of the distribution of $\bar{X}$ on repeated samplings from the same population will tend toward μ; (2) the standard deviation of the sampling distribution of $\bar{X}$ will be reasonably estimated by $s/\sqrt{N}$; and (3) the distribution of $\bar{X}$ will tend toward a normal distribution in form. Each of these theorems is true only under one or the other of the following two conditions:

1. They *will* be true if the population from which the samples are drawn is known to be normal.

2. They *may* be true if the size of the sample is sufficiently large. If the sample size is sufficiently large, they tend to be true regardless of the form of the population from which the sample is drawn.

Usually we cannot, in sociology, do much with the first assumption. We rarely know anything exact about the form of the population from which we draw samples, and what we do know usually leads us to suspect that the population is not normal. Yet the most powerful and exact statistical inferences are based on this first assumption: that the form of the population is known and that it is normal. This is usually justified on the grounds suggested in the second condition, and it is to this principle that we now turn.

The Central Limit Theorem and Tchebyscheff's Inequality

The *central limit theorem* is the fundamental law of theoretical statistics. By the central limit theorem the sampling distribution of any statistic, with remarkably few exceptions, will approach normality as sample size increases, regardless of the form of the population from which the samples are drawn, provided the population has a finite variance. Populations without finite variance (e.g., a distribution known as Cauchy's distribution) seldom come up in practice. This is, of course, one of the reasons why the normal distribution plays such an important part in modern statistics.

A closely related theorem is the *law of large numbers*. According to this theorem, as N becomes larger and larger the concentration of sample estimates around their own mean, which is in turn an estimate of the population parameter, becomes closer and closer—thus as N increases the statistic becomes closer and closer to the parameter.

We may illustrate this second theorem in terms of *Tchebyscheff's inequality*. Tchebyscheff's inequality is one form of the law of large numbers. It states that the area which is more than k sigmas from the mean under any distribution curve, *whatever its form*, is less than $1/k^2$. There is, for instance, *always* less than $1/2^2$, i.e., one quarter, of the area outside the 2σ range in any distribution (if it has a finite variance—but you are unlikely to run into an exception to this in practice). We may express this in two useful forms:

1. $$P(|x - \mu| > k\sigma) < 1/k^2$$

where k may be any number you care to choose. This says that if k is 3, the *proportion* of the curve (probability) on either side of 3σ from the mean of the population is less than $1/9$. In other words, at least 89% of the area is *inside* the range $\mu \pm 3\sigma$, no matter what the shape of the curve.

2. $$N(|x - \mu| > k\sigma) < N/k^2$$

This form is stated in terms of the *number* of observations rather than the proportion of the area. Suppose that N is 10 and k is 3; then this says that not more than one of the observations will be more than 3σ from the mean. You can try this easily for yourself; try getting some combination of 10 numbers, no two of which are identical, for which more than one of the numbers falls outside 3σ from the mean of the numbers (Deming's suggestion).

Now, if this is so, it follows of course, that it will be true of sampling distributions as well as populations or samples themselves. So for sigma in the above equations—usually in

(1)—put the standard error; e.g., for the sampling distribution of $\bar{X}$ you put $\sigma/\sqrt{N}$ for σ. This gives us a third form of Tchebyscheff's inequality.

3. $$P(|\bar{x} - \mu| > k\sigma/\sqrt{N}) < 1/k^2$$

where $\sigma/\sqrt{N}$ is the standard error of the mean.

In other words, for all possible samples of size N drawn from any universe, whatever its form, the probability is less than $1/k^2$ that the sample means will differ from μ by as much as $k\sigma/\sqrt{N}$.* (Try translating this for yourself, as we have for [1] above.) There are two critical features of this theorem. First, it is obvious that the term $\sigma/\sqrt{N}$ may be made smaller, for a fixed σ, by making N larger; so that increasing the sample size will have the effect of concentrating sample estimates of the mean more closely about μ, the true value of the mean. Second, Tchebyscheff's inequality, like the central limit theorem, makes no assumptions about the distribution of X_i in the population. It will be true regardless of the form of the distribution of X_i, depending only on the size of N.

Distribution-free and Nonparametric Methods

The three important principles on which our knowledge of sampling distributions is based—that $\bar{X}_i$ will tend to approximate μ, that $s_{\bar{x}}$ will estimate $\sigma_{\bar{x}}$, and that the distribution of $\bar{X}_i$ will tend to be normal—are, then, justified by the central limit theorem and the law of large numbers. The remarkable utility of these two theorems, and of the normal distribution as a consequence, is due to the fact that they do not assume any specific form of distribution of X_i in the population from which a sample is drawn.

There are, however, two limitations to the utility of these theorems. First, there is a problem of ambiguity; that is, it is difficult to say in any given case, if the form of the population is unknown, how large N must be in order that the normal distribution will, by the central limit theorem, approximate the sampling distribution of a given statistic. The central limit theorem is based on the idea that N, the sample size, shall approach infinity; in the terminology of calculus, the curves of the sampling distributions approach normality *in the limit*. This means that the *proof* of the theorem (its mathematical derivation as distinct from experimental evidence in its favor) shows that it *must* be true when N is infinitely (i.e. uncountably) large and the curves approach their limiting form. The chief problem, as Cochran (1953) remarks, is that it is difficult to say, in any given case, "how large must N be so that the normal is a good approximation," if the form of the population is unknown. The sampling distribu-

* You will notice that the standard error, or in general the standard deviations, in these inequalities use the population *parameter*, not the *sample* value; consequently for most purposes the inequality has largely theoretical significance. The exceptions are when you do have a fairly good idea of the population variance, say from the Census, or when you are willing to estimate it somehow and use the inequality to decide on the necessary sample size for an investigation.

tions of some statistics approach normality more slowly than others; and the sampling distribution of a given statistic approaches normality more slowly for some populations than for other populations. In other words, without knowing the form of our population, or at least *something* about it, we are not always sure whether or not to depend on the central limit theorem.

Second, many cases occur where it is in fact clear that N is too small to rely on the principles of large sample theory. In these cases, historically, recourse has been had to the t-distribution, which we introduced in Chapter 9. The t-distribution is associated with small samples; as N becomes larger, this distribution approaches a normal distribution in form. Its power depends on the fact that it does not presume a knowledge of $\sigma_{\bar{x}}$, but instead depends directly on $s_{\bar{x}}$ and on the number of degrees of freedom associated with its computation. The derivation of the t-distribution, however, assumes that the distribution of the population is known and is normal. To make the t test of the difference between means, even more restrictive assumptions are required.

Unlike the large sample case, in which statistical theory could apply under very general conditions and without stringent distribution assumptions, for some time no very general procedures were known for the small sample case. In recent years, however, statisticians have developed many new tests which may be applied under similarly general conditions. These tests are called *nonparametric* or *distribution-free* methods; the former because they usually require no assumptions about parameters, the latter because they usually require no, or few, assumptions about population distributions. Tchebyscheff's inequality, for example, is distribution-free, although it is not nonparametric (it uses σ, not s). The two terms, however, are usually used loosely and interchangeably to refer to the methods we will discuss in the remainder of this chapter. They all have the property that they apply under very general conditions and make few assumptions about populations.

An additional property of these methods is that they make less stringent demands than does, for example, the t test, on the metric properties of the variable in which we are interested. The t test demands that the variable under investigation be of type III in the sense defined in Chapter 1—in other words, that like age or income, it have equal intervals and an absolute zero point. The t test, therefore, does not apply to the case of orders or attributes (again as defined in Chapter 1). Nonparametric methods, on the other hand, do. The χ^2 test introduced in Chapter 10, for example, is a nonparametric test, designed to deal with attributes, or ordered polytomies such as those of the latter part of Chapter 7. Other methods, also suited to variables without any strict underlying measure, will be introduced in this chapter.

Thus, while one critical aspect of nonparametric methods is that they do not demand very stringent distribution assumptions, it is equally important that they demand less of the metric properties of sociological, or more generally, of social science variables.

The principal price paid for using these methods is that the inferences they permit are less precise than those set by parametric methods; the chief difficulty, for example, with Tchebyscheff's inequality is the very wide limits that it sets. If you have any information at all about the population you can set better limits. If, for instance, the population is continuous and unimodal, P is $4/9k^2$. Thus, if $k = 2$ we may say that at most $1/k^2 = 1/4 = 25\%$ of the area under a distribution curve is more than $\pm 2\sigma$ from the mean, even if we know nothing at all about the form of distribution. If in addition we know that the distribution is continuous and unimodal we may say that at most $4/[(9)(4)] = 11\%$ of the area is more than $\pm 2\sigma$ from the mean, a reduction of more than 50%. If we know that the distribution is normal, only 5% of the area is more than $\pm 2\sigma$ from the mean, a reduction of more than 50% again. More generally, when you *do* know something about the population form or parameters, you can make more exact statements than those resulting from the use of nonparametric methods (or distribution-free methods). You can always set narrower limits, or use more powerful tests, if you can meet the fairly strong assumptions underlying parametric tests. Nonparametric methods, therefore, are weaker, cruder; they use less information than parametric methods. Their utility is due to their very general application; because they do without certain kinds of information they can be used when the information is not available.

Confidence Intervals for Order Statistics

We first encountered the distribution problem in Chapters 3 and 4. The interpretation of the mean and variance, you will recall, is contingent on the form of the distribution of your observations. The solution we adopted for this problem was to rely only on the order of the observations, ignoring absolute magnitudes and the interval between observations. Diagrammatically, this is what we did:

We took this: X_1 X_2 X_3 $X_4 X_5 X_6 X_7 X_8 X_9 X_{10}$

| 1 | 2 | 3 | 4 | 5 | 6 | 7 | 8 | 9 | 10 |

The absolute value of each observation is read from the scale; this set of observations, for instance, is 1, 3, 3.7, 6.2, . . . 9.1.

And made this:

X_1 X_2 X_3 X_4 X_5 X_6 X_7 X_8 X_9 X_{10}

We have no measurement scale this time. We know what order the observations are in, but we do not know how large an interval there is between observations—this set of observations, then, is only 1st, 2nd, 3rd, 4th, . . . 10th.

In other words, we converted our observations into an ordered set rather than a measured set. Now we are going to do this again to solve the distribution problem in statistical inference. If we suspect that (1) our observations are drawn from a nonnormal population; and if further we suspect that (2) our sample is not large enough to justify application of the central limit theorem, then we convert our information to an order. (Frequently, also, we are given only an order, *without* metric values, to begin with. [See p. 329.]) Our measure of central tendency is the median, $\tilde{X}$. We will now show how to set confidence intervals around a median which make no assumptions about the form of distribution of our population.

Let us assume that the set of numbers in the figure above—in random order—is

$$1, \ 6.7, \ 3.7, \ 3, \ 7.2, \ 6.2, \ 8.1, \ 8.9, \ 9.1, \ 7.8$$

We put them in order and get:

$$1, \ 3, \ 3.7, \ 6.2, \ 6.7, \ 7.2, \ 7.8, \ 8.1, \ 8.9, \ 9.1$$

We find the median, which for 10 observations is the average of the 5th and 6th observations. This gives $[6.7 + 7.2]/2 = 6.95$.

Now we want an interval which we can confidently say contains M, the population median. As before, we mean by this that we desire a procedure for constructing intervals that assures us, over the long run, of being correct most of the time when we assert that M is contained within the interval. In a given case, we ask the probability that an interval between some two observations in our sample contains M; for example, we may desire the probability that an interval from the 2nd to the 9th observation, in a set of ten observations, contains M, i.e., that M is contained within the shaded area below.*

$$X_1 \ \boxed{X_2 \ \ X_3 \ \ X_4 \ \ X_5 \ \ X_6 \ \ X_7 \ \ X_8} \ \ X_9 \ \ X_{10}$$

The virtue of this question is that it can be answered without using the metric values of the observations, once they are in order. We are simply going to evaluate the probability of being located as much as a given *number of observations* to the right or left of M. The 8th observation may be almost exactly the same as $\tilde{X}$ in absolute value, or very different, depending on the shape and scale of the distribution. But we are only asking if M could be as much as three observations away from $\tilde{X}$, regardless of the scale of measurement or shape of the distribution. Just as in the case of the median itself, we are using only location, or position in an order. If we are given information about the metric values of the individual observations, we do not use it until we are through fixing our interval; we may then convert back to the original variate values if they are given.

The procedure we employ is not new to you. We use the computation of exact binomial probabilities and their summation, which you should understand if you have followed the discussion on pages 272–276. To find the probability that M is anywhere in the interval from X_2 to X_9, you sum the probabilities of being as far left or as far right of M as any one observation. To start with, we will assume that no observation is duplicated in value, so

---

* Note that the shaded area includes X_2 but excludes X_9. We actually think of a 0 term as a member of the set, so that *two* terms lie outside the shaded area on *both* sides, i.e., the diagram is really symmetrical. This becomes relevant when summing the required probabilities, which include a term for $P_{(0)}$.

that on every draw from the population we get an observation which is either to the left of, or to the right of, M. Like the coin-tossing model (where you get either a head or a tail), this gives you a probability of $1/2$, for any one draw, that a given observation is on a given side of M. (Remember that by definition the median is in the exact middle.) To get the probability that r of the observations, in N draws, are to the left, say, we have $\binom{N}{r}\left(\frac{1}{2}\right)^N$. The probability that r of them are to the right is the same. What we want, of course, is the probability that M lies between a *given pair* of the observations. We symbolize this probability with the expression $P(X_r < M < X_s)$, which is read, "the probability that M is more than X_r but less than X_s." In the example we are using, we want $P(X_2 < M < X_9)$, the probability that the population median is larger than the value of the second observation but less than the value of the ninth. This probability is

$$P(X_2 < M < X_9) = \sum_{2}^{8} \binom{10}{r}\left(\frac{1}{2}\right)^{10}$$

This is read exactly like the binomial problems in the previous chapter. The subscripts above and below the summation sign, $\sum$, are the crucial pieces of information. They tell you *which* terms of the binomial to include in the summation, or in other words, what values r is to take in $\binom{10}{r}$. These values correspond to the subscripts in the shaded area in the example above, 2, 3, 4, 5, 6, 7, 8. We will show how they are obtained when we come to the general case.

Working the problem out, it is easier to sum the probabilities for 0, 1, 9, and 10 than it is to get them for 2, 3, 4, etc., up to 8 as the formula instructs you to do. Since altogether they add up to 1, we can take

$$P(X_2 < M < X_9) = 1 - \binom{10}{0}\left(\frac{1}{2}\right)^{10} - \binom{10}{1}\left(\frac{1}{2}\right)^{10} - \binom{10}{9}\left(\frac{1}{2}\right)^{10} - \binom{10}{10}\left(\frac{1}{2}\right)^{10}$$

$$= 1 - 1/2^{10} - 10/2^{10} - 10/2^{10} - 1/2^{10}$$

$$= 1 - 22/1024$$

$$= 0.979$$

The expression with which we begin the computation is the same as the sum of the inside probabilities (the ones shaded in the example); it says, take 1 minus the sum of the outside probabilities (i.e., 1 minus the unshaded area) and the inside plus the outside areas add up to 1.

Now we know that 0.979 of the observations fall inside the area between the 2nd and

9th observations. Our level of significance is $1 - 0.979 = 0.021$, or about 2%. We usually agree to regard this as reasonable odds in our favor, so we decide to feel confident that M lies between X_2 and X_9, or in other words between 3 and 8.9.

Since it is obvious that the level of significance is $1 - P$ and this is equivalent to the sum of the terms on the right of the computation expression above, we need not bother taking 1 minus this sum. All we really need is the significance level. On the third line of the computations, for instance, instead of taking $1 - 22/1024$, simply take $22/1024$, which gives the significance level (2%) directly.

Now let us generalize this procedure. First, we allow duplication of values in the set; generalizing the notation, the probability in this case becomes

$$P(X_r < M < X_s) \geq \sum_{r}^{s-1} \binom{N}{r} \left(\frac{1}{2}\right)^N$$

which we read, "the probability that the population median, M, lies between any given two observations, say X_r and X_s, is equal to, *or more than*, ..." The crucial subscripts, which specify the range r is to take in computing the probability, are found above and below the summation sign. In general, these subscripts tell us, we begin the summation of the terms with the rth term, i.e., with the lower limit of the interval we desire to set, and go *up* to, but *not* including, the sth term, i.e., the upper limit of the interval. If we want the probability that M is between the 4th and 9th observations in a set of 12 observations, we sum the probabilities for 4, 5, 6, 7, 8 (or subtract terms 0, 1, 2, 3, 9, 10, 11, 12 from 1 if this is easier). In the general term $\binom{N}{r}$ these are the values we give to r.

This expression covers the case in which no duplication occurs and also the one in which duplication does occur; if there is no duplication then the probability is exactly equal to the expression on the right of $\geq$. If there is duplication, then the probability is greater. This means, of course, that the significance level is even smaller, so that your limits are even safer.

Continuing, we will allow N to increase to a moderate size, one too large to make computations simple. In this case we again approximate the binomial probabilities with the normal distribution. (Note: This does *not* mean that we assume anything at all about the distribution of the *population*; it is on the distribution of the r *index* in the formula that the approximation is based, and this tends to be normal for moderate and large N.) The interval is now given by counting $1.96\sqrt{N}/2$ observations on either side of the median, to get 95% confidence limits. For example, suppose there are 49 observations in a set. The median is the 25th observation. We count out $1.96\sqrt{49}/2 \cong 7$ observations on either side of the 25th observation ($\cong$ means "about" or "approximately"). Our interval, then, is from X_{18} to X_{32}. If N is 100, $\tilde{X}$ is between the 50th and 51st observations and the 95% confidence limits are $\tilde{X} \pm 1.96\sqrt{100}/2$ observations; this gives an interval approximately between the 40th and 60th observations.

We will let K_i designate the position of the ith observation in an array. If the observation X_1 is fourth largest of the observations, for example, we designate it K_4. We assume that an array is already formed, so that we begin with $K_1, K_2, K_3, \ldots K_{N-3}, K_{N-2}, K_{N-1}, K_N$.

1. $P_{(0)} + P_{(N)} = \qquad\qquad$; where $P_{(r)} = \binom{N}{r}\left(\dfrac{1}{2}\right)^N$

2. $P_{(0)} + P_{(1)} + P_{(N-1)} + P_{(N)} =$

3. $P_{(0)} + P_{(1)} + P_{(2)} + P_{(N-2)} + P_{(N-1)} + P_{(N)} =$

4. And so on until $\displaystyle\sum_0^{r-1} P_{(i)} + \sum_s^N P_{(i)} = 0.05$, or 0.01, whichever is desired.

1. We desire an interval $P(X_r < M < X_s) = 0.95$ or 0.99. The problem is to find r and s. It is usual to choose s in such a way that $s = N - r + 1$.

2. For ease of computation we proceed by finding $1 - P$ rather than P itself. (This reduces the number of binomial terms we are required to compute.) Begin with $P_{(0)}$ and $P_{(N)}$ and add, using the formula shown on line 1 at the left to evaluate the probabilities. If this equals or exceeds 5% (1%) the first step is sufficient. If not, enter on line 1.

3. If $1 - P$ is less than 5% (1%), add $P_{(1)}$ and $P_{(N-1)}$ to the sum entered on line 1. If the result equals or exceeds 5% (1%) the first two steps are sufficient. If not, enter on line 2.

4. Continue until the desired level of significance is reached.

5. Convert r and s from order statistics into their original metric values, if the original metric values are known.

6. If $N > 20$, count $z\sqrt{N}/2$ *observations* on either side of $\bar{X}$. For 95% intervals, for instance, use $z = 1.96$, or about 2.

Rank Correlation Methods

For a sociologist, rank correlation methods are among the most useful techniques he can learn. These methods measure the degree and direction of relationship in the bivariate and multivariate cases (i.e., where we have two or more observations made simultaneously of the same individuals), when the observations may be ordered but not measured. They are useful for two reasons: first, our data may be in this form to begin with—that is, we may not know the metric values of the observations, but may be able to order them; second, we may wish to convert known metric values into ordered positions (*ranks*) because this is a useful way of dealing with the distribution assumptions involved in making inferences from the Pearson product-moment correlation coefficient.

This is particularly important because inferences about correlation coefficients are more sensitive to distribution assumptions than inferences about the mean. In order to test the significance of the product moment coefficient several stringent assumptions are required. One of these, for instance, assumes a condition termed homoscedasticity—which means that the variance in a given column of the correlation table is equal to the variance in all the other columns. Second, for the most common test of the significance of r (using its standard error) we need a large N and the population correlation must not be too high; and to interpret the standard error exactly we assume not only normality of each univariate distribution, but also bivariate normality—i.e., a nice bell shape for the whole correlation surface, as it is called—and two univariate normals are not necessarily bivariate normal.

The simplest solution to this problem, particularly if N is less than 40 or so, is to convert the observations into ordered sets. The correlation between two ordered sets is measured in terms of the degree to which the two orders coincide; i.e., if the individual who is in the first position in order I is also first in order II, the individual who is in second position in I is also second in II, etc., the two orders are perfectly correlated. Interpretation of the significance of such a correlation requires no distribution assumptions.

Suppose that we have the following information. For fifteen officials of an organization we have their average number of informal luncheon contacts and the number of persons they name as luncheon partners who also name them, on a sociometric questionnaire.

TABLE 11-1.

Sociometric Status and Average Number of Luncheon Partners (Federal Law Enforcement Agency)

Official	1	2	3	4	5	6	7	8	9	10	11	12	13	14	15
Confirmed choices	5	8	3	5	6	7	5	9	11	6	6	10	6	7	4
Average number of partners	1.86	3.00	1.50	2.40	0.57	1.33	0.20	1.25	3.50	1.33	2.17	2.67	3.17	2.25	0.12

Source: Blau, 1955, p. 124.

Our first step, in converting these values into orders, is to make an array of each distribution. For the sociometric choices, for instance, we would have

11, 10, 9, 8, 7, 7, 6, 6, 6, 6, 5, 5, 5, 4, 3

and for the average number of luncheon partners actually observed we would have

3.50, 3.17, 3.00, 2.67, 2.40, 2.25, 2.17, 1.86, 1.50, 1.33, 1.33, 1.25, 0.57, 0.20, 0.12

Now we replace each individual's *variate value* by its *rank*, or position in the order. For the first order, for instance, official 9 gets a rank of 1, since he is the highest ranking sample member in this order, with 11 confirmed sociometric choices. The value 10, next in the order, is given a rank of 2, so official 12 has a 2, and so on. If two or three individuals have the same value we call this a "tie" and allocate the positions as follows: if two persons are tied we average their ranks and they both get the resulting average rank; if three are tied we again average their ranks and all three get the resulting average rank. At the same time the two, or three, ranks that are averaged are *used up*, so that the person following the tied individuals does *not* get one of the ranks that has been used in finding the average. He gets, instead, the rank that next follows. For instance, officials 6 and 14 are tied with 7 choices each. The 7's fall in the 5th and 6th positions in the order. Both officials get a rank of 5.5. Both positions 5 and 6 are used up and the ranking continues with position 7. Four officials share the value 6, and together they use up positions 7, 8, 9, and 10; they are all given 8.5; the next ranking is position 11, and so on. On the first order, then, we have:

Order I

Official	9	12	8	2	14	6	13	11	10	5	4	1	7	15	3
Rank	1	2	3	4	5.5	5.5	8.5	8.5	8.5	8.5	12	12	12	14	15

Similarly we replace the variate values on the average number of luncheon partners per day by ranks. We may, if we wish, use one of the orders as a prior order; that is, we can use order I to put the officials in order and then match it to their order on the second variable. That would give us,

Orders I and II

Official	9	12	8	2	14	6	13	11	10	5	4	1	7	15	3
Rank on I	1	2	3	4	5.5	5.5	8.5	8.5	8.5	8.5	12	12	12	14	15
Rank on II	1	4	12	3	6	10.5	2	7	10.5	13	5	8	14	15	9

Now we want to measure the correlation of the two orders. There are two coefficients, both easy to work with, which are used for this purpose. We will use Spearman's r_s here. (For Kendall's τ, see Kendall, 1955.) In order to compute Spearman's r_s we take the differences, d, between the two ranks of each individual case and we square them.

d(I–II)	0	−2	−9	1	−0.5	−5	6.5	1.5	−2	−4.5	7	4	−2	−1	6
d^2	0	4	81	1	0.25	25	42.25	2.25	4	20.25	49	16	4	1	36

We sum the squared differences, giving us 286, and enter this into the formula:

$$r_s = 1 - \frac{6\sum d^2}{N^3 - N}$$

$$= 1 - \frac{6(286)}{15^3 - 15}$$

$$= 1 - (1716/3360)$$

$$= 1 - 0.5107$$

$$= 0.49$$

Spearman's r_s, like other correlation coefficients, is designed to range from −1 (perfect unlike order, or negative correlation) to 1 (perfect like order, positive correlation).

The null hypothesis we ordinarily choose to test, when we come to the question of testing the significance of the rank correlation coefficient, is that the true correlation is 0. In other words, we assume that we have obtained a correlation of, say, 0.49, simply by chance, as a result of the accumulation of a series of random errors. We can make either a one-tailed or two-tailed test of this hypothesis. (See Chapter 9.) Our test, as usual, is based on the sampling distribution of r_s. This distribution is reasonably well known for the case when the true correlation is zero—which, of course, is why we chose this particular hypothesis. For other cases, somewhat less is known. Successive samples from a population in which the correlation is zero will give sample coefficients that are symmetrically distributed; and as

TABLE 11-2.

1% and 5% Significance Points for Tests of One-tailed and Two-tailed Hypotheses about Spearman's r_s (For N from 4 to 10)

N	Two-tailed test 1%	5%	One-tailed Test 1%	5%
4	none	none	none	1.000
5	none	1.000	1.000	0.900
6	1.000	0.886	0.943	0.829
7	0.893	0.750	0.893	0.714
8	0.857	0.714	0.833	0.643
9	0.798	0.666	0.783	0.600
10	0.765	0.632	0.746	0.564

Source: Siegel, 1956, p. 284; and Snedecor, 1946, p. 166.

N increases the distribution tends to become normal, regardless of the form of the population distribution. If N is less than 10, the significance of a given sample r_s can be evaluated directly from a table of the significance points of r_s, as in Table 11-2.

To read Table 11-2 you simply look on the line that represents the size of your sample (the number of observations) and the line will tell you how large r_s must be to be significant at the level designated at the head of the column. For instance, the table tells you that there is *no* value of r_s high enough to test a two-tailed hypothesis about ρ_s, the true population value (read "rho-s"), with only 4 observations; if $r_s = 1.000$, a one-tailed test (either $\rho_s \leq 0$ or $\rho_s \geq 0$) can be made at the 5% level. If you have 6 observations, a test of the hypothesis that $\rho_s = 0$ can be made. The value of r_s which you obtain must be 1.000, however, to be significant at the 1% level. If it is 0.886 or higher it is significant at the 5% level; and so on.

If N is greater than 10, as in the case we are using to illustrate the method, we use the t distribution as an approximation to the sampling distribution of r_s. We compute t from the following formula:

$$t = r_s\sqrt{(N-2)/(1-r_s^2)}, \quad \text{d.f.} = N - 2$$

where t is the usual t statistic

N is the number of observations

r_s is the Spearman rank order coefficient

d.f. is the number of degrees of freedom required to enter the table of the t distribution.

For the data we are using, then, we have

$$t = 0.49\sqrt{(15-2)/(1-0.49^2)}, \quad \text{d.f.} = 15 - 2$$
$$= 0.49\sqrt{(13)/(0.7599)}$$
$$= 0.49\sqrt{17.12}$$
$$= 0.49 \times 4.138$$
$$= 2.03$$

In the portion of the t table we have shown on page 242, we do not have significance points for d.f. = 13, but if you refer to Appendix Table 3, the probability of obtaining a t as large as or larger than 2.03 for 13 d.f. is between .05 and .10 for a two-tailed test ($H_0: \rho_s = 0$). Since we are interested only in a significant positive departure from zero ($H_0: \rho_s > 0$), we halve these probabilities, so that $P \leq .05$.

If there are many ties, the formula for r_s given above overestimates the correlation. In this case the somewhat complex formula that follows should be used, as it provides a better estimate of r_s.

$$r_s = 1 - \frac{\sum d^2}{\sqrt{1/6(N_1^3 - N_1) - T}\sqrt{1/6(N_2^3 - N_2) - U}}$$

where $T = \frac{1}{12}\sum(t_{1i}^3 - t_{1i})$; t_{1i} is the number of observations tied at the ith rank. In order

Computation design for Spearman rank correlation coefficient, r_s

K_i again designates an ordered position. K_{x_i} designates the position of the ith observation in an array of the X variable; K_{y_i} designates the position of the *same* observation in the Y array. If, for example, the first observation, O_1, is first in the X array and fourth in the Y array, the first row of the layout form at the right should read $K_{x_1} = 1$, $K_{y_1} = 4$,

$$K_{x_1} - K_{y_1} = -3,$$
$$(K_{x_1} - K_{y_1})^2 = 9$$

(1)	(2)	(3)	(4)	(5)
O_i	K_{x_i}	K_{y_i}	d	d^2
O_1	K_{x_1}	K_{y_1}	$K_{x_1} - K_{y_1}$	$(K_{x_1} - K_{y_1})^2$
O_2	K_{x_2}	K_{y_2}	$K_{x_2} - K_{y_2}$	$(K_{x_2} - K_{y_2})^2$
$\vdots$	$\vdots$	$\vdots$	$\vdots$	$\vdots$
O_N	K_{x_N}	K_{y_N}	$K_{x_N} - K_{y_N}$	$(K_{x_N} - K_{y_N})$

$$\sum (K_{x_i} - K_{y_i})^2 = \sum d^2 =$$

$$r_s = 1 - \frac{6 \sum d^2}{N^2(N-1)} =$$

$$t = r_s \sqrt{\frac{N-2}{1 - r_s^2}} = \qquad , \quad \text{d.f.} = N - 2.$$

1. Form an array of the observations on the X variable. (Start with the "best," smallest, "highest." You may choose the starting point at will, but you must be consistent on both X and Y, or the sign of r_s will be meaningless.) Order the observations on the variable Y in the same manner.

2. Replace the X value of each observation by its rank in the X array and the Y value of each observation by its rank in the Y array. In column 2 at the right enter ranks of the observations on the X variable and in column 3 enter ranks of the observations on the Y variable. Ranks in the same row must be for the *same* observation.

3. Take the difference between ranks and enter in column 4.

4. Square these differences, enter in column 5, and sum column 5.

5. Compute r_s from the formula at the left.

6. For $N > 10$, to test $H_0: \rho_s = 0$, use t, computed from the formula on line 4 with $(N-2)$ d.f. (ρ_s [read "rho sub-s"] is the population parameter corresponding to r_s.)

326 NONPARAMETRIC METHODS

I, for example, there are two observations tied at rank 5.5, three tied at rank 8.5, etc.; so that $T = \frac{1}{12}([2^3 - 2] + [3^3 - 3] + \ldots)$.

U means the same for the second rank order, i.e., $\frac{1}{12}\sum(u_{2i}{}^3 - u_{2i})$

The Difference Between r_s and γ

You may be confused about the difference between r_s and γ (gamma), since both measure the correlation between characteristics that are ordered. The difference is that with rank-correlation methods *each* observation has an exact and known place in the order. You know that official 9 is first on order I, that official 3 is last, etc. With γ you are dealing with *classes* which are ordered, rather than individual observations. The actual numbers are not *positions* in an order, but *frequencies* of membership in ordered classes.

If you can actually obtain the position of each individual in an order, and N is not staggeringly large, then you are better off using rank-correlation methods. They use more information and are consequently more sensitive and efficient than cross-classification of ordered classes for the same problem. When your data come to you originally in the form of a contingency table, however, you have to use γ. Both methods are of great importance to sociologists.

Replacing Variates with Signs Instead of Ranks

Distribution-free tests of significance break down into three broad classes: (1) those that use ranks; (2) those that use signs; and (3) those that use frequencies. The χ^2 method, for instance, happens to be a nonparametric test and uses frequencies; we have discussed the use of ranks, or positions in an order. It remains to discuss the use of signs. There are many nonparametric tests based on signs, but we will use here the one that seems most likely to be useful to sociologists; this is the so-called "median test."

The median test is suited to the same kinds of problem as the t test. We have observations on two groups, measured on the variate X, and we want to test the hypothesis that they are both random samples from a common population. But instead of working with means and variances we work with (a) medians and (b) directions with respect to the median. Our procedure is to pool the observations from the two groups and find the median of the combined distribution. Then we go back to dealing with the two separate groups again. In each group we assign a $+$ to values that are greater than the common median and a $-$ to values that are less than the common median. The results are entered into a 2×2 table, as shown on the following page.

	Sample 1	Sample 2
+	n_{+1}	n_{+2}
−	n_{-1}	n_{-2}

The plus means "above the common median"; the minus means "below the common median."

We then test for significance of association with χ^2.

Take, for instance, the results of the classic Asch experiments on group influences on cognitive judgments (Asch, 1952). In the Asch experiments groups of 7 subjects are asked to compare a standard vertical line and three comparison lines and to choose the comparison line that is the same length as the standard. Six of the subjects are instructed by the experimenter to make incorrect judgments after a few trials of the experiment have been run; one subject is called the "naïve" subject and it is his responses that we analyze. A control group (a group to which we do nothing, but which serves to give a baseline for measuring the effect of the experimental treatment given the other group) is set up in which the six instructed subjects make correct judgments throughout the experiment. The results are shown in Table 11-3.

TABLE 11-3.

Number of Critical Errors in Experimental and Control Groups (Asch Experiment on Cognitive Judgments)

X (*Number of Errors*)	0	1	2	3	4	5	6	7	8	9	10	11	12	*Total*
f_1 (Experimental group)	13	4	5	6	3	4	1	2	5	3	3	1	0	50
f_2 (Control group)	35	1	1	0	0	0	0	0	0	0	0	0	0	37

Source: Asch, 1952, p. 5.

The distributions are obviously such that we cannot use the t test here; the distributions are not normal and the variances are not equal. But despite the striking difference between the experimental and the control groups, we would still like to test the null hypothesis; i.e., that the differences could have been due to some random source of error.

Our first step is to pool both groups and find the median of the entire set of observations. This gives us:

Step 1: Pool the observations to find their median.

X	0	1	2	3	4	5	6	7	8	9	10	11	12	*Total*
f	48	5	6	6	3	4	1	2	5	3	3	1	0	87

$$\tilde{X} = l_{\tilde{x}} + \frac{(N/2 - \text{cum} f)}{f_{\tilde{x}}} i = 0 + (43.5/48) = 0.91$$

Now we go back and assign a $+$ or a $-$ to each observation, but at the same time regrouping them into their original samples. Here we will take the median as falling between the 0 and 1 classes. The 13 observations in the experimental group that are 0 will get a $-$ for being below the median, and the rest get a $+$ for being above. In the control group, 35 observations get a $-$ and the remaining two, a $+$.

Step 2: Give a sign to the observations to make a 2×2 table showing their distribution in the two groups.

	S_1	S_2	
$+$	37	2	39
$-$	13	35	48
	50	37	87

Now we can go ahead and test for independence by χ^2. Using the computation formula for the 2×2 case:

Step 3: Test for independence by χ^2. (See page 290.)

$$\chi^2 = \frac{87(1295 - 26 - \frac{87}{2})^2}{(39)(48)(37)(50)}$$

$$= \frac{87(1225.5)^2}{3,463,200}$$

$$= \frac{130,660,976}{3,463,200}$$

$$= 37.73, \quad P < 0.01$$

A χ^2 of 6.6 would have been significant at the 1% level, so this is highly significant.

The General Utility of Ranks, Signs, and Orders

It is hard to overemphasize the usefulness of order-statistics to the sociologist; but we have commented on this subject piecemeal, throughout the book, and we may have lost sight of the very general nature of their use, the several different reasons why they are becoming so prevalent in sociology. We will therefore try to set down the reasons in this section, giving it the character of a general summary of the use of positional characteristics.

1. First, you may have data that are inherently in the form of a rank order, or ordered classes, and obviously statistics based on orders are the appropriate methods to apply.

Computation design for the median test for two independent samples

You are given

$$S_1: \{X_{1i}\}$$

$$S_2: \{X_{2i}\}$$

where $\{X_{1i}\}$ customarily designates a set of observations, $X_{11}, X_{12}, \ldots$

	S_1	S_2	
$+$	n_{+1}	n_{+2}	n_+
$-$	n_{-1}	n_{-2}	n_-
	N_1	N_2	$N_1 + N_2$

1. $\tilde{X}_{s_1 s_2} =$

2. a. $n_{+1} =$
   b. $n_{-1} = N_1 - n_{+1} =$
   c. $n_{+2} =$
   d. $n_{-2} = N_2 - n_{+2} =$

3. $\chi^2 =$,   d.f. $= 1$

4. $P(\chi_1^2) =$

1. You are testing $H_0: M_1 = M_2$, i.e., that the two samples are drawn from populations having the same median.

2. Combine the observations from S_1 and S_2, the two samples given.

3. Order the combined set of observations.

4. Find the median of the combined set. Enter on line 1, at left.

5. a. Now take the set of observations X_{1i}: if $X_{1i} > \tilde{X}_{s_1 s_2}$, assign a plus sign;
      if $X_{1i} = \tilde{X}_{s_1 s_2}$, assign a plus sign;
      if $X_{1i} < \tilde{X}_{s_1 s_2}$, assign a minus sign.
   b. Now take the set of observations X_{2i}: if $X_{2i} > \tilde{X}_{s_1 s_2}$, assign a plus sign;
      etc., . . .

6. Count the frequency of observations which are both positive and in S_1, positive and in S_2, negative and in S_1, etc., and enter the frequencies in the fourfold table at the right, above.

7. Compute χ^2 for one degree of freedom, using the correction for continuity.

8. If $P\chi_1^2 < 0.05$, reject H_0.

2. You may, in addition, have data that are only quasi-measurable; that is, they are given a number value but you do not care to assume that in fact the observations are exactly measured. The exact significance of the interval between observations, you may suspect, is ambiguous.

3. Finally, you may have observations on a continuous variable, and have perfect faith in the measurability of the characteristic, but the distribution may not be normal in form and N may be small, so that the distribution of a sample statistic may not be presumed to be approximately normal by the central limit theorem.

In the first case, obviously there is no choice so far as the appropriate method of dealing with the data is concerned. In the other two cases you may choose to treat the observations as Type III (variable) characteristics, but it is best to apply methods using order rather than absolute magnitude of observations, even though in doing so you lose information. If N is large, you may wish to convert to an $r \times s$ contingency table with ordered classes; if N is manageable, you lose less information by using individual positions in the order. If you wish to make complex breakdowns, such as the multivariate cross-classifications of Chapter 8, a simple dichotomy at the median of a distribution is frequently the best practice.

Where We Stand

This concludes our discussion of elementary statistics. We began with problems of description, considering successively: (1) univariate measurement data; (2) bivariate measurement data; (3) univariate, bivariate, and multivariate enumeration data; and (4) problems of orders and ordered classifications in connection with these kinds of data. We then focused our interest on: (5) problems of statistical inference, including (a) parametric confidence intervals and tests of significance (in Chapter 9), (b) special problems of tests of significance for enumeration data, and (c) nonparametric confidence intervals and tests of significance (in this chapter). In connection with these topics we have also considered certain problems of univariate and bivariate order statistics.

We cannot do better, as a parting comment, than to paraphrase the preface: the task faced by the student is not that of learning how to compute a statistic, but rather that of learning how to make appropriate use of the statistic. The problem arises nowhere more frequently than with statistical inferences. Many sociologists are addicted to applying very exact methods (such as parametric confidence intervals, t tests) where they are not applicable. They are addicted also to inferring more from the results of a significance test than can be derived from the model underlying the test. Statistical tests seem to reassure many investigators that they have proved some substantive hypothesis if a significant probability is obtained, whereas in fact all they have done is tentatively to reject the possibility that an observed difference might have been due simply to chance, and even this inference is likely to be incorrect five times out of a hundred. The statistical test is only a part—and indeed a relatively small part—of the whole investigation, and careful thought about the substantive problem and the over-all design of the investigation (which may be guided by statistics but is not identical with statistics) is *not* replaced by applying, after the fact, a superficially exact statistical procedure.

Chapter 11

WORKBOOK EXERCISES

1. a. How many observations should be within 3σ of the mean of a set of 9 observations?   (Use Tchebyscheff's inequality.) ....

Within 2σ of the mean of a set of 12 observations? ....

b. Choose a set of 9 observations from Population I and show that the inequality gives the correct result.   Choose a set of 12 observations from Population IV and show the result again.   (*Note:* the inequality is so construed that *not more than* a certain number of observations lie outside the $k\sigma$ limits, but it is possible that *less than* this number lie outside the $k\sigma$ limits.)

....

....

....

2. In 20 samples of size 9 from Population I, how often would $\bar{X}$ exceed μ by more than 1.96σ?   (Use Tchebyscheff's inequality.) ....

....

How often would this occur if sample size were 49? ....

....

How would the answer given by Tchebyscheff's inequality differ if Population IV were used?

....

....

3. a. For each of the sampling distributions in the exercises of Chapter 9 you computed the proportion of the means (proportions, in Population II) within 2 and 3 standard deviations from the mean of the sampling deviation. Do the results conform to Tchebyscheff's inequality?

....

....

....

b. How does the interval set by Tchebyscheff's inequality differ from the interval defined by the theoretical normal distribution for Population III? If you knew that the population was normal which interval would you choose to work with? Why?

....

....

....

....

....

4. Write a Tchebyscheff inequality for the sampling distribution of a proportion. (I.e., put $\hat{p}$ for $\bar{X}$, P for μ, etc.) State briefly, in words, what this inequality says.

....

....

....

5. Draw 10 samples of size 10 from Population IV. Use the samples reading across (e.g., S_1 should read 2, 2, 1, 2, 5, 1, 5, 4, 7, 2). Then (1), compute the median for each sample; (2) set 95% confidence intervals for $S_1, S_2, \ldots S_5$, and 99% confidence intervals for $S_6, S_7, \ldots S_{10}$; and (3), compute M itself and observe how many of the intervals contain M.

$$S_1: \quad P(\qquad \leq M \leq \qquad) \geq 0.95$$

$$S_2: \quad P(\qquad \leq M \leq \qquad) \geq 0.95$$

$$S_3: \quad P(\qquad \leq M \leq \qquad) \geq 0.95$$

$$S_4: \quad P(\qquad \leq M \leq \qquad) \geq 0.95$$

$$S_5: \quad P(\qquad \leq M \leq \qquad) \geq 0.95$$

$$M =$$

.... of these intervals contain M. (This is .... %.)

S_6: $P($ $\leq M \leq$ $) \geq 0.99$

S_7: $P($ $\leq M \leq$ $) \geq 0.99$

S_8: $P($ $\leq M \leq$ $) \geq 0.99$

S_9: $P($ $\leq M \leq$ $) \geq 0.99$

S_{10}: $P($ $\leq M \leq$ $) \geq 0.99$

.... of these intervals contain M. (This is ....%.)

Use the space provided on page 343 for your work.

6. Davis and Havighurst (1946) report that the median age at weaning for 95 bottle-fed, middle-class white children was 10.7 months. Set 95% confidence intervals for this median. (*Note:* to do this you assume that the children are a random, independent sample which in fact they are not, in this study, so do not hastily generalize your result.)

....

....

....

....

7. The data in Table 1a (page 336) come from a study, by Clark (1949), of the relationship between occupational prestige, income, race, and first-admission rates into mental hospitals in Chicago and vicinity, 1922–1934. We show only the data for white-male admissions and income rank of occupation.

a. Compute r_s and test it for significance. Use the space provided on page 344.

b. Table 1b (page 336) shows the rank correlation between rates for specific psychoses and rank of occupational income. Test the significance of each of the coefficients; what does the table suggest? ($N = 19$.) Use the space provided on page 345.

8. In a variation on the Asch experiment (see page 328), Siegel and Fagan used 12 naïve subjects (i.e., subjects who were not instructed how to respond, as distinct from the "stooges" who were) on whom they measured not only conformity (yielding to the majority) but also authoritarianism and striving for social status. (Status striving was indicated by agreement with such statements as, "People shouldn't marry below their social level.") For conformity and status striving they obtained the results shown in Table 2 (page 337).

TABLE 1a.

Age-Adjusted First-Admission Rates by Occupation, White Males Aged 20–69, All Psychoses, Chicago, 1922–1934

(Rank Order of Occupations by Median Income of Occupation in Chicago, 1940)

Occupation	Rate per 100,000	Rank of Median Income
Large owners, higher income professionals	236	1 (highest)
Major salesmen (stock brokers, etc.)	328	5
Small tradesmen	349	8
Office workers	581	11
Police, firemen	597	6
Clergy, teachers, lower-income professionals	624	3
Engineers	829	2
Sub executives	843	7
Semiprofessionals	946	9
Salesmen	1009	13
Artists, musicians	1036	10
Barbers, beauticians	1213	15
Skilled workers	1254	12
Minor government employees	1314	4
Domestic workers	1492	16
Semiskilled and unskilled	1512	14
Peddlers	1747	18
Waiters	2058	17
Errand and office boys	9004	19 (lowest)

Source: Clark, 1949, p. 335, p. 338.

TABLE 1b.

r_s for Rank of Median Occupational Income by Occupational Rates of Selected Psychoses

Psychosis	r_s
Schizophrenia, all types	−0.71
Manic-depressives	−0.02
Senile psychoses	−0.57
Alcoholic psychoses	−0.78
General paralysis	−0.75
Other psychoses	−0.53

Source: Clark, 1949, p. 340.

TABLE 2.

Conformity in an Asch Situation and Strivings for Social Status

Student	Conformity Score (Number of Yields*)	Status Striving Score
A	0	42
B	0	46
C	1	39
D	1	37
E	3	65
F	4	88
G	5	86
H	6	56
I	7	62
J	8	92
K	8	54
L	12	81

Source: Siegel and Fagan, reported in Siegel, 1956, p. 208.
* The higher the number of yields, the higher the conformity; the higher the status-striving score, the higher the striving for status.

Compute r_s and test it for significance.   Use page 346.

9. The following experiment is a much simplified version of a study that is fundamental to the understanding of the operation of group norms.† (See Schachter, 1951, for the original experiment.)   Two hundred college students are assigned to extracurricular clubs on the basis of their expressed interest in these clubs.   One half are assigned to the type of club in which they showed moderate or great interest; this is called the *high-cohesion treatment.* (Cohesion means attachment to, or involvement in, the group.)   One half are assigned to a type of club in which they expressed little or no interest; this is called the *low-cohesion treatment.* One half of the high-cohesion treatment is further treated as follows: a story of a delinquent boy is read to the members and they are asked their opinions as to what should be done with the boy.   The story is so rigged that most subjects respond near the love-sympathy end of a 7-point attitude scale (this is called the *modal* response); at the same time in this half of the cohesive treatment a "stooge" is instructed to deviate markedly from the group in his opinion. One half of the low-cohesion treatment is further treated in exactly the same way.   The remaining groups (one half of the high and one half of the low) also have a "stooge" (the same people, in order to control for effects of personality) but he is instructed to give the *same*

† In the original experiment, mode and deviant were in the same group and a third "stooge," a "slider," who first was deviant and then shifted opinion, was used as well.   We have altered the design and used fictitious numbers to simplify the statistical treatment of the data.   The original also tests hypotheses about the relevance of the issue under discussion for pressures to communicate to the deviant and rejection of the deviant.

opinion as the modal response in the group. The hypotheses the experiment is designed to test are:

H_1: Rejection of deviants in high-cohesion groups is greater than rejection of the mode in high-cohesion groups.

H_2: Rejection of deviants in low-cohesion groups is greater than rejection of the mode in low-cohesion groups.

H_3: Rejection of deviants in high-cohesion groups is greater than rejection of deviants in low-cohesion groups.

a. First test the validity of the means of inducing differences in cohesion. The cohesion of the groups, once formed, is measured by responses to sociometric items which ask, for instance, "Do you want to remain a member of this group?" Did we really produce differences in cohesion? (Use χ^2.) Use the space below and page 347.

TABLE 3a.

Validity of Experimental Treatment for Cohesion

		Want to Remain Member		
		Yes	No	
Treatment given	High	98	2	100
	Low	65	35	100
		163	37	200

Source: Compare Schachter, 1951, p. 228.

b. Below we give the sociometric rankings of the deviant for each experimental treatment. These rankings (averages for each group) measure the rejection of the deviant and mode by the group at the end of the experimental session. (The higher the rank the greater the rejection.) The numbers are fictitious, but are of a similar order of magnitude as the original experimental results. Using the median test, test each of the three hypotheses of the experiment; show the formulation of your null hypothesis as well as the actual test of significance. Use the space provided on page 348.

TABLE 3b.

Average Sociometric Rankings of Deviant and Mode in High and Low Cohesive Groups
(Actual numbers fictitious)

Experimental Treatment	Ranking of "Stooge"*
High-cohesion with deviant	5.2, 6.1, 6.4, 7.0, 7.2, 7.3, 4.8, 8.4, 7.0, 6.4
High-cohesion with mode	4.5, 4.2, 3.0, 5.5, 4.0, 4.8, 5.2, 5.1, 4.5, 4.1
Low-cohesion with deviant	5.2, 6.0, 5.5, 5.0, 4.5, 6.3, 5.2, 4.8, 4.3, 5.7
Low-cohesion with mode	4.7, 4.1, 3.4, 5.3, 4.2, 4.6, 5.0, 5.8, 4.4, 4.2

Source: Compare Schachter, 1951, p. 235.

* There are 10 groups for each treatment; the entries are averages of the number of choices in each group.

10. Moving now into a field of study of a "natural" situation, the following investigation of two housing projects—for families of MIT students—also concerns the operation of group norms. (See Festinger, Schachter, and Back, 1950.) In this case, however, a somewhat different problem is encountered.

The following results are obtained during the study. With respect to attitudes toward and activity in a tenant's council: in one project ("Westgate West") there is an over-all pattern of homogeneity in opinion and activity—generally a favorable and active pattern; in the other project ("Westgate") there is homogeneity *within* each of the courts of the project, but marked heterogeneity of pattern *between* courts in the project taken as a whole. (In Westgate West tenants live in 17 barracks-like buildings; in Westgate they live in 9 courts, U-shaped in form.)

This raises two kinds of problems for the investigator: (1) To determine how the Westgate pattern arises; and (2) to discover for Westgate West whether uniformity of opinion among the N individuals implies that they are a meaningful group enforcing a common standard, or 17 meaningful groups having the same standard, or simply an accidental aggregate of individuals all of whom happen to have arrived at a similar opinion in individual, *independent* reactions to the same situation—i.e., no group norm is implied at all in this case.

One kind of evidence bearing on this problem concerns the correlation of individual interests and individual activity patterns in the two projects. In Westgate West a major determinant of activity in the council was how long the tenant expected to stay in the project—the longer he expected to stay, the more active he was. Most of the Westgate West tenants, however, were newcomers so that they tended to have similar interests in the organization. In Westgate, on the other hand, individual interests of this sort did *not* correlate with activity in the council. Here the major determinant of a given individual's activity in the council was whether or not *others in his group* were active.

Another kind of evidence concerns the treatment of those who deviate and the relation of deviation to cohesion. In general, those who deviate from the court norm in Westgate tend to be rejected on sociometric questions by others in the court, whereas those who deviate from the majority pattern in Westgate West are not similarly rejected.

The student is to finish this brief summary of the study by analyzing the remaining findings in Table 4, and then briefly discussing them.

TABLE 4.

Relationship of Deviance and Cohesion in Westgate and Westgate West

Westgate West				*Westgate*		
Building Number	*% Deviant*	*Cohesion Scores*		*Court*	*% Deviant*	*Cohesion Scores*
201–10	11	0.540		Tolman	23	0.529
211–20	10	0.500		Howe	23	0.500
221–30	10	0.590		Rotch	25	0.523
231–40	20	0.640		Richards	29	0.433
241–50	20	0.610		Main	29	0.527
251–60	20	0.630		Freeman	38	0.419
261–70	25	0.460		Williams	46	0.447
271–80	30	0.380		Miller	46	0.485
281–90	20	0.680		Carson	54	0.403
291–300	50	0.500				
301–10	50	0.640				
311–20	20	0.530				
321–30	33	0.520				
331–40	70	0.350				
341–50	30	0.500				
351–60	30	0.760				
361–70	40	0.560				

Source: Festinger, Schachter, and Back, 1950, p. 213, p. 214.

NAME..

SECTION..DATE...

a. Using the median test, show that the two projects do *not* differ significantly in the proportion of deviants per unit (court or building). When the 2×2 necessary for the test is set up, show that the correct test of significance is Fisher's exact test, not χ^2. Use χ^2, however, in making the actual test. Use page 349.

b. Using the median test, show that the projects *also* do not differ significantly in the cohesion of the units (court or building). Show whether one should use χ^2 or Fisher's exact test, but use χ^2. Use page 350.

c. Using rank correlation methods, show now that cohesion *is* related to conformity (measured by the proportion of deviants) in Westgate, but that the two are *not* related in Westgate West. Compute r_s for each project and test the obtained r_s for significance. Show the form of the null hypothesis in performing the test. Use page 351.

d. Now, finally, complete the investigator's report. (*Note:* the implication is that if a group norm exists, then the higher the cohesion of the group the greater the conformity to the group norm.) Discuss both the statistical treatment of the data and their substantive meaning. Use this page and page 342.

Problem 5

Problem 7a

Problem 7b

Problem 8

Problem 9a

Problem 9b

Problem 10a

Problem 10b

Problem 10c

Bibliography and References

Anderson, R. L., and Bancroft, T. A., 1952. *Statistical Theory in Research.* New York: McGraw-Hill.

Asch, S. E., 1952. "Effects of Group Pressures upon the Modification and Distortion of Judgments." In Swanson, G. E., Newcomb, T. M., and Hartley, E. L., eds., 1952. *Readings in Social Psychology.* New York: Henry Holt.

Berelson, B. R., Lazarsfeld, P. F., and McPhee, W. N., 1954. *Voting.* Chicago: The University of Chicago Press.

Blau, P. M., 1955. *Dynamics of Bureaucracy.* Chicago: The University of Chicago Press.

Centers, R., 1949. "Marital Selection and Occupational Strata." *Am. Jour. Soc.,* 54: 530–535.

Clark, K. B., and Clark, M. P., 1941. "Racial Identification and Preference in Negro Children." In Swanson, G. E., Newcomb, T. M., and Hartley, E. L., eds., 1952. *Readings in Social Psychology.* New York: Henry Holt.

Clark, R. E., 1949. "Psychoses, Income, and Occupational Prestige." In Bendix, R., and Lipset, S. M., eds., 1953. *Class, Status, and Power.* Glencoe: Free Press.

Clarke, A. C., 1952. "An Examination of the Operation of Residential Propinquity as a Factor in Mate Selection." *Am. Soc. Rev.,* 17:17–22.

Cochran, W. G., 1953. *Sampling Techniques.* New York: John Wiley.

Davis, A., and Havighurst, R., 1946. "Social Class and Color Differences in Child-Rearing." *Am. Soc. Rev.,* 11:698–710.

Deming, W. E., 1950. *Some Theory of Sampling.* New York: John Wiley.

Edwards, A. L., 1950. *Experimental Design in Psychological Research.* New York: Rinehart.

Edwards, A. L., 1955. *Statistical Methods for the Behavioral Sciences.* New York: Rinehart.

Faris, R. E. L., and Dunham, H. W., 1939. *Mental Disorders in Urban Areas.* Chicago: University of Chicago Press.

Federighi, E., 1950. "The Use of Chi-Square in Small Samples." *Am. Soc. Rev.*, 15: 777–779.

Festinger, L., Schachter, S., and Back, K., 1950. "The Operation of Group Standards." In Cartwright, D., and Zander, A., eds., 1953. *Group Dynamics.* Evanston: Row Peterson.

Finney, D. J., 1948. "The Fisher-Yates Test of Significance in 2 × 2 Contingency Tables." *Biometrika* 35, New Statistical Table No. 7.

Fisher, R. A., 1954. *Statistical Methods for Research Workers*, 12th ed. Edinburgh: Oliver and Boyd.

French, R. L., 1951. "Sociometric Status and Individual Adjustment among Naval Recruits." In Cartwright, D., and Zander, A., eds., 1953. *Group Dynamics.* Evanston: Row Peterson.

Freund, J. E., 1952. *Modern Elementary Statistics.* New York: Prentice-Hall.

Gist, N. P., and Halbert, L. A., 1956. *Urban Society*, 4th ed. New York: Crowell.

Goldhamer, H., and Marshall, A. W., 1953. *Psychosis and Civilization.* Glencoe: Free Press.

Goode, W. J., 1956. *After Divorce.* Glencoe: Free Press.

Goodman, L. A., and Kruskal, W. H., 1954. "Measures of Association for Cross-Classifications." *Jour. Am. Stat. Assn.*, 49:732–764.

Gorden, R. L., 1952. "Interaction between Attitude and the Definition of the Situation in the Expression of Opinion." *Am. Soc. Rev.*, 17:50–58.

Hagood, M. J., and Price, D. O., 1952. *Statistics for Sociologists*, 2nd ed. New York: Henry Holt.

Hatt, P. and Reiss, A., eds., 1951. *Urban Sociology.* Glencoe: Free Press.

Hawley, A. H., 1956. *The Changing Shape of Metropolitan America.* Glencoe: Free Press.

Henry, A. F., and Short, J. F., 1954. *Suicide and Homicide.* Glencoe: Free Press.

Horowitz, E. L., 1936. "Development of Racial Prejudice." In O'Brien, R. W., Schrag, C. C., and Martin, W. T., eds., 1951. *Readings in General Sociology.* Boston: Houghton Mifflin.

Hyman, H. H., 1955. *Survey Design and Analysis.* Glencoe: Free Press.

Hyman, H. H., and Sheatsley, P. B., 1947. "Some Reasons Why Information Campaigns Fail." In Swanson, G. E., Newcomb, T. M., and Hartley, E. L., eds., 1952. *Readings in Social Psychology.* New York: Henry Holt.

Kaplan, B., 1954. "A Study of Rorschach Responses in Four Cultures." *Papers of the Peabody Museum*, Vol. 42, No. 2, Cambridge, Mass.

Katz, D., and Hyman, H. H., 1947. "Industrial Morale and Public Opinion Methods." *Int. Jour. of Opinion and Attitude Research*, 1:13–29.

Katz, E., and Lazarsfeld, P. F., 1955. *Personal Influence*. Glencoe: Free Press.

Kaufman, H., 1944. "Prestige Classes in a New York Rural Community." In Bendix, R., and Lipset, S. M., eds., 1953. *Class, Status, and Power*. Glencoe: Free Press.

Kendall, M. G., 1955. *Rank Correlation Methods*, 2nd ed. London: Griffin.

Kish, L., 1953. "Selection of the Sample." In Festinger, L., and Katz, D., eds., *Research Methods in the Behavioral Sciences*. New York: Dryden Press.

Lander, B., 1954. *Towards an Understanding of Juvenile Delinquency*. New York: Columbia University Press.

Latscha, R., 1953. "Tests of Significance in a 2×2 Contingency Table: Extension of Finney's Table." *Biometrika* 40, New Statistical Table No. 17.

Lazarsfeld, P. F., and Kendall, P. L., 1950. "Problems of Survey Analysis." In Merton, R. K., and Lazarsfeld, P. F., eds., 1950. *Continuities in Social Research: Studies in the Scope and Method of "The American Soldier."* Glencoe: Free Press.

Lemert, E., 1951. *Social Pathology*. New York: McGraw-Hill.

Lipset, S. M., 1955. "Social Mobility and Urbanization." *Rural Soc.*, 20: 220–228.

Loomis, C. P., *et al*, 1953. "Social Status and Communication in Costa Rican Rural Communities." In Leonard, O. E., and Loomis, C. P., 1953. *Latin American Social Organization and Institutions*. E. Lansing: Michigan State College Press.

McCormick, T. C., 1934. "Rural Social Organization in South Central Arkansas. *Arkansas Agr. Exp. Station Bull. No. 313*. In Pearson, F. A., and Bennett, K. R., 1942. *Statistical Methods Applied to Agricultural Economics*. New York: John Wiley.

Marsh, C. P., and Coleman, A. L., 1956. "Group Influences and Agricultural Innovations: Some Tentative Findings and Hypotheses." *Am. Jour. Soc.*, 61: 588–594.

Menzel, H., 1950. "Comment on Robinson's 'Ecological Correlations and the Behavior of Individuals.'" *Am. Soc. Rev.*, 15:674.

Miller, D. C., 1945. "A Research Note on Mass Communication." *Am. Soc. Rev.*, 10: 691–694.

Mood, A. McF., 1950. *Introduction to the Theory of Statistics*. New York: McGraw-Hill.

National Resources Committee, 1939. "The Structure of Controls." In Bendix, R., and Lipset, S. M., eds., 1953. *Class, Status, and Power*. Glencoe: Free Press. (Original title: *The Structure of the American Economy*, Washington: Govt. Prtg. Office.)

Parten, M. B., 1950. *Surveys, Polls, and Samples*. New York: Harper.

Porterfield, A. L., and Talbert, R. H., 1954. "Crime in Southern Cities." In Vance, R. B., and Demerath, N. J., eds., 1954. *The Urban South*. Chapel Hill: University of North Carolina Press.

Robinson, W. S., 1950. "Ecological Correlations and the Behavior of Individuals." *Am. Soc. Rev.*, 15: 351–357.

Rogoff, N., 1953. *Occupational Mobility*. Glencoe: Free Press.

Rossi, P. H., 1955. *Why Families Move*. Glencoe: Free Press.

Schachter, S., 1951. "Deviation, Rejection, and Communication." In Cartwright, D., and Zander, A., 1953. *Group Dynamics*. Evanston: Row Peterson.

Schroeder, W. W., and Beegle, J. A., 1953. "Suicide: An Instance of High Rural Rates." *Rural Soc.*, 18: 45–52.

Selvin, H., 1957. "A Critique of Tests of Significance in Survey Research." *Am. Soc. Rev.*, 22: 519–527.

Shaw, C. L., and McKay, H. D., 1931. *Social Factors in Juvenile Delinquency*. Washington: Govt. Prtg. Office.

Shewhart, W. A., 1939. *Statistical Method from the Viewpoint of Quality Control*. Washington: Graduate School of the Dept. of Agriculture.

Siegel, S., 1956. *Nonparametric Statistics for the Behavioral Sciences*. New York: McGraw-Hill.

Siegel, S., and Fagan, J., n.d. "The Asch Effect under Conditions of Risk." In Siegel, 1956. pp. 204–212.

Snedecor, G. W., 1946. *Statistical Methods*, 4th ed. Ames: Iowa State College Press.

Sogge, T. M., 1954. "Industrial Classes in the United States, 1870–1950." *Jour. Am. Stat. Assn.*, 49: 251–253.

Stouffer, S. A., 1955. *Communism, Conformity, and Civil Liberties*. New York: Doubleday.

Stouffer, S. A., *et al*, 1950. *Measurement and Prediction*. Princeton: Princeton University Press.

Thibaut, J., 1950. "An Experimental Study of the Cohesiveness of Underprivileged Groups." In Cartwright, D., and Zander, A., eds., 1953. *Group Dynamics*. Evanston: Row Peterson.

U.S. Bureau of the Census. *Statistical Abstract of the United States*: *1951*, *1952*, and *1955*. Washington: Govt. Prtg. Office.

U.S. Treasury Dept., Internal Revenue Service, 1954. *Statistics of Income, 1950*. Washington: Govt. Prtg. Office.

Vance, R. B., and Demerath, N.J., 1955. *The Urban South*. Chapel Hill: University of North Carolina Press.

The World Almanac and Book of Facts for 1956, 1956. New York: N.Y. Telegraph and Sun.

Yule, G. U., and Kendall, M. G., 1950. *An Introduction to the Theory of Statistics*, 14th ed. New York: Hafner.

Zeisel, H., 1957. *Say It with Figures*, 4th ed. New York: Harper.

Zetterberg, H. L., 1952. "Cohesiveness as a Unitary Concept." Unpublished Ms.

Appendix

Table 1.   Table of Squares and Square Roots

Table 2.   Probabilities That Given Values of z Will Be Exceeded

Table 3.   Table of Critical Values of *t*

Table 4.   Table of Critical Values of Chi Square

Table I. Table of Squares and Square Roots

Number	Square	Square root	Number	Square	Square root	Number	Square	Square root
1	1	1.0000	41	16 81	6.4031	81	65 61	9.0000
2	4	1.4142	42	17 64	6.4807	82	67 24	9.0554
3	9	1.7321	43	18 49	6.5574	83	68 89	9.1104
4	16	2.0000	44	19 36	6.6332	84	70 56	9.1652
5	25	2.2361	45	20 25	6.7082	85	72 25	9.2195
6	36	2.4495	46	21 16	6.7823	86	73 96	9.2736
7	49	2.6458	47	22 09	6.8557	87	75 69	9.3274
8	64	2.8284	48	23 04	6.9282	88	77 44	9.3808
9	81	3.0000	49	24 01	7.0000	89	79 21	9.4340
10	1 00	3.1623	50	25 00	7.0711	90	81 00	9.4868
11	1 21	3.3166	51	26 01	7.1414	91	82 81	9.5394
12	1 44	3.4641	52	27 04	7.2111	92	84 64	9.5917
13	1 69	3.6056	53	28 09	7.2801	93	86 49	9.6437
14	1 96	3.7417	54	29 16	7.3485	94	88 36	9.6954
15	2 25	3.8730	55	30 25	7.4162	95	90 25	9.7468
16	2 56	4.0000	56	31 36	7.4833	96	92 16	9.7980
17	2 89	4.1231	57	32 49	7.5498	97	94 09	9.8489
18	3 24	4.2426	58	33 64	7.6158	98	96 04	9.8995
19	3 61	4.3589	59	34 81	7.6811	99	98 01	9.9499
20	4 00	4.4721	60	36 00	7.7460	100	1 00 00	10.0000
21	4 41	4.5826	61	37 21	7.8102	101	1 02 01	10.0499
22	4 84	4.6904	62	38 44	7.8740	102	1 04 04	10.0995
23	5 29	4.7958	63	39 69	7.9373	103	1 06 09	10.1489
24	5 76	4.8990	64	40 96	8.0000	104	1 08 16	10.1980
25	6 25	5.0000	65	42 25	8.0623	105	1 10 25	10.2470
26	6 76	5.0990	66	43 56	8.1240	106	1 12 36	10.2956
27	7 29	5.1962	67	44 89	8.1854	107	1 14 49	10.3441
28	7 84	5.2915	68	46 24	8.2462	108	1 16 64	10.3923
29	8 41	5.3852	69	47 61	8.3066	109	1 18 81	10.4403
30	9 00	5.4772	70	49 00	8.3666	110	1 21 00	10.4881
31	9 61	5.5678	71	50 41	8.4261	111	1 23 21	10.5357
32	10 24	5.6569	72	51 84	8.4853	112	1 25 44	10.5830
33	10 89	5.7446	73	53 29	8.5440	113	1 27 69	10.6301
34	11 56	5.8310	74	54 76	8.6023	114	1 29 96	10.6771
35	12 25	5.9161	75	56 25	8.6603	115	1 32 25	10.7238
36	12 96	6.0000	76	57 76	8.7178	116	1 34 56	10.7703
37	13 69	6.0828	77	59 29	8.7750	117	1 36 89	10.8167
38	14 44	6.1644	78	60 84	8.8318	118	1 39 24	10.8628
39	15 21	6.2450	79	62 41	8.8882	119	1 41 61	10.9087
40	16 00	6.3246	80	64 00	8.9443	120	1 44 00	10.9545

From Siegel, *Nonparametric Statistics for the Behavioral Sciences.* Abridged by permission from Sorenson, *Statistics for Students of Psychology and Education* (New York, McGraw-Hill Book Co., 1936).

Table 1. Table of Squares and Square Roots—(*Continued*)

Number	Square	Square root	Number	Square	Square root	Number	Square	Square root
121	1 46 41	11.0000	171	2 92 41	13.0767	221	4 88 41	14.8661
122	1 48 84	11.0454	172	2 95 84	13.1149	222	4 92 84	14.8997
123	1 51 29	11.0905	173	2 99 29	13.1529	223	4 97 29	14.9332
124	1 53 76	11.1355	174	3 02 76	13.1909	224	5 01 76	14.9666
125	1 56 25	11.1803	175	3 06 25	13.2288	225	5 06 25	15.0000
126	1 58 76	11.2250	176	3 09 76	13.2665	226	5 10 76	15.0333
127	1 61 29	11.2694	177	3 13 29	13.3041	227	5 15 29	15.0665
128	1 63 84	11.3137	178	3 16 84	13.3417	228	5 19 84	15.0997
129	1 66 41	11.3578	179	3 20 41	13.3791	229	5 24 41	15.1327
130	1 69 00	11.4018	180	3 24 00	13.4164	230	5 29 00	15.1658
131	1 71 61	11.4455	181	3 27 61	13.4536	231	5 33 61	15.1987
132	1 74 24	11.4891	182	3 31 24	13.4907	232	5 38 24	15.2315
133	1 76 89	11.5326	183	3 34 89	13.5277	233	5 42 89	15.2643
134	1 79 56	11.5758	184	3 38 56	13.5647	234	5 47 56	15.2971
135	1 82 25	11.6190	185	3 42 25	13.6015	235	5 52 25	15.3297
136	1 84 96	11.6619	186	3 45 96	13.6382	236	5 56 96	15.3623
137	1 87 69	11.7047	187	3 49 69	13.6748	237	5 61 69	15.3948
138	1 90 44	11.7473	188	3 53 44	13.7113	238	5 66 44	15.4272
139	1 93 21	11.7898	189	3 57 21	13.7477	239	5 71 21	15.4596
140	1 96 00	11.8322	190	3 61 00	13.7840	240	5 76 00	15.4919
141	1 98 81	11.8743	191	3 64 81	13.8203	241	5 80 81	15.5242
142	2 01 64	11.9164	192	3 68 64	13.8564	242	5 85 64	15.5563
143	2 04 49	11.9583	193	3 72 49	13.8924	243	5 90 49	15.5885
144	2 07 36	12.0000	194	3 76 36	13.9284	244	5 95 36	15.6205
145	2 10 25	12.0416	195	3 80 25	13.9642	245	6 00 25	15.6525
146	2 13 16	12.0830	196	3 84 16	14.0000	246	6 05 16	15.6844
147	2 16 09	12.1244	197	3 88 09	14.0357	247	6 10 09	15.7162
148	2 19 04	12.1655	198	3 92 04	14.0712	248	6 15 04	15.7480
149	2 22 01	12.2066	199	3 96 01	14.1067	249	6 20 01	15.7797
150	2 25 00	12.2474	200	4 00 00	14.1421	250	6 25 00	15.8114
151	2 28 01	12.2882	201	4 04 01	14.1774	251	6 30 01	15.8430
152	2 31 04	12.3288	202	4 08 04	14.2127	252	6 35 04	15.8745
153	2 34 09	12.3693	203	4 12 09	14.2478	253	6 40 09	15.9060
154	2 37 16	12.4097	204	4 16 16	14.2829	254	6 45 16	15.9374
155	2 40 25	12.4499	205	4 20 25	14.3178	255	6 50 25	15.9687
156	2 43 36	12.4900	206	4 24 36	14.3527	256	6 55 36	16.0000
157	2 46 49	12.5300	207	4 28 49	14.3875	257	6 60 49	16.0312
158	2 49 64	12.5698	208	4 32 64	14.4222	258	6 65 64	16.0624
159	2 52 81	12.6095	209	4 36 81	14.4568	259	6 70 81	16.0935
160	2 56 00	12.6491	210	4 41 00	14.4914	260	6 76 00	16.1245
161	2 59 21	12.6886	211	4 45 21	14.5258	261	6 81 21	16.1555
162	2 62 44	12.7279	212	4 49 44	14.5602	262	6 86 44	16.1864
163	2 65 69	12.7671	213	4 53 69	14.5945	263	6 91 69	16.2173
164	2 68 96	12.8062	214	4 57 96	14.6287	264	6 96 96	16.2481
165	2 72 25	12.8452	215	4 62 25	14.6629	265	7 02 25	16.2788
166	2 75 56	12.8841	216	4 66 56	14.6969	266	7 07 56	16.3095
167	2 78 89	12.9228	217	4 70 89	14.7309	267	7 12 89	16.3401
168	2 82 24	12.9615	218	4 75 24	14.7648	268	7 18 24	16.3707
169	2 85 61	13.0000	219	4 79 61	14.7986	269	7 23 61	16.4012
170	2 89 00	13.0384	220	4 84 00	14.8324	270	7 29 00	16.4317

Table I. Table of Squares and Square Roots—(*Continued*)

Number	Square	Square root	Number	Square	Square root	Number	Square	Square root
271	7 34 41	16.4621	321	10 30 41	17.9165	371	13 76 41	19.2614
272	7 39 84	16.4924	322	10 36 84	17.9444	372	13 83 84	19.2873
273	7 45 29	16.5227	323	10 43 29	17.9722	373	13 91 29	19.3132
274	7 50 76	16.5529	324	10 49 76	18.0000	374	13 98 76	19.3391
275	7 56 25	16.5831	325	10 56 25	18.0278	375	14 06 25	19.3649
276	7 61 76	16.6132	326	10 62 76	18.0555	376	14 13 76	19.3907
277	7 67 29	16.6433	327	10 69 29	18.0831	377	14 21 29	19.4165
278	7 72 84	16.6733	328	10 75 84	18.1108	378	14 28 84	19.4422
279	7 78 41	16.7033	329	10 82 41	18.1384	379	14 36 41	19.4679
280	7 84 00	16.7332	330	10 89 00	18.1659	380	14 44 00	19.4936
281	7 89 61	16.7631	331	10 95 61	18.1934	381	14 51 61	19.5192
282	7 95 24	16.7929	332	11 02 24	18.2209	382	14 59 24	19.5448
283	8 00 89	16.8226	333	11 08 89	18.2483	383	14 66 89	19.5704
284	8 06 56	16.8523	334	11 15 56	18.2757	384	14 74 56	19.5959
285	8 12 25	16.8819	335	11 22 25	18.3030	385	14 82 25	19.6214
286	8 17 96	16.9115	336	11 28 96	18.3303	386	14 89 96	19.6469
287	8 23 69	16.9411	337	11 35 69	18.3576	387	14 97 69	19.6723
288	8 29 44	16.9706	338	11 42 44	18.3848	388	15 05 44	19.6977
289	8 35 21	17.0000	339	11 49 21	18.4120	389	15 13 21	19.7231
290	8 41 00	17.0294	340	11 56 00	18.4391	390	15 21 00	19.7484
291	8 46 81	17.0587	341	11 62 81	18.4662	391	15 28 81	19.7737
292	8 52 64	17.0880	342	11 69 64	18.4932	392	15 36 64	19.7990
293	8 58 49	17.1172	343	11 76 49	18.5203	393	15 44 49	19.8242
294	8 64 36	17.1464	344	11 83 36	18.5472	394	15 52 36	19.8494
295	8 70 25	17.1756	345	11 90 25	18.5742	395	15 60 25	19.8746
296	8 76 16	17.2047	346	11 97 16	18.6011	396	15 68 16	19.8997
297	8 82 09	17.2337	347	12 04 09	18.6279	397	15 76 09	19.9249
298	8 88 04	17.2627	348	12 11 04	18.6548	398	15 84 04	19.9499
299	8 94 01	17.2916	349	12 18 01	18.6815	399	15 92 01	19.9750
300	9 00 00	17.3205	350	12 25 00	18.7083	400	16 00 00	20.0000
301	9 06 01	17.3494	351	12 32 01	18.7350	401	16 08 01	20.0250
302	9 12 04	17.3781	352	12 39 04	18.7617	402	16 16 04	20.0499
303	9 18 09	17.4069	353	12 46 09	18.7883	403	16 24 09	20.0749
304	9 24 16	17.4356	354	12 53 16	18.8149	404	16 32 16	20.0998
305	9 30 25	17.4642	355	12 60 25	18.8414	405	16 40 25	20.1246
306	9 36 36	17.4929	356	12 67 36	18.8680	406	16 48 36	20.1494
307	9 42 49	17.5214	357	12 74 49	18.8944	407	16 56 49	20.1742
308	9 48 64	17.5499	358	12 81 64	18.9209	408	16 64 64	20.1990
309	9 54 81	17.5784	359	12 88 81	18.9473	409	16 72 81	20.2237
310	9 61 00	17.6068	360	12 96 00	18.9737	410	16 81 00	20.2485
311	9 67 21	17.6352	361	13 03 21	19.0000	411	16 89 21	20.2731
312	9 73 44	17.6635	362	13 10 44	19.0263	412	16 97 44	20.2978
313	9 79 69	17.6918	363	13 17 69	19.0526	413	17 05 69	20.3224
314	9 85 96	17.7200	364	13 24 96	19.0788	414	17 13 96	20.3470
315	9 92 25	17.7482	365	13 32 25	19.1050	415	17 22 25	20.3715
316	9 98 56	17.7764	366	13 39 56	19.1311	416	17 30 56	20.3961
317	10 04 89	17.8045	367	13 46 89	19.1572	417	17 38 89	20.4206
318	10 11 24	17.8326	368	13 54 24	19.1833	418	17 47 24	20.4450
319	10 17 61	17.8606	369	13 61 61	19.2094	419	17 55 61	20.4695
320	10 24 00	17.8885	370	13 69 00	19.2354	420	17 64 00	20.4939

Table 1. Table of Squares and Square Roots—(*Continued*)

Number	Square	Square root	Number	Square	Square root	Number	Square	Square root
421	17 72 41	20.5183	471	22 18 41	21.7025	521	27 14 41	22.8254
422	17 80 84	20.5426	472	22 27 84	21.7256	522	27 24 84	22.8473
423	17 89 29	20.5670	473	22 37 29	21.7486	523	27 35 29	22.8692
424	17 97 76	20.5913	474	22 46 76	21.7715	524	27 45 76	22.8910
425	18 06 25	20.6155	475	22 56 25	21.7945	525	27 56 25	22.9129
426	18 14 76	20.6398	476	22 65 76	21.8174	526	27 66 76	22.9347
427	18 23 29	20.6640	477	22 75 29	21.8403	527	27 77 29	22.9565
428	18 31 84	20.6882	478	22 84 84	21.8632	528	27 87 84	22.9783
429	18 40 41	20.7123	479	22 94 41	21.8861	529	27 98 41	23.0000
430	18 49 00	20.7364	480	23 04 00	21.9089	530	28 09 00	23.0217
431	18 57 61	20.7605	481	23 13 61	21.9317	531	28 19 61	23.0434
432	18 66 24	20.7846	482	23 23 24	21.9545	532	28 30 24	23.0651
433	18 74 89	20.8087	483	23 32 89	21.9773	533	28 40 89	23.0868
434	18 83 56	20.8327	484	23 42 56	22.0000	534	28 51 56	23.1084
435	18 92 25	20.8567	485	23 52 25	22.0227	535	28 62 25	23.1301
436	19 00 96	20.8806	486	23 61 96	22.0454	536	28 72 96	23.1517
437	19 09 69	20.9045	487	23 71 69	22.0681	537	28 83 69	23.1733
438	19 18 44	20.9284	488	23 81 44	22.0907	538	28 94 44	23.1948
439	19 27 21	20.9523	489	23 91 21	22.1133	539	29 05 21	23.2164
440	19 36 00	20.9762	490	24 01 00	22.1359	540	29 16 00	23.2379
441	19 44 81	21.0000	491	24 10 81	22.1585	541	29 26 81	23.2594
442	19 53 64	21.0238	492	24 20 64	22.1811	542	29 37 64	23.2809
443	19 62 49	21.0476	493	24 30 49	22.2036	543	29 48 49	23.3024
444	19 71 36	21.0713	494	24 40 36	22.2261	544	29 59 36	23.3238
445	19 80 25	21.0950	495	24 50 25	22.2486	545	29 70 25	23.3452
446	19 89 16	21.1187	496	24 60 16	22.2711	546	29 81 16	23.3666
447	19 98 09	21.1424	497	24 70 09	22.2935	547	29 92 09	23.3880
448	20 07 04	21.1660	498	24 80 04	22.3159	548	30 03 04	23.4094
449	20 16 01	21.1896	499	24 90 01	22.3383	549	30 14 01	23.4307
450	20 25 00	21.2132	500	25 00 00	22.3607	550	30 25 00	23.4521
451	20 34 01	21.2368	501	25 10 01	22.3830	551	30 36 01	23.4734
452	20 43 04	21.2603	502	25 20 04	22.4054	552	30 47 04	23.4947
453	20 52 09	21.2838	503	25 30 09	22.4277	553	30 58 09	23.5160
454	20 61 16	21.3073	504	25 40 16	22.4499	554	30 69 16	23.5372
455	20 70 25	21.3307	505	25 50 25	22.4722	555	30 80 25	23.5584
456	20 79 36	21.3542	506	25 60 36	22.4944	556	30 91 36	23.5797
457	20 88 49	21.3776	507	25 70 49	22.5167	557	31 02 49	23.6008
458	20 97 64	21.4009	508	25 80 64	22.5389	558	31 13 64	23.6220
459	21 06 81	21.4243	509	25 90 81	22.5610	559	31 24 81	23.6432
460	21 16 00	21.4476	510	26 01 00	22.5832	560	31 36 00	23.6643
461	21 25 21	21.4709	511	26 11 21	22.6053	561	31 47 21	23.6854
462	21 34 44	21.4942	512	26 21 44	22.6274	562	31 58 44	23.7065
463	21 43 69	21.5174	513	26 31 69	22.6495	563	31 69 69	23.7276
464	21 52 96	21.5407	514	26 41 96	22.6716	564	31 80 96	23.7487
465	21 62 25	21.5639	515	26 52 25	22.6936	565	31 92 25	23.7697
466	21 71 56	21.5870	516	26 62 56	22.7156	566	32 03 56	23.7908
467	21 80 89	21.6102	517	26 72 89	22.7376	567	32 14 89	23.8118
468	21 90 24	21.6333	518	26 83 24	22.7596	568	32 26 24	23.8328
469	21 99 61	21.6564	519	26 93 61	22.7816	569	32 37 61	23.8537
470	22 09 00	21.6795	520	27 04 00	22.8035	570	32 49 00	23.8747

Table 1. Table of Squares and Square Roots—(*Continued*)

Number	Square	Square root	Number	Square	Square root	Number	Square	Square root
571	32 60 41	23.8956	621	38 56 41	24.9199	671	45 02 41	25.9037
572	32 71 84	23.9165	622	38 68 84	24.9399	672	45 15 84	25.9230
573	32 83 29	23.9374	623	38 81 29	24.9600	673	45 29 29	25.9422
574	32 94 76	23.9583	624	38 93 76	24.9800	674	45 42 76	25.9615
575	33 06 25	23.9792	625	39 06 25	25.0000	675	45 56 25	25.9808
576	33 17 76	24.0000	626	39 18 76	25.0200	676	45 69 76	26.0000
577	33 29 29	24.0208	627	39 31 29	25.0400	677	45 83 29	26.0192
578	33 40 84	24.0416	628	39 43 84	25.0599	678	45 96 84	26.0384
579	33 52 41	24.0624	629	39 56 41	25.0799	679	46 10 41	26.0576
580	33 64 00	24.0832	630	39 69 00	25.0998	680	46 24 00	26.0768
581	33 75 61	24.1039	631	39 81 61	25.1197	681	46 37 61	26.0960
582	33 87 24	24.1247	632	39 94 24	25.1396	682	46 51 24	26.1151
583	33 98 89	24.1454	633	40 06 89	25.1595	683	46 64 89	26.1343
584	34 10 56	24.1661	634	40 19 56	25.1794	684	46 78 56	26.1534
585	34 22 25	24.1868	635	40 32 25	25.1992	685	46 92 25	26.1725
586	34 33 96	24.2074	636	40 44 96	25.2190	686	47 05 96	26.1916
587	34 45 69	24.2281	637	40 57 69	25.2389	687	47 19 69	26.2107
588	34 57 44	24.2487	638	40 70 44	25.2587	688	47 33 44	26.2298
589	34 69 21	24.2693	639	40 83 21	25.2784	689	47 47 21	26.2488
590	34 81 00	24.2899	640	40 96 00	25.2982	690	47 61 00	26.2679
591	34 92 81	24.3105	641	41 08 81	25.3180	691	47 74 81	26.2869
592	35 04 64	24.3311	642	41 21 64	25.3377	692	47 88 64	26.3059
593	35 16 49	24.3516	643	41 34 49	25.3574	693	48 02 49	26.3249
594	35 28 36	24.3721	644	41 47 36	25.3772	694	48 16 36	26.3439
595	35 40 25	24.3926	645	41 60 25	25.3969	695	48 30 25	26.3629
596	35 52 16	24.4131	646	41 73 16	25.4165	696	48 44 16	26.3818
597	35 64 09	24.4336	647	41 86 09	25.4362	697	48 58 09	26.4008
598	35 76 04	24.4540	648	41 99 04	25.4558	698	48 72 04	26.4197
599	35 88 01	24.4745	649	42 12 01	25.4755	699	48 86 01	26.4386
600	36 00 00	24.4949	650	42 25 00	25.4951	700	49 00 00	26.4575
601	36 12 01	24.5153	651	42 38 01	25.5147	701	49 14 01	26.4764
602	36 24 04	24.5357	652	42 51 04	25.5343	702	49 28 04	26.4953
603	36 36 09	24.5561	653	42 64 09	25.5539	703	49 42 09	26.5141
604	36 48 16	24.5764	654	42 77 16	25.5734	704	49 56 16	26.5330
605	36 60 25	24.5967	655	42 90 25	25.5930	705	49 70 25	26.5518
606	36 72 36	24.6171	656	43 03 36	25.6125	706	49 84 36	26.5707
607	36 84 49	24.6374	657	43 16 49	25.6320	707	49 98 49	26.5895
608	36 96 64	24.6577	658	43 29 64	25.6515	708	50 12 64	26.6083
609	37 08 81	24.6779	659	43 42 81	25.6710	709	50 26 81	26.6271
610	37 21 00	24.6982	660	43 56 00	25.6905	710	50 41 00	26.6458
611	37 33 21	24.7184	661	43 69 21	25.7099	711	50 55 21	26.6646
612	37 45 44	24.7385	662	43 82 44	25.7294	712	50 69 44	26.6833
613	37 57 69	24.7588	663	43 95 69	25.7488	713	50 83 69	26.7021
614	37 69 96	24.7790	664	44 08 96	25.7682	714	50 97 96	26.7208
615	37 82 25	24.7992	665	44 22 25	25.7876	715	51 12 25	26.7395
616	37 94 56	24.8193	666	44 35 56	25.8070	716	51 26 56	26.7582
617	38 06 89	24.8395	667	44 48 89	25.8263	717	51 40 89	26.7769
618	38 19 24	24.8596	668	44 62 24	25.8457	718	51 55 24	26.7955
619	38 31 61	24.8797	669	44 75 61	25.8650	719	51 69 61	26.8142
620	38 44 00	24.8998	670	44 89 00	25.8844	720	51 84 00	26.8328

Table I. Table of Squares and Square Roots—(*Continued*)

Number	Square	Square root	Number	Square	Square root	Number	Square	Square root
721	51 98 41	26.8514	771	59 44 41	27.7669	821	67 40 41	28.6531
722	52 12 84	26.8701	772	59 59 84	27.7849	822	67 56 84	28.6705
723	52 27 29	26.8887	773	59 75 29	27.8029	823	67 73 29	28.6880
724	52 41 76	26.9072	774	59 90 76	27.8209	824	67 89 76	28.7054
725	52 56 25	26.9258	775	60 06 25	27.8388	825	68 06 25	28.7228
726	52 70 76	26.9444	776	60 21 76	27.8568	826	68 22 76	28.7402
727	52 85 29	26.9629	777	60 37 29	27.8747	827	68 39 29	28.7576
728	52 99 84	26.9815	778	60 52 84	27.8927	828	68 55 84	28.7750
729	53 14 41	27.0000	779	60 68 41	27.9106	829	68 72 41	28.7924
730	53 29 00	27.0185	780	60 84 00	27.9285	830	68 89 00	28.8097
731	53 43 61	27.0370	781	60 99 61	27.9464	831	69 05 61	28.8271
732	53 58 24	27.0555	782	61 15 24	27.9643	832	69 22 24	28.8444
733	53 72 89	27.0740	783	61 30 89	27.9821	833	69 38 89	28.8617
734	53 87 56	27.0924	784	61 46 56	28.0000	834	69 55 56	28.8791
735	54 02 25	27.1109	785	61 62 25	28.0179	835	69 72 25	28.8964
736	54 16 96	27.1293	786	61 77 96	28.0357	836	69 88 96	28.9137
737	54 31 69	27.1477	787	61 93 69	28.0535	837	70 05 69	28.9310
738	54 46 44	27.1662	788	62 09 44	28.0713	838	70 22 44	28.9482
739	54 61 27	27.1846	789	62 25 21	28.0891	839	70 39 21	28.9655
740	54 76 00	27.2029	790	62 41 00	28.1069	840	70 56 00	28.9828
741	54 90 81	27.2213	791	62 56 81	28.1247	841	70 72 81	29.0000
742	55 05 64	27.2397	792	62 72 64	28.1425	842	70 89 64	29.0172
743	55 20 49	27.2580	793	62 88 49	28.1603	843	71 06 49	29.0345
744	55 35 36	27.2764	794	63 04 36	28.1780	844	71 23 36	29.0517
745	55 50 25	27.2947	795	63 20 25	28.1957	845	71 40 25	29.0689
746	55 65 16	27.3130	796	63 36 16	28.2135	846	71 57 16	29.0861
747	55 80 09	27.3313	797	63 52 09	28.2312	847	71 74 09	29.1033
748	55 95 04	27.3496	798	63 68 04	28.2489	848	71 91 04	29.1204
749	56 10 01	27.3679	799	63 84 01	28.2666	849	72 08 01	29.1376
750	56 25 00	27.3861	800	64 00 00	28.2843	850	72 25 00	29.1548
751	56 40 01	27.4044	801	64 16 01	28.3019	851	72 42 01	29.1719
752	56 55 04	27.4226	802	64 32 04	28.3196	852	72 59 04	29.1890
753	56 70 09	27.4408	803	64 48 09	28.3373	853	72 76 09	29.2062
754	56 85 16	27.4591	804	64 64 16	28.3549	854	72 93 16	29.2233
755	57 00 25	27.4773	805	64 80 25	28.3725	855	73 10 25	29.2404
756	57 15 36	27.4955	806	64 96 36	28.3901	856	73 27 36	29.2575
757	57 30 49	27.5136	807	65 12 49	28.4077	857	73 44 49	29.2746
758	57 45 64	27.5318	808	65 28 64	28.4253	858	73 61 64	29.2916
759	57 60 81	27.5500	809	65 44 81	28.4429	859	73 78 81	29.3087
760	57 76 00	27.5681	810	65 61 00	28.4605	860	73 96 00	29.3258
761	57 91 21	27.5862	811	65 77 21	28.4781	861	74 13 21	29.3428
762	58 06 44	27.6043	812	65 93 44	28.4956	862	74 30 44	29.3598
763	58 21 69	27.6225	813	66 09 69	28.5132	863	74 47 69	29.3769
764	58 36 96	27.6405	814	66 25 96	28.5307	864	74 64 96	29.3939
765	58 52 25	27.6586	815	66 42 25	28.5482	865	74 82 25	29.4109
766	58 67 56	27.6767	816	66 58 56	28.5657	866	74 99 56	29.4279
767	58 82 89	27.6948	817	66 74 89	28.5832	867	75 16 89	29.4449
768	58 98 24	27.7128	818	66 91 24	28.6007	868	75 34 24	29.4618
769	59 13 61	27.7308	819	67 07 61	28.6082	869	75 51 61	29.4788
770	59 29 00	27.7489	820	67 24 00	28.6356	870	75 69 00	29.4958

Table I. Table of Squares and Square Roots—(*Continued*)

Number	Square	Square root	Number	Square	Square root	Number	Square	Square root
871	75 86 41	29.5127	921	84 82 41	30.3480	961	92 35 21	31.0000
872	76 03 84	29.5296	922	85 00 84	30.3645	962	92 54 44	31.0161
873	76 21 29	29.5466	923	85 19 29	30.3809	963	92 73 69	31.0322
874	76 38 76	29.5635	924	85 37 76	30.3974	964	92 92 96	31.0483
875	76 56 25	29.5804	925	85 56 25	30.4138	965	93 12 25	31.0644
876	76 73 76	29.5973	926	85 74 76	30.4302	966	93 31 56	31.0805
877	76 91 29	29.6142	927	85 93 29	30.4467	967	93 50 89	31.0966
878	77 08 84	29.6311	928	86 11 84	30.4631	968	93 70 24	31.1127
879	77 26 41	29.6479	929	86 30 41	30.4795	969	93 89 61	31.1288
880	77 44 00	29.6648	930	86 49 00	30.4959	970	94 09 00	31.1448
881	77 61 61	29.6816	931	86 67 61	30.5123	971	94 28 41	31.1609
882	77 79 24	29.6985	932	86 86 24	30.5287	972	94 47 84	31.1769
883	77 96 89	29.7153	933	87 04 89	30.5450	973	94 67 29	31.1929
884	78 14 56	29.7321	934	87 23 56	30.5614	974	94 86 76	31.2090
885	78 32 25	29.7489	935	87 42 25	30.5778	975	95 06 25	31.2250
886	78 49 96	29.7658	936	87 60 96	30.5941	976	95 25 76	31.2410
887	78 67 69	29.7825	937	87 79 69	30.6105	977	95 45 29	31.2570
888	78 85 44	29.7993	938	87 98 44	30.6268	978	95 64 84	31.2730
889	79 03 21	29.8161	939	88 17 21	30.6431	979	95 84 41	31.2890
890	79 21 00	29.8329	940	88 36 00	30.6594	980	96 04 00	31.3050
891	79 38 81	29.8496	941	88 54 81	30.6757	981	96 23 61	31.3209
892	79 56 64	29.8664	942	88 73 64	30.6920	982	96 43 24	31.3369
893	79 74 49	29.8831	943	88 92 49	30.7083	983	96 62 89	31.3528
894	79 92 36	29.8998	944	89 11 36	30.7246	984	96 82 56	31.3688
895	80 10 25	29.9166	945	89 30 25	30.7409	985	97 02 25	31.3847
896	80 28 16	29.9333	946	89 49 16	30.7571	986	97 21 96	31.4006
897	80 46 09	29.9500	947	89 68 09	30.7734	987	97 41 69	31.4166
898	80 64 04	29.9666	948	89 87 04	30.7896	988	97 61 44	31.4325
899	80 82 01	29.9833	949	90 06 01	30.8058	989	97 81 21	31.4484
900	81 00 00	30.0000	950	90 25 00	30.8221	990	98 01 00	31.4643
901	81 18 01	30.0167	951	90 44 01	30.8383	991	98 20 81	31.4802
902	81 36 04	30.0333	952	90 63 04	30.8545	992	98 40 64	31.4960
903	81 54 09	30.0500	953	90 82 09	30.8707	993	98 60 49	31.5119
904	81 72 16	30.0666	954	91 01 16	30.8869	994	98 80 36	31.5278
905	81 90 25	30.0832	955	91 20 25	30.9031	995	99 00 25	31.5436
906	82 08 36	30.0998	956	91 39 36	30.9192	996	99 20 16	31.5595
907	82 26 49	30.1164	957	91 58 49	30.9354	997	99 40 09	31.5753
908	82 44 64	30.1330	958	91 77 64	30.9516	998	99 60 04	31.5911
909	82 62 81	30.1496	959	91 96 81	30.9677	999	99 80 01	31.6070
910	82 81 00	30.1662	960	92 16 00	30.9839	1000	100 00 00	31.6228
911	82 99 21	30.1828						
912	83 17 44	30.1993						
913	83 35 69	30.2159						
914	83 53 96	30.2324						
915	83 72 25	30.2490						
916	83 90 56	30.2655						
917	84 08 89	30.2820						
918	84 27 24	30.2985						
919	84 45 61	30.3150						
920	84 64 00	30.3315						

Table 2. Probabilities That Given Values of z Will Be Exceeded

The probabilities shown are for the upper-tail.

z	0	1	2	3	4	5	6	7	8	9
0.0	.5000	.4960	.4920	.4880	.4840	.4801	.4761	.4721	.4681	.4641
0.1	.4602	.4562	.4522	.4483	.4443	.4404	.4364	.4325	.4286	.4247
0.2	.4207	.4168	.4129	.4090	.4052	.4013	.3974	.3936	.3897	.3859
0.3	.3821	.3783	.3745	.3707	.3669	.3632	.3594	.3557	.3520	.3483
0.4	.3446	.3409	.3372	.3336	.3300	.3264	.3228	.3192	.3156	.3121
0.5	.3085	.3050	.3015	.2981	.2946	.2912	.2877	.2843	.2810	.2776
0.6	.2743	.2709	.2676	.2643	.2611	.2578	.2546	.2514	.2483	.2451
0.7	.2420	.2389	.2358	.2327	.2296	.2266	.2236	.2206	.2177	.2148
0.8	.2119	.2090	.2061	.2033	.2005	.1977	.1949	.1922	.1894	.1867
0.9	.1841	.1814	.1788	.1762	.1736	.1711	.1685	.1660	.1635	.1611
1.0	.1587	.1562	.1539	.1515	.1492	.1469	.1446	.1423	.1401	.1379
1.1	.1357	.1335	.1314	.1292	.1271	.1251	.1230	.1210	.1190	.1170
1.2	.1151	.1131	.1112	.1093	.1075	.1056	.1038	.1020	.1003	.0985
1.3	.0968	.0951	.0934	.0918	.0901	.0885	.0869	.0853	.0838	.0823
1.4	.0808	.0793	.0778	.0764	.0749	.0735	.0721	.0708	.0694	.0681
1.5	.0668	.0655	.0643	.0630	.0618	.0606	.0594	.0582	.0571	.0559
1.6	.0548	.0537	.0526	.0516	.0505	.0495	.0485	.0475	.0465	.0455
1.7	.0446	.0436	.0427	.0418	.0409	.0401	.0392	.0384	.0375	.0367
1.8	.0359	.0351	.0344	.0336	.0329	.0322	.0314	.0307	.0301	.0294
1.9	.0287	.0281	.0274	.0268	.0262	.0256	.0250	.0244	.0239	.0233
2.0	.0228	.0222	.0217	.0212	.0207	.0202	.0197	.0192	.0188	.0183
2.1	.0179	.0174	.0170	.0166	.0162	.0158	.0154	.0150	.0146	.0143
2.2	.0139	.0136	.0132	.0129	.0125	.0122	.0119	.0116	.0113	.0110
2.3	.0107	.0104	.0102	.0099	.0096	.0094	.0091	.0089	.0087	.0084
2.4	.0082	.0080	.0078	.0075	.0073	.0071	.0069	.0068	.0066	.0064
2.5	.0062	.0060	.0059	.0057	.0055	.0054	.0052	.0051	.0049	.0048
2.6	.0047	.0045	.0044	.0043	.0041	.0040	.0039	.0038	.0037	.0036
2.7	.0035	.0034	.0033	.0032	.0031	.0030	.0029	.0028	.0027	.0026
2.8	.0026	.0025	.0024	.0023	.0023	.0022	.0021	.0021	.0020	.0019
2.9	.0019	.0018	.0018	.0017	.0016	.0016	.0015	.0015	.0014	.0014
3.0	.0013	.0013	.0013	.0012	.0012	.0011	.0011	.0011	.0010	.0010

Table 2 is adapted from Wallis and Roberts, *Statistics, A New Approach* (Glencoe, Ill., Free Press, 1956), by permission of the authors and publishers. The digits heading the columns are additional digits for the values of z shown in the first column. Thus, the probability corresponding to z = 1.32 is found in the row in which "1.3" appears at the left and the column in which "2" appears at the top. The probability is 0.0934. For two-tailed probabilities take 2P. For the area to the left of the ordinate at z take 1 — P. For the area between the mean and z take 0.5 — P.

Table 3. Table of Critical Values of *t*

df	.10	.05	.025	.01	.005	.0005
	.20	.10	.05	.02	.01	.001
1	3.078	6.314	12.706	31.821	63.657	636.619
2	1.886	2.920	4.303	6.965	9.925	31.598
3	1.638	2.353	3.182	4.541	5.841	12.941
4	1.533	2.132	2.776	3.747	4.604	8.610
5	1.476	2.015	2.571	3.365	4.032	6.859
6	1.440	1.943	2.447	3.143	3.707	5.959
7	1.415	1.895	2.365	2.998	3.499	5.405
8	1.397	1.860	2.306	2.896	3.355	5.041
9	1.383	1.833	2.262	2.821	3.250	4.781
10	1.372	1.812	2.228	2.764	3.169	4.587
11	1.363	1.796	2.201	2.718	3.106	4.437
12	1.356	1.782	2.179	2.681	3.055	4.318
13	1.350	1.771	2.160	2.650	3.012	4.221
14	1.345	1.761	2.145	2.624	2.977	4.140
15	1.341	1.753	2.131	2.602	2.947	4.073
16	1.337	1.746	2.120	2.583	2.921	4.015
17	1.333	1.740	2.110	2.567	2.898	3.965
18	1.330	1.734	2.101	2.552	2.878	3.922
19	1.328	1.729	2.093	2.539	2.861	3.883
20	1.325	1.725	2.086	2.528	2.845	3.850
21	1.323	1.721	2.080	2.518	2.831	3.819
22	1.321	1.717	2.074	2.508	2.819	3.792
23	1.319	1.714	2.069	2.500	2.807	3.767
24	1.318	1.711	2.064	2.492	2.797	3.745
25	1.316	1.708	2.060	2.485	2.787	3.725
26	1.315	1.706	2.056	2.479	2.779	3.707
27	1.314	1.703	2.052	2.473	2.771	3.690
28	1.313	1.701	2.048	2.467	2.763	3.674
29	1.311	1.699	2.045	2.462	2.756	3.659
30	1.310	1.697	2.042	2.457	2.750	3.646
40	1.303	1.684	2.021	2.423	2.704	3.551
60	1.296	1.671	2.000	2.390	2.660	3.460
120	1.289	1.658	1.980	2.358	2.617	3.373
∞	1.282	1.645	1.960	2.326	2.576	3.291

(Top sub-heading: Level of significance for one-tailed test — .10, .05, .025, .01, .005, .0005; Level of significance for two-tailed test — .20, .10, .05, .02, .01, .001.)

Table 4. Table of Critical Values of Chi Square

Probability under H_0 that $\chi^2 \geq$ chi square

df	.99	.98	.95	.90	.80	.70	.50	.30	.20	.10	.05	.02	.01	.001
1	.00016	.00063	.0039	.016	.064	.15	.46	1.07	1.64	2.71	3.84	5.41	6.64	10.83
2	.02	.04	.10	.21	.45	.71	1.39	2.41	3.22	4.60	5.99	7.82	9.21	13.82
3	.12	.18	.35	.58	1.00	1.42	2.37	3.66	4.64	6.25	7.82	9.84	11.34	16.27
4	.30	.43	.71	1.06	1.65	2.20	3.36	4.88	5.99	7.78	9.49	11.67	13.28	18.46
5	.55	.75	1.14	1.61	2.34	3.00	4.35	6.06	7.29	9.24	11.07	13.39	15.09	20.52
6	.87	1.13	1.64	2.20	3.07	3.83	5.35	7.23	8.56	10.64	12.59	15.03	16.81	22.46
7	1.24	1.56	2.17	2.83	3.82	4.67	6.35	8.38	9.80	12.02	14.07	16.62	18.48	24.32
8	1.65	2.03	2.73	3.49	4.59	5.53	7.34	9.52	11.03	13.36	15.51	18.17	20.09	26.12
9	2.09	2.53	3.32	4.17	5.38	6.39	8.34	10.66	12.24	14.68	16.92	19.68	21.67	27.88
10	2.56	3.06	3.94	4.86	6.18	7.27	9.34	11.78	13.44	15.99	18.31	21.16	23.21	29.59
11	3.05	3.61	4.58	5.58	6.99	8.15	10.34	12.90	14.63	17.28	19.68	22.62	24.72	31.26
12	3.57	4.18	5.23	6.30	7.81	9.03	11.34	14.01	15.81	18.55	21.03	24.05	26.22	32.91
13	4.11	4.76	5.89	7.04	8.63	9.93	12.34	15.12	16.98	19.81	22.36	25.47	27.69	34.53
14	4.66	5.37	6.57	7.79	9.47	10.82	13.34	16.22	18.15	21.06	23.68	26.87	29.14	36.12
15	5.23	5.98	7.26	8.55	10.31	11.72	14.34	17.32	19.31	22.31	25.00	28.26	30.58	37.70
16	5.81	6.61	7.96	9.31	11.15	12.62	15.34	18.42	20.46	23.54	26.30	29.63	32.00	39.29
17	6.41	7.26	8.67	10.08	12.00	13.53	16.34	19.51	21.62	24.77	27.59	31.00	33.41	40.75
18	7.02	7.91	9.39	10.86	12.86	14.44	17.34	20.60	22.76	25.99	28.87	32.35	34.80	42.31
19	7.63	8.57	10.12	11.65	13.72	15.35	18.34	21.69	23.90	27.20	30.14	33.69	36.19	43.82
20	8.26	9.24	10.85	12.44	14.58	16.27	19.34	22.78	25.04	28.41	31.41	35.02	37.57	45.32
21	8.90	9.92	11.59	13.24	15.44	17.18	20.34	23.86	26.17	29.62	32.67	36.34	38.93	46.80
22	9.54	10.60	12.34	14.04	16.31	18.10	21.24	24.94	27.30	30.81	33.92	37.66	40.29	48.27
23	10.20	11.29	13.09	14.85	17.19	19.02	22.34	26.02	28.43	32.01	35.17	38.97	41.64	49.73
24	10.86	11.99	13.85	15.66	18.06	19.94	23.34	27.10	29.55	33.20	36.42	40.27	42.98	51.18
25	11.52	12.70	14.61	16.47	18.94	20.87	24.34	28.17	30.68	34.38	37.65	41.57	44.31	52.62
26	12.20	13.41	15.38	17.29	19.82	21.79	25.34	29.25	31.80	35.56	38.88	42.86	45.64	54.05
27	12.88	14.12	16.15	18.11	20.70	22.72	26.34	30.32	32.91	36.74	40.11	44.14	46.96	55.48
28	13.56	14.85	16.93	18.94	21.59	23.65	27.34	31.39	34.03	37.92	41.34	45.42	48.28	56.89
29	14.26	15.57	17.71	19.77	22.48	24.58	28.34	32.46	35.14	39.09	42.56	46.69	49.59	58.30
30	14.95	16.31	18.49	20.60	23.36	25.51	29.34	33.53	36.25	40.26	43.77	47.96	50.89	59.70

Table 4 is abridged from Table IV of Fisher and Yates: *Statistical Tables for Biological, Agricultural, and Medical Research*, published by Oliver and Boyd Ltd., Edinburgh, by permission of the authors and publishers. For larger values of *df*, the expression $\sqrt{2\chi^2} - \sqrt{2df - 1}$ defines *z* and probabilities may be read off from Table 1.

Table 3 is abridged from Table III of Fisher and Yates: *Statistical Tables for Biological, Agricultural, and Medical Research*, published by Oliver and Boyd Ltd., Edinburgh, by permission of the authors and publishers. Values of *t* are in the body of the table. The probability designated "Level of significance for one-tailed test" is the probability of exceeding *t* in one direction. The probability designated "Level of significance for two-tailed test" is simply 2*P*.

Index

abscissa, 21
analysis of variance, 265
Anderson, R. L., 18, 344
a priori probability, 230–231
array, 27
  definition of, 15–16
Asch, S. E., 328, 344
association, 2, 291
  chi-square test of significance of, 328
  in contingency tables, 284
  gamma as measure of, 181–183
  interpretation of, 208–209
  lambda measure of, 171, 174–177, 183, 186, 284
  measures of, and independence, 167–168
  measures of, in 2×2 tables, 168–171
  multivariate, formula for, 205–208
  percentage difference as measure of, 163–167
  phi coefficient as measure of, 169–171, 172, 183, 186
  Q as measure of, 169, 170, 171, 172, 181, 182, 183, 186
  specification of, 209–212
  spurious, 203, 206, 207, 208, 212
  test of, in before-and-after case, 291
  (*see also* confounding factors, independence)
attributes
  cross-classification of, 131–133
  definition of, 4–5, 125
  dichotomous, 126
  multivariate, form of tables of, 201–203
average, 28, 53
  definition of, 41
average deviation, 69

average value (*see* central tendency)

Back, K., 340, 341, 345
Bancroft, T. A., 18, 344
base
  choice of, in computing rate, 130–131
Beegle, J. A., 216, 217, 347
Bendix, R., 344, 346
Bennett, K. R., 346
Berelson, B. R., 132, 146, 149, 202, 207, 344
binomial distribution, 271, 272, 280
binomial probabilities, 318, 319
  approximation of normal distribution to, 276, 279–280
  exact, computation of, 272–276
biserial coefficient, 186–187
Blau, P. M., 113, 322, 344
Bureau of the Census, U.S., 143, 144, 145, 164, 347

Cartwright, D., 345, 347
Cauchy's distribution, 314
cell frequencies, 126
census tracts, 130
Centers, R., 182, 288
central limit theorem, 314–315, 331
central tendency, 15 (*see also* mean, median, mode)
"chance," 231
characteristics, types of, 4–9
chi-square
  applied to general $r \times s$ table, 288–289, 291
  and median test, 328–329
  table of, 282, 366
chi-square test, 271, 284, 316

as approximation to exact test, 286–288
  correction for continuity for, 281–282, 287, 289, 290
  in goodness-of-fit case, 280–283
  as nonparametric test, 327
"chunks," 232
Clark, K. B., 294, 297, 302, 303
Clark, M. P., 294, 297, 302, 303
Clark, R. E., 335, 336, 344
Clarke, A. C., 86, 344
class, 18
  open-ended, 51
class frequency, 18
class interval, 18, 19, 21, 27
  (*see also* grouping)
class limits
  real, 18, 19
  recorded, 20
classifications, logical criteria for, 125, 126
Cochran, W. G., 315, 344
coding
  definition of, 42
  by step deviations, 44
coefficient of contingency, 168
coefficient of determination, 108
coefficient of predictability, 171
Coleman, A. L., 11, 12, 13, 346
computation design
  for chi-square, 290
  of confidence intervals for median, 321
  of exact binomial probabilities, 277–278
  of gamma measure of association, 184–185
  for lambda measures of association, 178
  for mean of grouped data, 46
  for median of grouped data, 50
  for median test, 330

of Q and phi coefficient from fourfold tables, 172
  for r from grouped observations, 106–107
  for regression constants and error variance from grouped data, 110
  for Spearman's rank correlation coefficient, 326
  for t test, 245
  use of, 45
  for variance and standard deviation, 74
confidence intervals, 233–235
  interpretation of, 236, 238
  for median, 317–320
  for $_p$, 235–236
  for X, 236–237
confounding factors, 203–205
  (*see also* association, spurious)
contingency table, 134–135
  asymmetrical, 135–140
  examples of, 143–151
  measure of association in, 167–168
  percentaging, 135–141
  $r \times s$ table
    application of chi-square to, 288–289, 291
    d. f. in, 288
  symmetrical, 140–141
continuity
  concept of, 19
  correction for, 281–282, 287, 289, 290
continuous variables, 8
correlated observations, effects on tests of significance, 248
correlation, 2, 100–101
  curvilinear, 108
  defined, 93
correlation coefficient, 93, 100
covariance, 98, 102

curve
  normal, 25–27
    reading table of, 78–80
  skewed, 23, 26
  (*see also* distribution)

Davis, A., 335, 344, 345
degrees of freedom, 282
  and *t* distribution, 241–244
  in 2 × 2 table, 287–288
delta, 168, 205–206, 212, 255
Demerath, N. J., 346
Deming, W. E., 232, 233, 249, 314, 344
description, 52
deviations, from mean, 68–73
d. f. (*see* degrees of freedom)
dichotomy, of attributes, 4–5
discrete variables, 8
dispersion, 15, 28
  measures of
    defined, 67, 67–80
    location-based, 75–77
distribution
  bimodal, 24, 51
  Cauchy's, 314
  multimodal, 24
  sampling, 234, 235
  types of, 21–25
  types of curves in, 26
  unimodal, 24
distribution assumptions, 313, 314, 316, 322
distribution-free methods, 315–317
  (*see also* nonparametric methods)
Dunham, H. W., 119, 345

ecological correlation, 109
ecological fallacy, 109
Edwards, A. L., 42, 79, 169, 186, 236, 248, 249, 345
enumeration data, 4, 125
  (*see also* attributes, chi-square, *and* proportions)
epsilon measure, of percentage difference, 164, 165, 166, 167
error variance, 99, 100
  computation of, from grouped data, 110
exact binomial probabilities, computation of, 272–276
exact test
  chi-square approximation to, 286–288
  Fisher's, 284–286, 288
expected values
  how obtained, in goodness-of-fit cases, 280–281
  how obtained, in test for independence, 286–287

F test of significance, 246–247
factorial sign, 273
Fagan, J., 335, 338, 347
Faris, R. E. L., 119, 345
Federighi, E., 285, 345
Festinger, L., 340, 341, 345
Finney, D. J., 285, 345
Fisher's exact test, 284–286, 288
formula
  for addition of ultimate frequencies, 204
  for average deviation, 69
  for averaging proportions, 129
  for averaging two means, 52
  for cell frequency of independent attributes, 167
  for chi-square, 286, 290
    corrected for continuity, 282, 290
    for 2 × 2 table, 290
  for computation for grouped data, 105, 106
    for ungrouped data, 102
  for confidence interval containing the median, 320, 321
  for correlation coefficient, *r*, definition of, 101
  defining percentage, proportion and ratio, 128
  defining percentage change, 131
  for definition of *t*, 240
  for delta, observed-expected cell-frequency, 168
  for error variance
    computation of, ungrouped data, 100
    definition of, 99
    standard error of estimate, grouped data, 110
  for Fisher's exact test, 285
  for gamma, 181, 183, 185
  for general term of binomial expansion, 273, 277
  for lambda, 176, 177, 178
  for linear relationship, 95
  mathematical, 41
  for mean, definition of, 41
  for mean, grouped data, 45, 46
  for median, grouped data, 48, 50
  for midpoints, 20
  for multivariate association, 206
  for phi coefficient, 169, 170, 172
  for quartiles, grouped data, 76
  for range, 67
  for regression coefficients, 97–98
  for regression equation, 97
  for semi-interquartile range, 75

for Spearman *r_s*, 324, 326
  corrected for ties, 325, 327
for standard deviation, definition of, 70
for standard error of difference between two means from independent samples, 240, 241, 245
for standard error of difference between two proportions from independent samples, 279
for standard error of estimate, 99
for standard error of mean, 237, 238
for standard error of proportion, 234, 238
for standard normal variable, 78
for *t*-test of significance of *r_s*, 325, 326
for Tchebyscheff's inequality, 314, 315
for variance, computation, grouped data, 72, 74
  ungrouped data, 71
for variance, definition of, 70
for Yule's *Q*, 169, 170, 172
fourfold tables, measures of association in, 168–171
French, R. L., 81, 82, 345
frequency, 18
frequency distribution, 18
frequency polygon, 22–23, 30–31
Freund, J. E., 52, 345

gamma, as measure of association, 181–183, 186, 323, 327
Gist, N. P., 126, 345
Goldhamer, H., 203, 345
Goode, Wm. J., 37, 147, 288, 289, 345
Goodman, L. A., 169, 171, 174, 180, 345
goodness-of-fit cases, 291
  chi-square test in, 280–283
  degrees of freedom for, 282
Gorden, R. L., 17, 345
grouped data
  mean for, 42–45
  quartiles from, 76
  r from, 102–107
  standard deviation from, 72, 73
grouping, 17–19, 27
  error, 19, 42
  (*see also* class intervals)
guessed mean, 42, 43
Guttman, L., 171

Hagood, M. J., 51, 272, 345
Halbert, L. A., 126, 345

Halbwachs, M., 210
Hartley, E. L., 344, 345
Hatt, P., 57, 345
Havighurst, R., 335, 344
Hawley, A. H., 58, 345
Henry, A. F., 345
histogram, 21–22, 29–30
homogeneity of variance
  as assumption in *t*-test, 246
  test for, 246–247
homoscedasticity, 322
Horowitz, E. L., 55, 345
Hyman, Herbert, 13, 151, 201, 345, 346
hypothesis, null, 240–244, 245, 248
  one-tailed, 243–244
  two-tailed, 243–244
hypothesis, test of
  (*see* test of significance)

ideal bowl experiment, 232–233
independence, 163
  chi-square test for, 329
  in classical definition of probability, 231
  definition of, 167–168
  in 2 × 2 tables, 283–288
inequality, Tchebyscheff's, 314–315, 316
inference, 52
  logic of, 249
interpolation term, 48
interval scales, 8
intervening variable, 208, 212, 213
intrinsic order, 6–7
invariance of form, 27

Kaplan, B., 33, 345
Katz, D., 13, 346
Katz, Elihu, 211, 346
Kaufman, H., 87, 88, 346
Kendall, M. G., 5, 102, 103, 171, 205, 323, 347
Kendall, P., 201, 209, 346
Kish, L., 249, 346
Kruskal, W. H., 169, 171, 174, 180, 345
kurtosis, 26, 27

lambda, as measure of association, 171, 174–177, 183, 186, 284
  limitation of, 177–180
Lander, Bernard, 108
large sample theory
  compared to small sample theory, 237, 239
  confidence intervals in, 233–237
  logic of, 313–314
law of large numbers, 314, 315
Latscha, R., 285, 346

Lazarsfeld, P. F., 132, 146, 149, 201, 202, 207, 209, 211, 344, 346
least-squares method, 97, 99
Lemert, E., 37, 346
Leonard, O. E., 346
leptokurtosis, 26, 27
Lipset, S. M., 344, 346
Literary Digest poll, 1936, 232
Loomis, C. P., 283, 346

McCormick, T. C., 279, 346
McKay, H. D., 31, 85, 347
McPhee, W. N., 132, 146, 149, 202, 207, 344
manifold classification, 125, 126
definition of, 5, 6
marginals, 134
Marsh, C. P., 11, 12, 13, 346
Marshall, A. W., 203, 345
Martin, W. T., 345
mean
definition of, 41–42
deviations from, 68–73
for grouped data, 42–45
guessed, 42, 43
sensitivity of, to extreme values, 47
standard error of, 237
use of, 52
means
averaging of, 52
standard error of differences between, 240, 241
measurement data, 8
(*see also* continuous variables, correlation coefficient, discrete variables, mean, median *and* mode)
median
computation of, for grouped data, 48–51
for ungrouped data, 47–48
confidence intervals for, 317–320
definition, 45, 46
use of, 52
median test, 327–329
Menzel, H., 109, 346
Merton, R. K., 346
midpoint, 18
finding, 20, 21
Miller, D. C., 59, 346
mode
definition of, 51
use of, 52
model, mathematical, v–vi
Mood, A. McF., v, 1, 346
multivariate attributes, analysis of, 213
general form of tables of, 201–203
multivariate population, 4

National Resources Committee, 145, 346
negative linear relationship between variables, 95–96
Newcomb, T. M., 344, 345
nonparametric methods, 315–317
chi-square method as, 327
precision of, compared to parametric methods, 317
nonparametric tests, 246
normal curve, 25–27, 78–80
areas under, 73
normal distribution, 271, 272, 280, 313, 315, 317, 331
approximation of, to binomial probabilities, 276, 279–280
null hypothesis, 240–244, 245, 248
one-tailed, 243–244
two-tailed, 243–244

O'Brien, R. W., 345
observations
correlated, 248
definition of, 16
open-ended class, 51
order
definition of, 5–8
intrinsic, 6–7
rank, 8
order statistics, 47
(*see also* gamma, median, nonparametric methods, quartiles, *and* rank correlation)
orders, utility of, 329, 331
ordinate, 21

parameter, 233, 234, 238, 241, 255
Parten, M. B., 346
partials, 202
Pearson, F. A., 168, 346
Pearson product-moment correlation coefficient (*see* product-moment correlation coefficient)
percentage, 128, 129, 137
direction of, 133
percentage change, 129, 131
percentaging
rules for direction of, 135–139
phi coefficient, as measure of association, 169–171, 172, 183, 186
platykurtosis, 26, 27
point-biserial coefficient, 186–187
Poisson distribution, 272, 280
polyotomous classification, 126
polyotomy, definition of, 5
population, 1, 2, 229, 230
parameters of, 255
types of, 3–4

Porterfield, A. L., 116, 117, 346
positive linear relationship between variables, 94
predictability, coefficient of, 171
Price, D. O., 51, 272, 345
probabilities, exact binomial, computation of, 272–276
probability
classical definition of, 230–231
conditional, 174
defined as relative frequency, 173
definition of, 173–174
samples, 233
product-moment correlation coefficient, 169, 186–187, 322
computation of, from grouped data, 102–107
from ungrouped data, 101–102
interpretation of, 108–109
proportion, 128, 129
confidence intervals for, 234
sampling distribution of, 272–275
test for applicability of normal approximation to, 272
significance of difference between, 276, 279–280
standard error of, 235
standard error of difference between, 279

Q, as measure of association, 169, 170, 171, 172, 181, 182, 183, 186
quarter, 85
quartiles
defined, 75
from grouped data, 75–76
from ungrouped data, 75–76
quasi-variables, 5–8
association between, 180–182
(*see also* orders)
quota sampling, 233

r, 93, 101
(*see* product-moment correlation coefficient)
r_s, significance of, 323, 324, 325, 326, 327
randomness, departures from, effect on inferences about populations, 232–233
random numbers, 251
random sampling, 249
systematic, 231
range, 67–68
rank correlation methods, 322–327
ties in, 323, 325

rank order, 8, 327
ranks, utility of, 329, 331
rates, 129–130
definition of, 5
specific, 205
ratio, 127–128, 133
real limits, 18, 19
recorded limits, 20
regression
curvilinear, 96
linear, 94–98
regression coefficient, 94
regression equation, 93
regression techniques, defined, 93
Reiss, A., 57, 345
replication, 165
residual category, 126
residual sum of squares, 99, 100
Robinson, W. S., 109, 346
Rogoff, N., 133, 347
Rossi, Peter, 150, 347
"rounding" error, 43, 141

samples, 1, 2, 229, 230
nonrandom, 232–233
probability, 233
random
simple, 231
stratified, 231
types of, 231–232
sample statistics, notation for, 255
sampling distribution, 232, 234, 235
statistics of experimental approximations of, 255
sampling frame, 231
Schachter, S., 338, 339, 340, 341, 345, 347
Schrag, C. C., 345
Schroeder, W. W., 216, 217, 347
Selvin, Hanan, 291, 347
semi-interquartile range, 75, 76–77
set of observations, 16
Shaw, C. L., 31, 85, 347
Sheatsley, P. B., 151, 345
Shewhart, W. A., 232, 347
Short, J. F., 345
Siegel, S., 291, 335, 338, 347
sigma, 42
significance, test of (*see* test of significance)
signs, utility of, 329, 331
skewness, 23
slope, 94
small sample theory
nonparametric, 316
(*see also* confidence interval for median, median test *and* rank correlation)
parametric (*see* *t*-test *and* *t*-distribution)

Snedecor, G. W., 247, 251, 252, 347
Sogge, T. M., 131, 144, 347
Spearman's r_s, 323, 324, 325, 326
standard deviation, 69, 70, 71, 72
  computation design for, 73
  interpretation of, 73
  of sampling deviation, 234, 235
  units, 78
standard error, 240
  of difference between proportions, 279
  of estimate, 99–100, 110
standard normal variables, 78
standard scores, 78
statistic, sample estimate, 233, 238
statistical inference, 2
statistics
  application of, v–vi
  definition of, 1
  descriptive, 2, 15
  order, 47
  use of, 331–332
Stouffer, Samuel, 136, 146, 177, 179, 215, 216, 347
stub, 5
sum of squares, 70, 71, 98, 101
  residual, 99, 100
Swanson, G. E., 344, 345
symbols, 42, 255
  functions of, 16–17

T, measure of association, 168
t distribution, 237, 241–244, 272, 316

complete table of, 366
portion of table of, 242
t test, 240
  assumptions underlying, 244–248, 265
  metric requirements for, 316
table
  complete table, chi-square, 366
  complete table, normal distribution, 365
  complete table, t distribution, 366
  1% and 5% points for significance of Spearman's r_s, N from 4 to 10, 324
  portion of normal distribution, 79
  portion of table of chi-square, 282
  portion of 5% points of F distribution, 247
  portion of table of t-distribution, 242
  sampling distribution of $_p$ for $N = 6$, $P = 0.5$, 275
  of squares, square roots, 358
tabulation, 17–18
Talbert, R. H., 116, 117, 346
Tchebyscheff's inequality, 314–315, 316
test of significance, 239–244, 246–247
  chi-square
    goodness-of-fit test, 280–283
    test for independence, 284, 286–290

difference between two proportions, small sample case, 272–275, 277–278
  large sample case, 276, 279
F test, 246–247
Fisher's exact test, 284–286
interpretation of, 283, 289, 291
median test, 327–329, 330
for proportions, 271
for Spearman r_s, 324–325
t-test, 239–248
(see also null hypothesis, one-tailed and two-tailed)
tetrachoric correlation coefficient, 187
Thibaut, J., 264, 265, 266, 347
third moment, of distribution, 23
Tschuprov, A. A., 168
Type I data
  definition of, 4
  (see also enumeration data)
Type II data, 5–8
  (see also order)
Type III data, 8
  (see also measurement data)

ultimate class frequencies, 134
U.S. Bureau of the Census, 143, 144, 145, 164, 347
U.S. Treasury Dept., 43, 44, 72, 347
universe, 1, 2, 229, 230

univariate frequencies, 134
univariate population, 3

values, expected, how obtained in goodness-of-fit cases, 280–281
Vance, R. B., 346
variability (see dispersion, measures of)
variable, 8
  intervening, 208, 212, 213
variance, 69, 70, 71, 72, 74
  analysis of, 265
  error, 99
  homogeneity of, 246–247
variance ratio, 246

weight, 52
World Almanac, 118, 356

Yule, G. U., 5, 102, 103, 167, 171, 205, 347
Yule's Q, 169, 170, 171, 172, 181, 182, 183, 186, 283, 284, 286

Zander, A., 345, 347
Zeisel, Hans, 135, 138, 139, 166, 210, 347
zero order frequencies, 134
Zetterberg, Hans L., 239, 246, 248, 347